TRANSISTORS: THEORY AND APPLICATIONS

TRANSISTORS
Theory and Applications

by **ABRAHAM COBLENZ,** B.E.E., M.E.E.
Transistor Products, Inc., Waltham, Mass.
formerly with
Signal Corps Engineering Laboratories

and **HARRY L. OWENS,** E.E.
Signal Corps Engineering Laboratories

FIRST EDITION

1955

McGRAW-HILL BOOK COMPANY, INC.

New York   Toronto   London

TRANSISTORS: Theory and Applications

Library of Congress Catalog Card Number: 54-9692

II

THE MAPLE PRESS COMPANY, YORK, PA.

PREFACE

This book had its inception during a casual conversation in 1952 at the Evans Signal Laboratory, Belmar, N. J., between one of the authors and Mr. Richard J. Gale. Mr. Gale was then organizing a series of intramural electronics and physics courses for laboratory engineers. It was agreed that a course on transistors would be given if not less than 20 engineers indicated an interest by attending an orientation class. To a lecture room normally seating approximately 80, over 100 engineers and physicists came in response to a single announcement.

Two series of lectures were given at Evans Signal Laboratory and another at Coles Signal Laboratory. Near the conclusion of the lectures, Mr. James D. Fahnestock, then associate editor of *Electronics* magazine, invited the authors to write a series of articles based on the lectures. Whereas approximately six articles were originally decided upon, the series was extended to eleven upon an indication of reader interest far beyond expectations. The first eleven chapters, exclusive of the historical chapter, appeared consecutively in *Electronics* magazine from March, 1953, until January, 1954.

Because of widespread reader interest, the authors were invited to publish the articles in book form, and this series, considerably expanded and revised, forms the basis of this volume.

The authors hope it will be a practical and useful guide and reference to those entering this fascinating field, as well as to those already in it. The information contained in this volume has been obtained from a very large number of publications, articles, conference notes, and verbal contributions, as well as original work by the authors.

The book covers the theory of transistors from the vantage point of the electronics technician or engineer and includes those aspects of transistor manufacture which have a bearing on transistor characteristics and applications. The theoretical matter is presented with a

v

minimum of mathematics and with pronounced emphasis on the applications to working circuits.   It is intended for technicians of all grades
who are in the electronics field and whose mathematical preparation
may be limited.   Mathematical analyses that were felt to be essential to a complete presentation, such as those in Chapter 12, may be
omitted, restricting the reading to the commentaries.   In general,
the mathematical presentations are usually so completely discussed in
words that, if they are glossed over, no major points useful to the
reader will be lost.

In addition to the cooperation of Mr. Richard J. Gale and Mr. James
D. Fahnestock, acknowledgment for guidance and assistance is due to
Professor Karl Lark-Horovitz of Purdue University; to Dr. Wolfgang
W. Gaertner and to other members of the Solid State Devices Branch
and Thermionics Branch of the Signal Corps Engineering Laboratories
for consultation, advice, and review of many of the formulas; to engineers of other branches of the Laboratories who have assisted in many
ways; and to Louise H. Owens, Lillian Coblenz, and Diana Coblenz
for assistance with typing. The authors gratefully acknowledge the
encouragement and support of Dr. H. A. Zahl and Lt. Col. W. M. Van
Harlingen, Office of the Director of Research, Signal Corps Engineering
Laboratories.   Thanks are also due to the Office of Technical Information and Patent Office, through whose efforts clearance for the material
in this book was obtained; finally, to the Western Electric Co., the
General Electric Co., R.C.A., and to the Raytheon Mfg. Co. for per-
mission to reproduce photographs.

Abraham Coblenz
Harry L. Owens

CONTENTS

Chapter 13. MANUFACTURING PROCESSES 202

Chapter 14. SILICON 238

Chapter 15. SPECIAL TOPICS 249

FOREWORD

The study of solids had to await the development of a broad and comprehensive science of indirect measurement because of the relative inaccessibility of the interior of the solid. Many decades of experimental and mathematical experience were required with the gases and liquids before man was able to show any significant progress in the study of the solid phases of matter. Prior to the past twenty years, the literature on solid state research was very limited. In the last decade the study of solids has received an impetus in the form of the transistor which may make the solid state one of our well-understood sciences.

The worth of the discovery of the transistor transcends the value of the transistor *per se*. As information accumulated regarding the copper-oxide and related rectifiers, the germanium and silicon crystal rectifiers and mixers, the piezoelectric crystals, the halide crystals, and finally the transistor, the realization dawned that there are solid materials to which you need merely attach electrodes and lo! a remarkable electronic device is born! The potentialities of this concept are unlimited—truly infinite. With the discovery that in addition to a host of other functions, such as rectification, mixing, infrared detection and radiation detection in general, modulation, frequency stabilization, etc., solid state devices are capable of amplification, the previously known or estimated applications of solid materials to electronics has been increased by at least an order of magnitude. The discovery of the transistor thus not only represents a step in the deciphering of the cryptogram of the solid state, but it also focuses the spotlight on the practical importance of solid state physics. It is generally agreed that we are embarking on a vast frontal movement to exploit the intrinsic potentialities of the solid.

It will be for history to determine whether the discovery of the transistor deserves to be ranked as one of the great inventions of this century, but there can be no doubt that the transistor has far-reaching significance in electronics and electrical communications, in which fields it will probably lead to major changes and advances. Transistors have captured the interest and imagination of lay and technical men alike, and confidence in transistors has been reflected in an extensive investment in research, development, and applicatious. Although many problems remain to be solved, sufficient progress has been made to warrant serious study of circuit and system applications for transistors. It is evident that contributions to this important subject can best be made by those who have become thoroughly conversant with the principles of transistor theory and applications.

Transistor progress during the past six years is truly remarkable. Units which have been developed sufficiently for commercial application are becoming available in quantity. The outlook is for continued progress through the improvement of existing types and the discovery and development of new types. These developments will unquestionably stimulate circuit application work which, in turn, will further stimulate the research and development effort on the devices themselves. It is of interest in this connection to observe that there have crept into the parlance of transistor engineers the words "transistors and transistor-like devices." Clearly, therefore, we are heading not only toward improved and new transistors but also toward entirely new solid state devices.

LIST OF SYMBOLS

Symbol	Meaning
a	ratio of output loop current to input loop current
B	base
c	velocity of light, 3×10^{10} cm per sec
C	capacitance
C	collector
CG	current gain
CG_o	over-all current gain
db	decibel, $= 10 \log_{10} P_{\text{out}}/P_{\text{in}}$
e	charge on the electron, 1.6×10^{-19} coulomb
e_g	ac generator voltage
E	emitter
E_c	applied dc collector supply voltage
E_e	applied dc emitter supply voltage
E_{int}	ac voltage at output of stage I
g_{11}	small-signal short-circuit input conductance
g_{12}	small-signal short-circuit feedback conductance
g_{21}	small-signal short-circuit transfer conductance
g_{22}	small-signal short-circuit output conductance
GB	grounded base, or common base
GC	grounded collector, or common collector
GE	grounded emitter, or common emitter
h_{11}	small-signal short-circuit input impedance
h_{12}	small-signal open-circuit feedback potential ratio
h_{21}	small-signal short-circuit current transfer ratio
h_{22}	small-signal open-circuit output admittance
i	ac current
i_e	emitter current, or current through r_e ($+$ toward junction point J)
i_{e1}	ac emitter current in loop 1

i_{e2} ac emitter current in loop 2
I dc current
I_b dc base current
I_c dc collector current
I_e dc emitter current
k Boltzmann's constant, 1.38×10^{-16} erg per degree Kelvin
m mass
n density of electrons, in electrons per cm³
p density of holes, in holes per cm³
P power
PG power gain
PG_o over-all power gain
P_o power output
r_b base resistance
r_b' equivalent base resistance at high frequencies;

$$r_b' \cong \frac{h_{11} I_e - 0.025}{(1 - \alpha_{ce}) I_e} \text{ at room temp.}$$

r_c collector resistance
r_e emitter resistance
r_m mutual resistance
r_{11} small-signal open-circuit input resistance
r_{12} small-signal open-circuit reverse transfer resistance
r_{21} small-signal open-circuit forward transfer resistance
r_{22} small-signal open-circuit output resistance
R dc resistance
R_b' added series base resistance
R_b $R_b' + r_b$
R_e $R_e' + r_e$
R_e' added emitter series resistance
R_g generator resistance (or impedance)
$R_{g\text{II}}$ generator resistance of second stage in cascaded arrangement
R_i input resistance, or driving point resistance
R_{i_I} input resistance of stage I
R_{i_II} input resistance of stage II
R_{i_III} input resistance of stage III
R_L load resistance
R_{L_1} load resistance of first stage (external) in cascaded arrangement
R_{L_2} load resistance, second stage
R_H Hall coefficient
R_o output resistance
R_{o_III} output resistance of stage III
T temperature

V_c	dc voltage at collector
V_e	dc voltage at emitter
VG	voltage gain
VG_o	over-all voltage gain
Y_{11}	small-signal short-circuit input admittance
Y_{12}	small-signal short-circuit feedback admittance
Y_{21}	small-signal short-circuit transfer admittance
Y_{22}	small-signal short-circuit output admittance
Z_{11}	small-signal open-circuit input impedance
Z_{12}	small-signal open-circuit reverse transfer impedance
Z_{21}	small-signal open-circuit forward transfer impedance
Z_{22}	small-signal open-circuit output impedance
α	current amplification factor
α_{cb}	collector-to-base current amplification factor
α_{eb}	emitter-to-base current amplification factor
α_{ce}	collector-to-emitter current amplification factor
β	temperature coefficient of energy gap, $\Delta E_g/\Delta T$
ΔE_g	width of energy gap, or forbidden band, usually in electron volts
μ_e	electron mobility, in cm per sec per volt per cm
μ_h	hole mobility, in cm per sec per volt per cm
ρ	resistivity, in ohm-cm
ρ_i	intrinsic resistivity, in ohm-cm
τ	lifetime, usually given in μsec

NOTES: 1. Capital letters usually refer to externally added circuit elements; lower case letters to internal, or equivalent T (or π) parameters.

2. Capital letters usually refer to dc values; lower case letters to ac values.

TRANSISTORS: THEORY AND APPLICATIONS

1 A SHORT HISTORY OF TRANSISTORS

A. INTRODUCTION

It has become generally established that scientific progress is the result of well-organized research teams. The day of the garret scientist, working alone in a near-bare loft by the flickering light of an oil lamp is almost past. For the scope of knowledge in any one field is so vast that few individuals can fully master it. In addition, an individual effort is dwarfed by the large-scale attack upon the frontiers of our technical knowledge by incalculable numbers of scientific workers in many great laboratories with virtually unlimited facilities. Even in purely theoretical contributions, the facilities available in these million-dollar laboratories are almost indispensable to original work; in experimental investigations the facilities of large laboratories are even more essential. With industry alerted to the lucrative financial rewards possible by just a single discovery from its privately supported research, the flow of funds of all types to private and university laboratories has made it possible to increase the numbers of groups working on research projects and to enable them to proceed without the impediments of limited facilities, funds, or personnel. Thus scientific teamwork is the keynote of modern scientific progress. Each team of theoretical and experimental scientists is able to start with the contributions of earlier investigations and to make further inroads into new and unknown areas in the world of science.

The transistor has been described as an outstanding illustration of the value of teamwork in modern research. The patent papers may show it to be the invention of J. Bardeen and W. H. Brattain, but their discovery was made possible only through the success of previous contributions and with the help of coworkers who specialized in many fields of endeavor,

B. CRYSTAL DETECTORS BEFORE 1920

Silicon is the most plentiful element on earth, next to oxygen, and its existence appears to have been known as far back as the time of the alchemists. Though it is so plentiful, it is not found free in nature, but as one of the forms of silicon dioxide (SiO_2) such as sand, quartz, flint, etc.[1] It was first separated and identified as an element in 1823 by the Swedish chemist Jöns Jakob Berzelius (1779–1848).

At the time of his preparation of the orderly scheme of chemical elements which is now commonly called the periodic table, Dmitri Ivanovich Mendelyeev (1834–1907) predicted that the missing element in his periodic table[2] below silicon and titanium would have many of the properties of the adjacent elements, and he called it eka-silicon (Sanskrit: *eka*, next in order or one). In 1886, Clemens Alexander Winkler (1820–1896), a German chemist, extracted a substance from argyrodite ($4Ag_2S,GeS_2$), a complex silver and germanium sulfide, found in the Himmelsfurst mine, Freiberg, Saxony, Germany.[3] Winkler analyzed the argyrodite and was able to identify all but about 7 per cent of the mineral, whereupon he assumed the existence of a new element which he called germanium (Latin, Germany). Germanium has since been found also in zinc ores, silicate materials, certain coals, and germanite,[4,5] ($7CuS\text{-}FeS\text{-}GeS_2$, Tsumeb mine, southwest Africa).

When Heinrich Rudolph Hertz (1857–1894) found a means for detecting electromagnetic waves in 1888, he used a crude loop with metal spheres brought into juxtaposition across which a spark jumped when the correct conditions were attained. A marked improvement was afforded by Sir Oliver Joseph Lodge (1851–1940) in adapting the coherer invented by Prof. Édouard Branly (1846–1940), a French scientist. Guglielmo Marconi (1874–1937) used the coherer in early experiments with an automatic "decoherer" to loosen the electrically welded iron filings which were the heart of the device, after each impulse. The iron filings were simply held in a glass tube with provisions for leading the signal in and out. The great disadvantage of the coherer was that it would reproduce dots and dashes only. About 1901 Prof. Reginald Aubrey Fessenden (1866–1932)[6] developed an improved detector involving a Wollaston wire dipped into a solution of nitric acid. It was able to detect continuous signals as well as dots and dashes, but the liquid component was an obvious disadvantage. In 1883 Thomas Alva Edison (1847–1931) noted the passage of current between a filament and metallic anode in an evacuated bulb. In 1903 John Ambrose Fleming (1849–1945) used Edison's discovery to make the first vacuum-tube diode detector for radio signals.

The first observations of the phenomenon of asymmetric conduction were apparently made by Munck in 1835.[7] No practical use of the fact that metals in contact with certain minerals and compounds would perform the unilateral conductivity essential in detection was made until about 1906 when Henry Harrison Chase Dunwoody (1842–1933), then with the De Forest Wireless Company, but who had served in the United States Signal Corps and had been retired as a brigadier general, invented the carborundum crystal detector. It was not a whisker type of detector, however, but used a piece of electric-furnace carborundum between brass holders.[8] Carborundum (SiC) must have suggested the idea of silicon to Greenleaf Whittier Pickard (1877–) who filed a patent in 1906 for a crystal detector in the form we know today—a cat whisker in contact with the crystal. It was also discovered that other minerals such as galena (PbS), iron pyrites (FeS$_2$), chalcopyrite (CuFeS$_2$), and zincite (ZnO) might be used in crystal detectors. It is noteworthy that the lead ore galena, also called galenite, occurs in various forms known as cuproplumbite (5Cu$_2$S·PbS), alisonite (3Cu$_2$S·PbS), altaite (lead telluride, PbTe), or clausthalite (lead selenide, PbSe), and so on, so that many of the galena crystals used in early radio days were often combined in various proportions with these and other related compounds. In the March 10, 1924, edition of Circular 74 of the Bureau of Standards, Radio Instruments and Measurements, appears the following: "A perikon detector, chalcopyrite-zincite was used . . . " indicating the wide usage of these mineral detectors before the displacement of these by the silicon and germanium crystal detectors.

C. GERMANIUM RECTIFIERS[6]

Probably due to the less frequent occurrence of germanium compared with silicon, and due also to the comparative novelty of the element, the rectifying action of germanium was not observed until about nine years after Pickard's invention of the silicon point contact crystal detector. In 1915, Carl Axel Fredrick Benedicks[9] (1875–), a Swedish inventor, first discussed the point contact rectifying action of germanium. This discovery appears to have increased interest in the element, for in the following years recovery of germanium from the chloride and the oxide was achieved. Germanium was also successfully purified. In the years following Pickard's discovery, and up to the discovery of the transistor, much of the theory of semiconductors was developed. But it was not until 1946 that Walter H. Brattain, of the Bell Telephone Laboratories, described rectification by semiconductor to semiconductor contact.[10] He discussed semiconductor crystals formed into a point and obtained a series showing how specific combinations of crystals produce predictable rectification directions, depending on the column of the periodic table in which the element belongs. Robert G. Sachs of Purdue University, in the same year, proposed a multicontact theory of rectification[11] which hinted at the invention to follow. In 1947, L. Sosnowski of the Admiralty Research Laboratories, Teddington, Middlesex, England, wrote to the *Physical Review* in which he said: "it should be possible to apply the theory advanced . . . if sufficiently close contact could be made between N and P type samples of, say, silicon, to observe rectificating and photo-voltaic effects. The results briefly reported by Brattain,* seem to indicate the suggested results do occur."[12] Thus was born the idea of a PN junction, upon which are based the NPN and PNP junction transistors.

The existence of surface states was first postulated by Ignace Tamm,[13] and in the same work the concept of surface energy levels that are bound was introduced. Mott and Gurney[14] say of the Tamm levels (first edition, 1940): "We do not know of any very definite experimental evidence about the existence of Tamm levels . . . . "

D. DISCOVERY OF THE TRANSISTOR

The high-back-voltage germanium rectifier was discovered by Seymour Benzer at Purdue University in the fall of 1942. Because of wartime restrictions, no public disclosures were made until 1944.[15] As Torrey and Whitmer[16] point out, the crystal rectifiers available prior to this discovery were inadequate for application as second detectors in radar receivers and in similar applications because of low-reverse-voltage limitations. Considerable interest was aroused by the discovery that the high-inverse-voltage characteristics could be obtained in germanium crystal rectifiers. Scaff and Theurer initiated work on the high-reverse-voltage diodes at the Bell Telephone Laboratories at about this time,[17] and high-voltage crystal diodes using silicon were subsequently explored by the University of Pennsylvania.[18]

At the Bell Telephone Laboratories, an experimental as well as a theoretical attack on the high-back-voltage rectifier was made, the latter under the supervision of William Shockley. As the investigation progressed, certain unexplainable phenomena were considered (small contact potential between P- and N-type silicon,[19] immobility of induced charges on thin films of semiconductors, and independence of rectifying properties with metals having different work functions); to explain these, John Bardeen[20] revived the Tamm levels and pro-

* See Ref. 10.

posed an explanation based on surface states and electrons in bound energy levels at the surface. The explanation not only fitted the phenomena indicated above, but also correctly predicted the results of additional experiments made immediately thereafter to check the hypothesis. If free electrons in the semiconductor can become bound on the surface, will the contact potential vary with the concentration of donors (or acceptors) of the material? If free electrons can become bound on the surface, will the contact potential change when light is used to alter the number of electrons available by bombardment of the surface with light? The experimental data said "yes" to both questions.

Brattain and Bardeen[21] next tried an electrolyte in contact with a semiconductor surface, apparently reasoning that the liquid would obtain the best "contact" to these surface charges. Of particular interest was the effect of such surface charges on the characteristics of the high-back-voltage rectifier, then the cynosure of electronic interest, and the technique of using the electrolyte was applied to it. They found that the density of the surface states could be varied by application of a potential across the electrolyte. A logical, but not necessarily obvious, next step was to control the density of the surface electrons by a metallic contact near the whisker of the high-back-voltage rectifier. The control of these surface charges by the added electrode (cat whisker) completed the structure now known as a "transistor" (TRANSfer resISTOR). The first public announcement of the transistor was made in June, 1948 (patent No. 2,524,035 filed June 17, 1948).

E. THE TRANSISTOR AFTER 1948

In July of 1949, W. Shockley of the Bell Telephone Laboratories published a theoretical analysis[22] wherein it was shown that because a PN junction can inject a hole current into an adjacent N-type material it performs essentially the function of an emitter. Accordingly, he predicted that a PNP type of transistor, consisting of area contacts rather than point contacts, should be a practical device. Approximately six months later, Goucher et al.,[23] in a letter to the editor of the Physical Review, published experimental data supporting the PN-junction theory proposed by Shockley, using PN diodes formed by addition of gallium to high-back-voltage N-type germanium. Hall and Dunlap[24] published results of a diffusion method of making PN junctions, but it was not until the end of 1951 that PNP transistors, prepared by the diffusion method, were reported.[25]

At about this time also, J. N. Shive[26] reported the practical development of a phototransistor, using a point contact on N-type germanium. A brief history of the phototransistor appears in an article by Shive.[27]

Early in 1951, Shockley reported on theory and experiment of NPN transistors.[28]   This was the first public report on the feasibility of this type of transistor.   Also presented at this time was the theory of the PNPN "hook" transistor.   In 1952, Shockley reported on the theory of a unipolar field-effect transistor,[29] but it was not until some time later that experimental models of the theoretically predicted units could be constructed.   During 1953 numerous investigations were in progress to determine the utility of other elements and intermetallic compounds for possible transistor applications.[30,31]

F. CONFERENCES ON SEMICONDUCTOR DEVICES

No historical treatment of transistors should be concluded without mention of the IRE-AIEE semiconductor symposia. If a final, unequivocal proof were needed to show that research and development in the twentieth century is a team effort, the semiconductor conferences furnish that proof.

On June 13, 1949, at the tube conference held at Princeton University, one session was devoted exclusively to semiconductor devices. This was the Seventh Annual Conference on Electron Device Research. Twelve papers were presented on transistors and crystal diodes, and the meetings ran over into two sessions.

At the Eighth Annual Conference on Electron Device Research at the University of Michigan on June 21 and 22, 1950, semiconductor sessions were again held.   The papers presented included fifteen reports of semiconductor research.

On June 21 and 22 of the following year, at the Ninth Annual Conference on Electron Device Research held at the University of New Hampshire, three semiconductor sessions were required, and somewhat more than twenty papers were presented.

By 1952, semiconductor work had increased to the extent that it was deemed advisable to organize a separate conference on semiconductor device research.   This conference was held at the University of Illinois, Urbana, Ill.   On June 19 and 20, six sessions were held in which over thirty papers were presented.

The following year (1953) the conference was renamed Conference on Transistor Research and was held at Pennsylvania State College, July 6 to 8.   Over 100 papers were submitted, of which time permitted the presentation of only 46.   A record attendance of 261 was noted.

In 1954, the Conference on Semiconductor Device Research, AIEE-

IRE, met at the University of Minnesota, Minneapolis, Minn., on June 28, 29, and 30. Over 275 solid state physicists and engineers heard and discussed informally 70 papers on transistor research. Most frequently discussed were surface states and silicon.

Since only scientific and professional personnel who are "active workers" in the solid state field as evidenced by contributions to the art are extended invitations, it seems fair to say that the attendance of this number of engineers and physicists bears witness to the scientific and industrial importance of the information presented at these conferences.

Much of the material discovered in the years from 1948 to the present was first reported at these conferences, usually much earlier than formal publication. The sessions have become an effective means for interchange of scientific information by semiconductor-device research workers from all parts of the country. It is almost an understatement to mention that these symposia have contributed materially to the advancement of the transistor art.

REFERENCES

1. "Handbook of Chemistry and Physics," 34th ed., p. 330, Chemical Rubber Publishing Co., Cleveland, Ohio, 1952–1953.
2. Chalmers, T. W.: "Historic Researches," pp. 128ff., Morgan Brothers, Ltd., London, 1949.
3. Chalmers, T. W., "Historic Researches," p. 135, Morgan Brothers, Ltd., London, 1949.
4. "Handbook of Chemistry and Physics," 34th ed., p. 316, Chemical Rubber Publishing Co., Cleveland, Ohio, 1952–1953.
5. Dana, Edward Salisbury: "Textbook of Mineralogy," John Wiley & Sons, Inc., New York, 1932.
6. Archer, Gleason L.: "History of Radio to 1926," pp. 67ff., American Historical Society, Inc., New York, 1938.
7. Cornelius, E. C.: Germanium Crystal Diodes, *Electronics*, pp. 118–223, February, 1946.
8. MacLaurin, W. Rupert: "Invention and Innovation in the Radio Industry," p. 118, The Macmillan Company, New York, 1949.
9. Benedicks, C.: *Intern. Z. f. Metallog.*, Vol. 7, p. 225, 1915.
10. Brattain, W. H.: *Phys. Rev.*, Vol. 69, p. 682, 1946.
11. Sachs, R. G.: *Phys. Rev.*, Vol. 69, p. 682, 1946.
12. Sosnowski, L.: *Phys. Rev.*, Vol. 72, p. 642, 1947 (letter dated Aug. 22, 1947).
13. Tamm, I.: *Z. Physik*, Vol. 76, p. 849, 1932.
14. Mott, N. F., and R. W. Gurney: "Electronic Processes in Ionic Crystals," p. 86, Oxford University Press, London, 1950.
15. Benzer, S.: The High Voltage Germanium Rectifier, *National Defense Research Council 14–342*, Purdue University, Nov. 1, 1944.

16. Torrey, Henry C., and Charles A. Whitmer: "Crystal Rectifiers," pp. 361ff., McGraw-Hill Book Company, Inc., New York, 1948.

17. Scaff, J. H., and H. C. Theurer: Final Report on Preparation of High Back Voltage Germanium Rectifiers, NDRC 14–555, Bell Telephone Laboratories, Oct. 24, 1945.

18. Lewis, M. N., J. H. Taylor, R. J. Gibson, Jr., and W. E. Stephens: High Back Voltage Silicon, NDRC 14–453, University of Pennsylvania, June 28, 1945.

19. Meyerhoff, W. E.: Contact Potential Difference in Silicon Crystal Rectifiers, *Phys. Rev.*, Vol. 71, pp. 727–735, May 15, 1947.

20. Bardeen, J.: Surface States and Rectification at a Metal-Semiconductor Contact, *Phys. Rev.*, Vol. 71, pp. 717–727, May 15, 1947.

21. Bardeen, John, and Walter H. Brattain: Physical Principles Involved in Transistor Action, *Phys. Rev.*, Vol. 75, pp. 208–225, Apr. 15, 1949.

22. Shockley, W.: The Theory of PN Junctions in Semiconductors and PN Junction Transistors, *Bell System Tech. J.*, Vol. 28, pp. 435–489, July, 1949.

23. Goucher, F. S., G. L. Pearson, M. Sparks, G. K. Teal, and W. Shockley: Theory and Experiment for a Germanium PN Junction, *Phys. Rev.*, Vol. 81, p. 637, Feb. 15, 1951.

24. Hall, R. N., and W. C. Dunlap: PN Junctions Prepared by Impurity Diffusion, *Phys. Rev.*, Vol. 80, p. 467, Nov. 1, 1950.

25. Saby, J. S.: Recent Developments in Transistors and Related Devices, *Tele-Tech.*, Vol. 10, pp. 32ff., December, 1951.

26. Shive, J. N.: The Phototransistor, *Bell Labs. Record*, Vol. 28, pp. 337–342, August, 1950; also A New Germanium Photoresistance Cell, *Phys. Rev.*, Vol. 76, p. 575, Aug. 14, 1949.

27. Shive, J. N.: Properties of the M-1740 Photocell, *Proc. IRE* Vol. 40, No. 11, pp. 1410ff, November, 1952.

28. Shockley, W., M. Sparks, and G. K. Teal: PN Junction Transistors, *Phys. Rev.*, Vol. 85, pp. 151–162, July 1, 1951.

29. Shockley, W.: A Unipolar "Field-Effect" Transistor, *Proc. IRE*, Vol. 40, No. 11, pp. 1365–1376, November, 1952.

30. Breckenridge, R. G., and W. R. Hosler: Electrical Properties of Titanium Dioxide Semiconductors, *Phys. Rev.*, Vol. 91, pp. 793–802, Aug. 15, 1953.

31. Breckenridge, R. G.: Semiconducting Intermetallic Compounds, *Phys. Rev.*, Vol. 90, p. 488, May 1, 1953.

2 HOLES AND THE TRANSISTOR

This chapter provides an introduction to transistors, tells why technically qualified personnel will find this field attractive, and indicates the size of the transistor field.

1. ADVANTAGES AND USES

Figure 2-1 shows a number of experimental transistors, point contact and junction, manufactured prior to 1952. Figure 2-2 shows

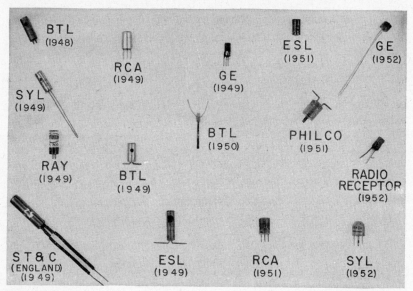

Fig. 2-1. Early transistors, manufactured prior to June, 1952. (Courtesy of the manufacturers shown.)

typical point contact and junction transistors manufactured after 1952. These units occupy about one thousandth of the volume, represent one hundredth of the weight, and require about one tenth of the power of the average type of radio receiving tube; yet they will perform many of the functions of vacuum tubes.

Transistors are capable of being used in circuits to provide amplification, oscillation, pulse generation, pulse counting, pulse storage, gating, pulse delay, coincidence gating, and so on. They are more rugged

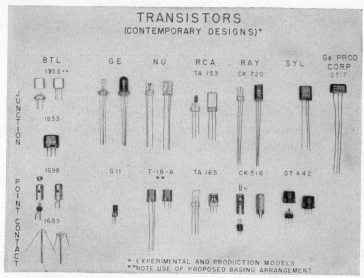

Fig. 2-2. More recent transistor types, including use of in-line two-and-one base arrangement. (*Courtesy of the manufacturers shown.*)

than vacuum tubes in general, and their life has already been demonstrated to be about three times the normal life of a vacuum tube; the expected life has been extrapolated to 70,000 hr.[1]

2. OUTLOOK FOR TRANSISTORS

The transistor was invented in 1948, and at that time the total investment of private and government funds in transistor work, as such, was limited to perhaps five-figure numbers. Increasing confidence in the potential utility of the transistor has resulted in both acceleration and expansion of the transistor development activity. Currently, industry and government-sponsored programs are valued at many millions of dollars. The youthfulness of this field and the extraordinary promise it holds forth to capable technicians in the field of electronics and electricity render it extremely fruitful for the development of new and ingenious circuit and system applications. Virtually every important work in the field of transistors today has an element of newness and may properly be considered a contribution to the art.

In this virgin and unexplored field the need for electronic engineers and technicians specially trained in the transistor art is urgent and continually increasing. This book should serve to initiate technical people with varied backgrounds in electronics into this fascinating subject.

Transistors, which are a product of the relatively new science of solid state physics, are expected to replace receiving tubes in some applications and to make possible entirely new electronic equipment. The very large investments in transistors by leading tube manufacturers indicate that the long-term outlook for this new circuit element is sound and inviting.

3. AIM AND LEVEL OF PRESENTATION

Presently available literature on transistors includes many highly technical discourses on specialized topics of limited interest to the average reader. The purpose of this book is to present the principles of transistor operation in simple language suited to the needs of the practical technician. No single text appears to fill the needs of practical men in the field who do not have the time to get acquainted with such abstruse subjects as quantum mechanics, vector analysis, and differential equations.

4. NEW IDEAS ARE INVOLVED

Transistor theory represents a radical departure from vacuum-tube theory. The reader must be prepared to give careful thought to certain concepts of physics which are not difficult but are noticeably different from the principles with which he has become acquainted in his study of vacuum-tube theory and electronics. A scientific open-mindedness and a willingness to accept ideas that may appear to contravene long-established or long-accepted concepts will be found not only desirable but almost essential. In order to fully appreciate these new concepts, the reader may find rereading of the chapters very helpful.

5. ELECTRON THEORY AND SEMICONDUCTORS

The flow of electrons accounts for both alternating and direct current. This theoretical explanation can be found in virtually all textbooks on ac and dc theory, electrons, and electrical phenomena in general.

A close scrutiny of the supporting evidence, however, reveals that electron flow is simply a convenient theory used to explain the phenomenon known as electric current—that electric current is a flow of electrons is not a scientific law.   No one has ever crept into a conductor or electrolyte and witnessed the actual flow of electrons.   The theoretical explanation is the result of indirect experimental evidence, and while this evidence is sound and withstands very critical examination, the conclusions based upon it must be viewed as an inference or a hypothesis and not as a law of nature.

The fact that electron flow as an explanation for electric current is only a theory is strikingly demonstrated by experimental results in which the data obtained cannot be explained by the use of electron theory alone.   Just such a case exists in the field of semiconductor materials that exhibit conducting properties in a range between insulators and conductors.   A particularly important phenomenon in transistor action is observed that does not lend itself to a direct explanation by means of electron theory alone.

6. RUDIMENTS OF THE TRANSISTOR

Consider the arrangement shown in Fig. 2-3.   A small block of a semiconductor material such as germanium or silicon is placed in electrical contact with a conducting metal which is then grounded, as shown at B of the figure.   On the top of the semiconductor block, spaced a few thousandths of an inch apart, are two cat whiskers such as were common in connection with the cat whisker galena crystals used as detectors in the early days of radio.

The cat whisker marked C is negative with respect to the semiconductor block by virtue of the battery E_c with its negative terminal connected to the cat whisker.   A milliammeter is shown in series with this connection, and the current indicated will be designated as I_c. The circuit indicated may be considered as a crystal diode biased in the reverse or high-resistance direction.   If the applied voltage E_c is approximately 10 volts, I_c may perhaps be of the order of 1 ma. (The figures used here are not intended to be significant; only orders of magnitude are important.)

Analyzing the observed data from the standpoint of electron theory, one would say simply that electrons flow from the cat whisker to the base through the semiconductor material under the influence of the applied potential E_c and it is the flow of these electrons which gives the meter indication I_c.   The dashed lines from C to B in the figure show the approximate flow or streamlines of electrons within the semiconductor block.

At the cat whisker marked E the polarity of the applied potential E_e is opposite to that at C; the positive terminal of the battery is connected to the cat whisker. A milliammeter in series with this circuit, if switch S_1 were closed, would then indicate the current in the EB circuit, and since the diode on the E side is connected in the forward or low-resistance direction, a very small potential at E_e when the switch is closed, say of the order of 0.5 volt, will cause a current flow of the order of perhaps 1 ma.

If the reader will, for a moment, imagine the C circuit open and S_1 closed, then, as before, I_e indicates the current flowing in the EB circuit

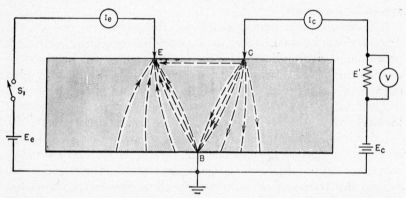

Fig. 2-3. Basic circuit arrangement for point contact transistor, showing internal electron flow lines, without the use of the hole concept.

because of electron flow from B to E. Again, as before, the dashed lines indicate the streamlines of electrons in the EB circuit within the semiconductor material.

7. CURRENT AMPLIFICATION

Now consider the CB circuit closed as shown and S_1 open. As mentioned above, under the specified conditions, I_c will be about 1 ma. When S_1 is closed, an extraordinary phenomenon, loosely described as transistor action, is observed—the current in the CB circuit increases markedly and may, in a typical case, reach 2 or 3 ma. Note that when S_1 is closed, and I_c increases by a factor of two or more, the emitter current remains, for all practical purposes, the same as with the C circuit open, approximately 1 ma. Typical transistors yield current amplifications of this magnitude, but exceptional units have produced current gains as great as 100. In any case, a significant and highly important current amplification is observed.

8. ELECTRON THEORY INSUFFICIENT TO EXPLAIN TRANSISTOR ACTION

It is instructive, following the remarks made at the beginning of this chapter, to attempt to explain the observed data by means of electron theory alone.

This is no simple undertaking. If the reader will carefully trace polarities around the circuit, he will observe that the E terminal is actually positive with respect to the C terminal. One might then expect that electron flow within the semiconductor block would be from C to E, making less electrons available to contribute to the conduction process from C to B, and therefore one might, at a first glance, expect I_c to decrease.

If fewer electrons were available for the conduction process, the current would be smaller, and the observed increase in I_c is certainly perplexing. Extraordinary and unconventional variations would be required in electron theory per se to explain how the two divergent streams of electrons in the material can cause an interaction which will lead to the current amplification observed, particularly in view of the electric field which tends to draw electrons from the CB stream.

It is virtually impossible to explain the phenomenon delineated by means of the electron theory alone, and certain reinforcing or auxiliary concepts must be introduced to complement electron theory in order to explain this transistor action properly. It is necessary to point out very carefully that the phenomena observed in semiconductors which lead to effects such as the one described do not require a modification of electron theory, but they imperatively demand an important additional concept.

In proceeding to a more critical examination of what must be the nature of such an auxiliary concept in order to explain phenomena such as the one just described, it is necessary to probe deeply into the relation between a theory and the supporting data. In practice, a body of facts and experimental data accumulates, and thereafter a hypothesis may be proposed which seeks to explain all the data. This is the normal progress of the scientific method. Both experience and the philosophy of the method have shown that merely because a given hypothesis adequately accounts for the observed experimental data, it does not preclude the possibility that another hypothesis may exist which will equally well explain what has been observed. The only way then of deciding between two such satisfactory theories is to endeavor to find some further facts which one or the other of the two theories will not satisfactorily explain. In our case, electron theory explains a host of phenomena already well known but does not preclude the possibility that an addition to electron theory not only will equally well explain the great number of experiments in ac and dc circuits but will, in addition, explain transistor action in a semi-conductor. We must next examine the external evidence upon which we base our knowledge of the direction of flow of current and the nature of the current carriers.

9. DIRECTION OF CURRENT FLOW

Our knowledge of the direction of electric current flow is most fre-quently based on the direction of the magnetic field associated with electric current. The left-hand rule for electron flow states that, if the left hand grasps a conductor so that the fingers point in the direc-tion of the lines of flux, then the thumb will point in the direction of electron flow. From this rule it may be shown that if the electrons in a wire flow in a loop clockwise, in the plane of the paper the reader now sees, the north pole would be above the paper toward the reader and the south pole under the paper.

10. ROWLAND'S EXPERIMENT[2]

About 1889 a well-known physicist, H. A. Rowland, performed a simple but extremely important experiment. In equally spaced sec-tors of an ebonite disk were placed negative charges obtained by the time-honored method of rubbing cat's fur against a glass rod. The sectors were separated by raised portions so that each sector contained its own set of charges. This ebonite disk was then rotated at high speed, and it was observed that a magnetic field was present identical to what would have been expected if a flow of electrons had occurred in a loop of wire in the same direction of rotation. If the plane of the disk were parallel to the plane of the paper, the north pole for clockwise rotation of the disk would be above the paper toward the reader—exactly as for the case discussed above.

When these negative charges were removed and replaced by positive charges and the ebonite disk was then rotated *counterclockwise*, the same direction of magnetic field was observed, north toward the reader if the disk is again considered parallel to the plane of the paper.

The significance of this experiment must not be overlooked. It is now clear that if our ideas about the direction of electric current are based on the direction of the resultant magnetic field, and they most fre-quently are, then when we assume that electric current is flowing from left to right because electrons are flowing from left to right, the phe-nomenon we are observing, namely, the magnetic field, could also be caused by positive charges moving from right to left.

Rowland's classical experiment indicates that the external or phenomenological manifestations are the same. When we say electric current we never, unless by special training, think of the motion of positive charges, and in this way we subconsciously exclude the possibility that the carriers may be positive. Once we consider this possibility, our habit of associating electric current with the flow of electrons leads to this anomalous situation about the direction of flow.

In the transistor studies that are to follow, it is essential that the reader bear in mind the possibility that electric current may be due to the flow of positive charges as well as of negative charges. The possibility that these two processes may be simultaneously active in an electronic semiconductor material is fundamental to the theory of transistor action.

11. HOLES—PRELIMINARY DEFINITION

Modern theory of the structure of matter pictures the atom as containing a core or nucleus with electrons outside of this nucleus rotating about it. This subject will be covered in a full chapter subsequently. It may be said here that the present picture of approximately what the electrons look like as they rotate about the nucleus is given in Fig. 2-4.

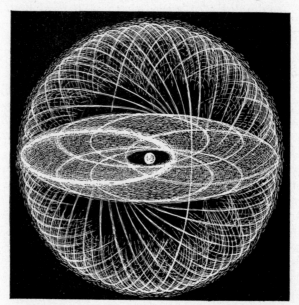

PATH OF ELECTRONS AROUND NUCLEUS

Fig. 2-4. The "smeared-out" picture of electrons and nucleus. The net charge is zero.

The electrons are pictured as a sort of smeared-out or hazy region about the nucleus as the figure shows. For purposes of this introductory discussion, let us grant that the cloud shown about the nucleus is due to electrons.

If we were to remove one electron by some means such as bombardment of the atom, for instance, a net positive charge would be left since the atom with its normal complement of electrons is electrically neutral or has a net zero charge. By removing an electron from the picture presented in Fig. 2-4, we have created in the atom a sort of

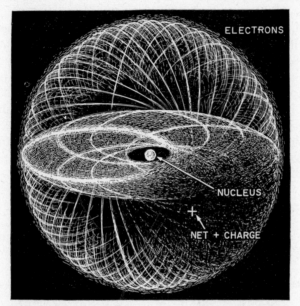

Fig. 2-5. The smeared-out picture of electrons and "holes" in the atom.

rarified area where an electron is not particularly likely to be found; this area looks like a hole (see Fig. 2-5). A positive charge is associated with the hole.

The picture presented is not an entirely accurate description of a hole, and a more satisfactory definition of a hole will be given later. The rather crude picture is intended only for the purpose of introducing this new concept, which is essential in the analysis of transistor action. Having established that electric current can be carried by positive charges, and considering a net positive charge as a hole, it follows that electric current can be carried by holes. The physicist uses the word "hole" in transistor theory differently from its usage in normal everyday conversation.

12. HOLE AS A PARTICLE

Because this concept of holes is so essential to the study of transistors, a few more ideas regarding its nature may be in order. The concept of a hole came into existence in the study of the physics of solids because it was found to be a convenient physicomathematical abstraction for specifying the behavior of atomic structures in the solid. By endowing the hole with a definite mass, a definite positive charge, a definite velocity, and an associated energy—in short, by treating it as a true particle—much useful and practical information about specific materials, particularly the semiconductors, can be obtained.[3] It can be shown that holes are acted upon by electric and magnetic fields in exactly the way one would expect a particle with the mass of an electron and a positive charge to react under equal conditions. A particularly important aspect of hole behavior is its attraction by a point of negative potential. The reader will find it convenient in all future thinking about holes to consider them equivalent to positively charged electrons, that is, particles with mass equal to the mass of the electron and charge equal to that of the electron but of opposite sign. The more accurate definition of a hole to be given later will not conflict with this simple picture.

13. EFFECT OF HOLES

Having introduced these preliminary concepts, let us return to the laboratory-observed phenomenon discussed in connection with Fig.

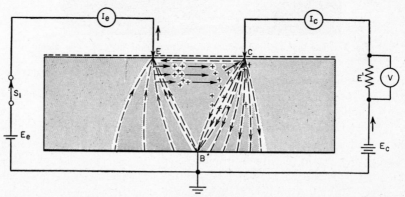

Fig. 2-6. Essentials of transistor action, using the concept of holes, with S_1 closed.

2-3. In Fig. 2-6 is shown essentially the same arrangement, electrically, as in Fig. 2-3. Let us try now to see how the introduction of the concept of holes can lead to a plausible explanation for the phenomenon of current amplification previously discussed.

14. CURRENT AMPLIFICATION—WITH HOLE CONCEPT

As electrons leave the germanium block at point E because of battery E_e, holes are created in the material in consonance with the elementary principles just discussed, wherein electrons removed by any means from their atomic location give rise to holes, as shown in Fig. 2-5. Under the influence of the electric field (note that point C is negative with respect to point E), the holes drift toward the C side of the circuit. We have already seen that ordinarily the current I_c is small because the number of electrons available for conduction is inadequate to support a larger flow.   If the reader will recall his experience with the behavior of a negative space charge from vacuum-tube theory, he will realize that the presence of a positive space charge due to holes between C and B can create a strongly attracting region for electrons in this space. Electrons from neighboring sites are thus attracted into the CB region and add to the available electrons for conduction.   The result is a circuit which possesses lower resistance because of the abundance of electrons.   The evidence that the circuit has lower resistance is that current I_c will increase appreciably when switch S_1 is closed.

This is a rather crude explanation of what happens, and later on, when the necessary additional background theory has been developed, a more accurate and sophisticated explanation will be presented.   The introduction of the additional concept of holes assists in the explanation of transistor action involving current amplification.   Before introduction of the concept of holes, no satisfactory explanation for transistor action was apparent.

15. SUPPORTING EVIDENCE FOR EXISTENCE OF HOLES

It must not be inferred, merely because this is an elementary explanation, that the hypothesis presented here regarding the motion of holes is merely a guess.   There is a good and sound body of evidence to support this hypothesis, and a particularly interesting experiment along these lines will be described.   In transistor parlance, the cat whisker at point C is known as a collector and the cat whisker at point E is known as the emitter.   Assume that the physical position of the emitter is fixed and that the spacing between emitter and collector is varied by moving the collector whisker.   It has been mentioned in the description of a hole that it can be acted upon by a magnetic field.   In addition, holes do not actually flow from the emitter to the collector in perfectly straight lines.   The motion of the holes toward the collector is due to the force of the electric field plus an ordinary diffusion action; the electrons traverse curved paths from emitter to collector, possibly approximating arcs of circles.

16. HOLE CHARACTERISTICS—RECOMBINATION

If a magnetic field of proper direction is applied across the slab, the diffusion of the holes into the slab is restricted and the current of holes can be made to flow more nearly in a straight line. As the holes move from emitter to collector, many of them collide with an electron associated with an atom, recombine, and disappear. This recombination is always going on and is one of the important phenomena in transistor action. The subject of recombination will be discussed more fully later on, but for this chapter it is sufficient to point out that, unlike the electron, the hole has a finite life. Typical values of average hole lifetime for single-crystal germanium lie in the range from a few microseconds to several thousand microseconds. The velocity of a hole is a fixed quantity. The velocity of the hole multiplied by its lifetime will determine the distance the hole will travel before recombination.

Since a straight line is the shortest distance between two points, it is clear that holes starting from the emitter that follow a straight line between emitter and collector will travel further before disappearing because of recombination as compared to those which travel in a curved path. The magnetic field, by forcing the holes into the upper portion of the block, compels them to follow paths which are more nearly straight lines. Experimentally it is observed that transistor action is obtainable at the collector in the presence of a magnetic field when the collector is physically spaced farther away from the emitter[4] than it is possible to space it when the magnetic field is turned off. This experimental fact, sometimes called the Suhl effect, tends to strengthen our belief that positive particles of some kind flow from emitter to collector in the case of the arrangement shown in Fig. 2-3.

17. SUMMARY

Summarizing the major points of this chapter, the reader is urged to retain the following essential points:

1. Transistor action in units of the type illustrated in Fig. 2-2 is characterized by power amplification.

2. It is necessary to introduce the concept of holes in order to explain transistor action.

3. For practical purposes, a hole may be considered to be a positively charged particle with a positive mass.

4. In the study of transistors, the reader must be prepared to consider and master new concepts which may be radically different from many of the scientific principles he has studied previously.

REFERENCES

1. The Transistor, Selected Reference Material on Characteristics and Applications, Contr. DA 36-039 sc-5589 (Task 3), p. 5, prepared by Bell Telephone Laboratories for Western Electric Co., Inc., New York, 1951.
2. Starling, S. G.: "Electricity and Magnetism for Advanced Students," Longmans, Green & Co., Ltd., London, 1935.
3. Shockley, W.: "Electrons and Holes in Semiconductors," pp. 178ff., D. Van Nostrand Company, Inc., New York, 1950.
4. Suhl, H., and W. Shockley: *Phys. Rev.*, Vol. 75, No. 10, pp. 1617–1618, May 10, 1949.

3 A GLIMPSE OF QUANTUM MECHANICS

In Chap. 2 an approximate explanation of transistor action was given. This introductory treatment of transistor theory demonstrates that the field of transistors is intimately connected with the study of solid materials in general and with semiconductors in particular. The principles governing the behavior of solid materials are collectively referred to as solid state theory.

18. SEMICONDUCTOR TERMS

Like any other specialized branch of the sciences, the field of semiconductors uses its own terms and definitions. This nomenclature cannot be explained in all cases by using the concepts normally encountered in electronics. New and very general concepts which describe the basic behavior of matter and energy must be introduced to aid in explaining clearly the terms commonly used in semiconductor and transistor work.

As an illustration, in the study of transistors it is difficult to avoid the use of such terms as energy levels, forbidden bands, and quantum states. The explanation of these terms may be more readily understood if the reader is first introduced to some of the fundamental principles of quantum mechanics. Accordingly, a few of the elementary principles will be given in this chapter as preparation for further study of semiconductors and transistors.

Consider an airtight box whose inside walls are lined with a thick layer of felt. Over the felt has been deposited a heavy, uniform layer of lampblack to provide a smooth, flat inside surface. Such an enclosure absorbs all the frequencies in the light of visible range and reflects none, and is called a black body.[1] It is very significant in the field of physics because of all the absorbers of radiation known a black body is the most perfect.

If energy in the form of radiation (heat or light) were introduced into this box through a tiny hole in one end, it would bounce back and forth from wall to wall, ultimately being almost totally absorbed. The energy would merely raise the temperature of the black body. It can be shown that this simple structure is the ideal absorber and the ideal radiator. Physicists have found that the behavior of the black body can be described in relatively simple mathematical terms.

A bolometer[2] is a device capable of measuring minute amounts of heat energy. It consists of a very sensitive Wheatstone bridge. One arm of the bridge is a very fine coated wire used as a probe. When heat energy falls on this fine wire, the change in resistance of the wire is measured by the Wheatstone bridge. With suitable calibration, the readings of the Wheatstone bridge can be converted into energy values in some convenient unit such as ergs. In this way physicists for nearly a hundred years have been able to measure minute amounts of heat or radiant energy. By using single-colored or single-frequency filters it is possible with the aid of the bolometer to determine the amount of energy contained in each frequency component of the radiation being studied.

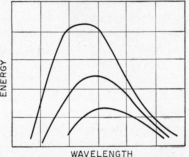

Fig. 3-1. Curves of black-body radiation, showing variation of energy with wavelength. The peaks of energy increase in absolute magnitude with temperature and shift toward the shorter wavelengths.

19. BLACK-BODY RADIATION

Now, we have just said that the black body is the most perfect radiator. This implies that of all possible radiators not only will the black body give off the maximum amount of radiant energy, but also that the radiant energy will contain the widest range of frequencies. If one makes a tiny hole in the black body and inserts a bolometer probe, for a given temperature of the black body the variation or distribution of the energy with frequency is shown by the curves in Fig. 3-1. Much can be said about these curves, but it is actually not important for future applications in the study of transistors. The reader need merely note that these curves are obtained by a straightforward process from a simple and fundamental experiment.

The bolometer is capable of measuring temperature very accurately. The experiment described above can be made under careful control and with almost no special equipment. The distribution of black-body radiation was known to physicists as far back as the 1890s.

The data were so accurate and fundamental it was felt that if the physicists could explain the curves obtained, whatever theory of matter was proposed as a basis for the explanation stood an excellent chance of being the ultimately correct theory of the structure of matter.

It must be understood that at the time we are speaking about, at the turn of the century, the tremendous strides in science that have been made in the last 50 years were unknown. Physicists were groping about for a theory of the structure of matter which would explain such phenomena as were then known, for instance, this black-body radiation. Since the black body is such a simple structure, so easily described by the very elementary laws of thermodynamics (which is the science of the flow of heat), it was felt that this black-body radiation was an ideal phenomenon on which to test such theories of the structure of matter as might be conceived by the best brains at the turn of the century. Some of the outstanding physicists who lived about the year 1900 tried their hand at proposing a theory of matter on the basis of which a formula could be obtained involving the energies, the wavelength, and the temperature which would give a curve that would fit Fig. 3-1. Based on the knowledge available at that time in the fields of mathematics and physics, the best brains in the world of these sciences, alone and in combination, tried to arrive at a theory of matter which would result in a mathematical curve to fit these black-body radiation curves, but to no avail.[3]

20. PLANCK'S THEORY TO EXPLAIN BLACK-BODY RADIATION

An obscure professor of thermodynamics, Max Planck, came to the conclusion that one or more of the fundamental assumptions that were being made by these eminent physicists must be inadequate or entirely incorrect. Planck asked himself what assumption must be made, regardless of whether it was reasonable or not, in order that the theory of matter based on this assumption would lead to a mathematical expression to fit the curve.

Generally speaking, this kind of thinking is both unscientific and unwise. It is called an *ad hoc* theory, that is, it is a theory compounded to fit a specific set of facts and these facts only, ignoring various associated phenomena. While such a theory usually fits the facts, it is frowned upon by the scientific world, because in nearly all cases of such *ad hoc* theories, it is not long before additional data are uncovered which the theory, made to fit only a specific set of facts, fails to explain. For this reason, the physicists of the day paid very little attention to Planck's hypothesis.

What was it that Planck actually proposed? Planck found that he could write a mathematical expression to fit the curve of black-body radiation if he assumed that the molecules of the material of which the black body was made, namely, the molecules of the lampblack, could oscillate or vibrate under the action of the heat energy supplied and that each molecule thus became a little generator of high-frequency energy or an oscillator. Thus far his assumption was not too far different from that made by the other physicists. But Planck broke sharply from the assumptions made by the others when he said that these microscopic oscillators can generate energy only in integral multiples of a unit amount of energy which we shall call simply E (*i.e.*, the least amount of energy that any oscillator could have would be E ergs or joules or any other unit of energy). Thereafter, all other oscillators might generate $2E$, $3E$, $10E$, $72E$, and so on, but never, say, $2.5312E$ ergs or units of energy, or $3.5E$ units, or $7.7E$ units. In short, the basic unit of energy E could be multiplied only by an integer, or a whole number, when describing the energy of any other oscillator, and all intermediate values of energy were arbitrarily omitted from further consideration in Planck's theory. This hypothesis received little attention for several years.

21. PHOTOELECTRIC EFFECT—EINSTEIN[4]

When light strikes certain surfaces such as zinc, electrons are knocked out from the metal surface. If a metal plate is then placed near the metal surface in a vacuum and made positive with respect to the zinc plate, electrons will flow to the positive plate and an electric current can be detected. Phototubes are made which employ this principle.

It might seem perfectly reasonable that, if the intensity of the light shining on the zinc plate is increased, the energy with which the light strikes the zinc atoms will be increased and the electrons knocked out from the zinc plate would have greater energy. This sounds reasonable but is entirely wrong. The actual fact observed experimentally is that the intensity of the light has nothing to do with the energy of electrons knocked out—it determines only the number of electrons liberated from the zinc plate. To get higher energy electrons out, the frequency of the light must be increased. The reader may be mildly surprised to learn that to get more electrons out or to increase the current, the intensity of the light must be increased; but, if higher energy electrons are required, the frequency of the light must be increased, using light toward the violet end of the spectrum.

The fact that the higher energy electrons are freed by the higher

frequencies of light was well known around 1905.   As in the case of
black-body radiation, physicists were unable to establish the mathematical relationship between energy and frequency.   When quite a
young man, Einstein tried to find this mathematical relationship.   He
found that, if he applied Planck's idea that the energy imparted to
the zinc plate by the light could occur only in integral multiples of a
fixed unit of energy E, there was a possibility that he could supply a
suitable equation.   For this basic unit of energy E, Planck had written
simply

$$E \text{ is proportional to } f, \text{ the frequency}$$

or

$$E = \text{constant} \times f$$

This constant, which is now known as Planck's constant, is given by
6.53×10^{-27} erg sec and is usually designated by the letter h.   So the
equation that Planck wrote for this basic unit of energy is

$$E = hf \tag{3-1}$$

The reader will observe that the unit of Planck's constant is erg
seconds and that of f is cycles per second.   In physics "cycles" is not
a bona fide unit, and the units of frequency will usually be found to
be given by "per second" or (time)$^{-1}$.   Dimensionally, $hf = E$

$$\text{erg seconds} \times \frac{1}{\text{seconds}} = \text{ergs}$$

With this convention the reader will see that the units of E are erg
seconds, times per second or erg which is the unit of energy, and the
relation is dimensionally correct.   Starting with this assumption of
Planck's and applying it to the photoelectric effect described above,
Einstein wrote an equation which stated simply that the kinetic energy
of an electron emitted from the photosensitive surface, $\frac{1}{2}mv^2$, is this
Planck energy hf minus a constant w_o which depends on the nature of
the photosensitive metal and is called a work function.   Thus Einstein
wrote

$$\tfrac{1}{2}mv^2 = hf - w_o \tag{3-2}$$

The reader should not concern himself too much with this equation as
it is merely incidental to the main subject, and a complete understanding of it, while desirable, will not be essential for our work.   The
important thing is that, by applying Planck's radically new idea,
Einstein derived this photoelectric equation which has been experimentally established as being correct and accurate and which fills
the need mentioned above for a quantitative formula to explain the

photoelectric effect. However, a single application like this one does not prove a theory, and the physicists of the time were not greatly impressed by an isolated success of so radical a theory.

22. SPECTRA AND THE QUANTUM THEORY[5]

Consider a pair of carbon electrodes with the lower one scooped out to form a hollow in the top where it faces the upper one. Into this hollow, pour a small quantity of fine chips of some element like copper or aluminum. In front of the space between the two carbon electrodes is placed a suitable prism. The reader is probably acquainted with the dispersion of light by a glass prism. We have all, at one time or another, seen how white light focused as a beam on a prism is broken up by the prism into its component colors or frequencies, the highest frequencies being bent most. This is how the range of colors, violet, indigo, blue, green, yellow, orange, red, is obtained, the violet being the highest frequency light. When an electric arc is struck between the carbon electrodes prepared as above, the nature or composition of the arc is affected by the element placed in the hollow. The element is vaporized by the heat of the arc, producing a large number of frequencies in the arc, and these are dispersed or separated by the prism. If a suitably treated photographic plate is placed nearby, lines will appear at regularly spaced intervals on the photographic plate, and these lines are referred to as a spectrogram. The instrument which produces the spectrogram is called a spectroscope, and the science which covers this subject is called spectroscopy.

The reason for the great importance of spectroscopy is that, for every element or compound, an experienced spectroscopist can tell exactly what elements were present in the sample from the spacing, width, and number of the lines. These spectrograms are "read" by recognizing the frequency corresponding to each line because the prism disperses the radiation components according to frequency in a unique and reproducible manner. For a long time scientists tried to understand why the frequencies were related in certain specific ways and tried to predict new lines in certain elements. Because of the importance of spectroscopy in metallurgical work, many capable physicists around 1905 concerned themselves with the problem of understanding and accounting for the observed lines. As they did not properly understand the fundamental laws of spectra, they were mostly content to derive empirical laws on the basis of which they could account for the observed lines. They could not derive these formulas from considerations of the structure of matter.

23. BOHR'S THEORY OF SPECTRAL FREQUENCIES

A number of series, or groups, of lines were known for the element hydrogen. From chemical findings it was known that hydrogen had only one electron associated with its nucleus. To explain the observed series, a physicist named Bohr tried to apply the Planck concepts about the energy occurring in discrete jumps to the orbit of the hydrogen electron. Not only did his theory fit the observed facts about the hydrogen atom and electron, but with very little difficulty Bohr was able to propose a simple formula which explained the frequencies of the lines in the hydrogen- and helium-atom spectra.

His formula went further—it predicted where to look for new lines beyond the range of equipment then available. When improved apparatus had been developed, the lines were found as Bohr had predicted. Thus, by application of Planck's rather radical innovation, Bohr was able to provide a satisfactory formula for the frequencies of the lines in the hydrogen series. Previous attempts to provide a formula based on classical concepts had failed.

24. SUCCESSES OF PLANCK'S THEORY

By this time, the Planck hypothesis had really begun to stack up an imposing array of successes. In addition to its use in the photoelectric equation, black-body radiation, and the frequency of spectral lines, Planck's hypothesis had been used by Debye in a highly successful theory of specific heat of solids. Also as a sort of corollary to Bohr's successful theoretical model of the hydrogen atom, it explained one of the most perplexing conflicts of the old or classical theory. It would seem reasonable that, if an electron rotates about a nucleus, the only way you can explain its not falling right into the nucleus, considering the negative charge on the electron and the positive charge on the nucleus, would be by assuming that its centrifugal force keeps it at a distance from the nucleus as a result of its circling motion. As long as it keeps on rotating it must be using up energy, and according to the old theory a rotating electron must, of necessity, keep radiating energy due to its motion. Granting that the amount of energy radiated is small, over a sufficiently long period of time enough energy would surely be radiated for the electron to rotate successively with less and less velocity until it fell into the nucleus. But of course we know that this does not happen, and yet this is an inexorable consequence of the old or classical theory.

The physicists who persisted in sticking to the classical theory were forced to admit that this glaring inconsistency in their old theory was very simply answered by quantum theory which, insisting that energy can be radiated in fixed bits or quanta only, does not require that an electron rotating about the nucleus radiate any energy at all. About 1913 the outstanding successes of Planck's hypothesis had convinced the physicists and mathematicians of the day that it had great merit. Let us examine somewhat more closely the precepts of Planck's theory.

25. THE CONCEPT OF DISCRETE ENERGY INCREMENTS

To the physicist, mechanics means the body of laws, all the mathematics and formulas, all the theorems and axioms, in short, all the rules that govern the description and explanation of a given science. Quantum mechanics is the body of rules and laws and mathematics which determines our description of the phenomena of nature in terms of quanta, or discrete amounts of something, such as energy or momentum. The ideas about the laws of nature as conceived prior to the advent of the quantum hypothesis are known as classical mechanics. The reader can imagine an experiment in which he raises the molecule of a substance a very small, an infinitesimally small, amount Δd. Potential energy may be defined as the weight of a body times the distance through which it is raised. If the change in height of the molecule is given by Δd, the change in its potential energy is given by $W \Delta d$. If we can make Δd extremely small, we can also make $W \Delta d$ quite small and thus change the energy by as small an amount as we please. But Planck's hypothesis says we cannot do this—the least amount by which energy may be changed is given by $E = hf$, where h is Planck's constant and f is a frequency associated with the molecule. Certainly the concept of energy varying in jumps or quanta does not appeal to the common sense as much as energy varying smoothly or having a continuous distribution. As we will see later, many of our ideas on logic are rudely disturbed by the mandates of quantum mechanics. The success of quantum mechanics lies in its ability to explain experimental data and to indicate new avenues of experimental investigation. Logic is subjective, and if the reader had been trained to think in terms of quanta or the discrete distribution of energy, he would probably be equally confused by a theory of continuous distribution of energy.

Quantum mechanics is introduced in these chapters on transistors because quantum mechanics is essential in the discussion of microscopic dynamics and because to understand transistor theory it is necessary to study the submicroscopic structure of a metal.

Because of the discreteness in the distribution of energy, particularly for electrons when within the field of influence of the nucleus, one does not speak of energy in general but speaks of "energy levels." An energy level means a specific fixed value of energy which is some whole number multiplied by hf. By speaking of an energy level, we imply that an adjacent energy value is another level not less than hf units of energy above or below the first-mentioned energy level. One can never find an energy level, say, $0.63hf$ or any other fraction of energy units above or below the first-mentioned energy level. Physically there are many ways of measuring the energy of an electron, and these measurements of energy are quite accurate and consistently confirm the preceding assertion. These are the facts we must accept even though we may wonder why no intermediate values are observed. We shall frequently be talking about energy levels, and the reader must understand that this means a discrete value of energy. The nearest possible adjacent level must be hf energy units above or below.

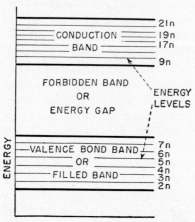

Fig. 3-2. Energy of a quantized particle, such as an electron. Only the ordinate is to scale. Figure shows how the energy of the particle, according to quantum mechanics, can change in discrete amounts only, often in large jumps.

26. ENERGY BANDS IN SEMICONDUCTORS[6]

For many reasons, such energy levels frequently occur in groups, and such a series of energy levels is called an energy band. There are some series of energy levels that are never observed experimentally. In other words, electrons have never been found that have energy levels in this series. Such groups of energy levels are called forbidden bands or energy gaps. The concept of energy bands and forbidden energy levels is of particular importance in the study of semiconductors and transistor theory.

The abscissa on Fig. 3-2 has no scale; a vertical series of points would do just as well. The ordinate is an arbitrary measure of energy in suitable units. At the top of Fig. 3-2 is shown a series of energy levels marked with possible, though not necessarily realizable, energy values, and this set of energy levels or ensemble of energy levels, as it is sometimes called, constitutes a band. It is called a conduction band to indicate that, in our discussion of germanium, electrons with energy levels that fall within this band are usually the ones which are taking part in the conduction process or are carriers of electric current. Below this conduction band, other energy levels are theoretically possible. In the case of germanium, at room temperature electrons that have energy values that fall in this range are never observed. These energy levels, which are not observed experimentally, constitute a forbidden band or energy gap.

27. ENERGY GAPS FOR SILICON AND GERMANIUM

An electron volt is a convenient measure or unit of energy used by physicists in the quantitative description of electrical phenomena. It is the energy acquired by an electron in falling through a potential difference of 1 volt. In terms of this measure of energy, the energy gap or forbidden bandwidth for the semiconductor germanium is about 0.7 electron volt and for silicon, another semiconductor used in transistors, 1.11 electron volts.[7] By contrast, this energy gap or forbidden band for a conducting metal is zero electron volts wide (*i.e.*, nonexistent). The width of the energy gap is a convenient way of classifying conductors, semiconductors, and insulators.

Refer again to Fig. 3-2. Below the forbidden band shown in Fig. 3-2 is a series of possible energy levels which in ensemble form a band. In a later chapter we shall see why it is called a valence-bond band. For the present we may say that these electrons are bound or fixed in their energy levels. These electrons cannot readily change their energy level or wander about under the influence of electric fields. Within the valence-bond band, one electron may usually be found at each of the possible energy levels. As the electrons cannot readily change their energy level, the entire band ordinarily remains filled and for this reason is sometimes referred to as the filled band. It follows that the conduction band may also be called the unfilled band.

28. VALENCE-BOND BAND (FILLED BAND)

The levels in the valence-bond band are below the levels in the conduction band. If sufficient energy is imparted to electrons in the valence-bond band by heating the material for example, electrons may acquire sufficient energy to jump across the energy gap and acquire the energies of the levels in the conduction band. The electrons never land within the forbidden band. Either they will acquire enough energy to appear suddenly at levels in the conduction band, or they will stay in the valence-bond band.

29. QUANTUM ANALYSIS AND MATHEMATICS

One other aspect of quantum mechanics may be added here to show again its difference from classical mechanics. The reader has seen mathematical proofs of certain physical phenomena; for instance, in any elementary text will be found a derivation of the law that

$$S = 0.5gt^2 + v_o t + s_o$$

indicating the distance a body will have fallen, after t sec, if it falls under the acceleration due to gravity g, with an initial velocity v_o, and an initial distance s_o from some reference height.   In classical mechanics, one would start with Newton's second law of motion and go through a series of logical, mathematically and physically consistent steps, to arrive at the result.

In quantum mechanics such a logical sequence of events is unnecessary and usually not found.   The original equation in quantum mechanics is a mathematical invention on the part of some great physicist-mathematician which has no physical counterpart or meaning whatever, or it need not have.   The equation is solved for its variables by a self-consistent mathematical process, entirely devoid of any physical meaning.   Only the result, the last equation, has meaning.

30. SCHROEDINGER'S EQUATION

As an illustration, the energy levels we have been discussing are all derivable from a very famous equation of mathematical physics called Schroedinger's equation[8]:

$$A \frac{\partial^2 \psi}{\partial x^2} + V\psi = B \frac{\partial \psi}{\partial t}$$

The E's in the solution are the energy levels that are possible or permitted, and the ψ's are the quantum states.   But the equation itself has no physical meaning whatever, and neither do the intermediate steps used in solving for the permissible energy levels and quantum states.   The reader can see again how quantum mechanics is unconcerned with what our minds consider as logical, common sense, or an orderly physical process—it seeks only to explain our experimental data, and this it does quite effectively.

31. SUMMARY

In summary, the following are the salient points of this chapter and should be retained for further study of transistor theory:

1. An electron, when in the sphere of influence of the nucleus, has certain possible, discrete values of energy, or energy levels, which are integer multiples of hf, f being a frequency associated with the electron. No intermediate values of energy are permitted.

2. When speaking of such an electron, one always speaks of its energy level; groups or ensembles of energy levels are called bands.

3. For a semiconductor, there is a conduction band, a forbidden band or energy gap, and a valence-bond band.

4. One electron can be distinguished from another by specification of its quantum state.

5. In quantum mechanics, every mathematical step does not necessarily have physical meaning—only to the last equation or result can there be imparted a physical significance.

REFERENCES

1. Richtmeyer, F. K., and E. H. Kennard: "Introduction to Modern Physics," pp. 145ff., McGraw-Hill Book Company, Inc., New York, 1947.
2. Pender, H., and K. McIlwain: "Electrical Engineers' Handbook," p. 15–04, John Wiley & Sons, Inc., New York, 1950.
3. Richtmeyer, F. K., and E. H. Kennard: "Introduction to Modern Physics," pp. 170ff., McGraw-Hill Book Company, Inc., New York, 1947.
4. Jauncey, G. E. M.: "Modern Physics," pp. 207–208, D. Van Nostrand Company, Inc., New York, 1938.
5. Bode, W. R.: "Chemical Spectroscopy," Chap. III, John Wiley & Sons, Inc., New York, 1943.
6. Glasstone, S.: "Theoretical Chemistry," pp. 142ff., D. Van Nostrand Company, Inc., New York, 1944.
7. Shockley, W.: "Electrons and Holes in Semiconductors," p. 22 (energy to break bond), D. Van Nostrand Company, Inc., New York, 1950.
8. Rojansky, V.: "Introductory Quantum Mechanics," p. 81, Prentice-Hall, Inc., New York, 1946; and Richtmeyer, F. K., and E. H. Kennard: "Introduction to Modern Physics," pp. 259ff., McGraw-Hill Book Company, Inc., New York, 1947.

4 THE ELECTRON

In this chapter, aspects of the nature of the electron which are important in the study of transistors will be presented. The popular concept of the electron as a small "ball of fire" is usually adequate for the study of electronics but inadequate for the study of semiconductors used in transistors. The mental picture of the electron to be developed not only is satisfactory for transistor theory, but is also more in keeping with the principles of modern physics than the oversimplified ball-of-fire idea. In the study of transistor theory, it is necessary to examine the microscopic structure of the solid material because attention is focused on the interaction of an electron with its environment within the solid. This chapter on the nature of the electron, and the previous chapter on quantum mechanics, will provide the reader with the background necessary for a basic understanding of the principles of semiconductors.

32. PARTICLE PICTURE OF THE ELECTRON

There is considerable evidence that the electron is a small solid-like particle sometimes called a "corpuscle." Some of the experiments which strengthen the idea of a corpuscular electron are already known to the reader. For instance, the electrons emitted from a hot filament in a cathode-ray tube are known to strike the fluorescent screen and by their bombardment create a small bright spot. A simple explanation of this bright area is based on the assumption that the electrons are small solid particles whose action on the screen is analogous to the action of the sand in a sandblasting gun such as used to clean walls.

One of the proofs that electricity is granular in nature and occurs in integral multiples of a reference or unit amount was established by Millikan[1] in his oil-drop experiment. In this experiment, fine drops of oil were suspended between the plates of a condenser. Each drop of oil was electrically charged. By adjusting the electric field between the plates, the gravitational force on these oil drops was carefully counterbalanced by the strength of the electric field, and the rate of rise or fall of the drops was measured. From computations it was then evident that in all cases the charged oil drop behaved as if it carried a

charge which was some integer times a fixed amount of charge. This fixed amount of charge is now considered to be the charge on the electron. Our belief that the electron is corpuscular in nature is based in part on the results of this experiment.

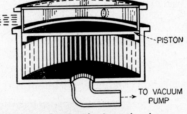

Fig. 4-1. Sectional view showing essentials of Wilson cloud chamber. When the air in the upper chamber is suddenly expanded by rapid downward motion of the piston, the water vapor in the air, on cooling, will condense on charged particles which may be in the chamber.

33. CLOUD-CHAMBER EXPERIMENT

Another in the series of experiments which furnishes evidence that the electron is corpuscular in nature is the Wilson cloud-chamber[2] experiment, Fig. 4-1. This experiment is based on the fact that, if air saturated with water vapor is allowed to expand suddenly and is then cooled, it condenses upon any charged particles that may be suspended within it. If these particles are moving through the chamber under the influence of an electric field, a track can be observed which marks the path of the charged particles as the water vapor

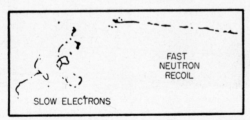

Fig. 4-2. Tracks of electrons as may be seen in a Wilson chamber. Fast electrons, such as may be accelerated by high potentials, will leave straight tracks like the neutron recoil track on the right.

condenses upon them. An electron, which is a charged particle, in passing through such a cloud chamber, will leave a distinct and observable track, Fig. 4-2. By suitably arranging electron emitters and positively charged plates in a Wilson chamber, the paths of two or more electrons may be made to intersect, sometimes resulting in a collision of two electrons. It is possible to show that the directions after collision are exactly what you would expect if two hard spherical bodies, like steel bearings, were to collide under comparable initial conditions.

The cathode-ray phenomenon, the oil-drop experiment, and the Wilson cloud-chamber experiment are examples of the large body of evidence that is available to support our belief that the electron behaves like a small solid particle or corpuscle.

34. ELECTRON DIFFRACTION

The important concept contained in this chapter is that, while some very convincing experimental data are available to prove that the elec-

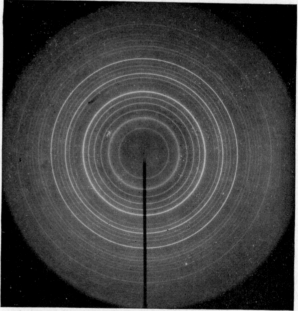

Fig. 4-3. A diffraction pattern such as may be observed due to electron diffraction through nickel crystals.   The pattern is for thallium chloride ($TlCl_3$) and shows the circular patterns obtained in such diffraction processes.

tron behaves like a corpuscle, it is a paradox that equally convincing data are available to prove that the electron behaves like a wave.   The experimental results to be described can be interpreted only by assuming that the electron is a wave just as the experimental results described in the preceding section may be explained only by assuming that the electron is a particle.   A wave is considered to be an energy front which varies or oscillates at a definite frequency, but has itself no physical or tangible existence.

In general, light travels in straight lines. However, when it passes through a fine slit in an opaque material, a certain amount of bending into the areas that would otherwise be in perfect shadow is observed. This diffraction, as the spreading or bending is called, results in areas of reinforcement and interference which appear on a suitable screen as a characteristic pattern, Fig. 4-3. It is important to note that only waves can be diffracted; the diffraction of a particle has no meaning.

An accurate determination of the wavelength of light can be made by use of the diffraction phenomenon if the width of the slit and the distance to the screen on which the light is focused after passing through the slit are known. This is one of the important methods for measuring the wavelength of light. One requirement for such an experiment, however, is that the width of the slit through which the light passes must be of the order of magnitude of the wavelength; otherwise the amount of the diffraction is negligible. By mechanical ruling techniques using scratches made by a diamond tip, diffraction slits as narrow as 10^{-5} cm can be produced. Certain materials have their atoms arranged in layers, and the space between the layers may serve as a diffracting slit for radiations of very short wavelength. For nickel, the spacing between atomic layers is of the order of 10^{-8} cm.

35. DE BROGLIE'S PREDICTION*

On the basis of a mathematical analysis, De Broglie predicted that electrons should be subject to diffraction in the same way that light waves are diffracted when they pass through a fine slit in a piece of opaque material. About 1927 two experimental physicists, Davisson and Germer, devised an experiment to test De Broglie's hypothesis by passing electrons through a nickel slab.[3] Since only a wave can suffer diffraction, a diffraction pattern should be obtained only if the electron possesses wave properties. On the strength of De Broglie's prediction, Davisson and Germer performed the electron-diffraction experiment using nickel crystals and obtained clear and unmistakable diffraction patterns, such as in Fig. 4-3. As stated in the preceding paragraph, if the width of the slit and the distance to the surface on which the pattern appears are known, the wavelength of the incident radiation

* The great interest in quantum mechanics which gathered momentum with Bohr's formulas for the spectral lines led to a rapid development of quantum mechanics and its extension by men such as De Broglie to an even more general and powerful science called "wave theory." It was from the fundamental concepts of wave theory that De Broglie predicted the wavelength of the electron and therefore the possibility for diffraction of the electron.

can be computed. When such a computation was made for this experiment, the value of λ (wavelength) obtained agreed almost perfectly with that predicted by De Broglie.[4]

Physicists have considered that there is a finite probability that the diffraction patterns observed may be explained on the basis of collisions between the electrons and the atomic layers in the nickel crystal. The probability of collisions is influenced by the following:

1. The diameter of the electron as obtained from data where its corpuscular nature is evident is of the order of 10^{-13} cm.

2. The atomic layers of the nickel crystals are spaced 10^{-8} cm apart.

3. From 1 and 2, the spacing is 100,000 times the diameter of the electron.

4. The current used in the experiment was only 10 to 15 electrons per second.

5. The dimensions of the atomic layers are very large compared with the diameter of the electron.

Taking into consideration all these facts, it is possible to show that the probability of collisions between electrons and atomic layers is negligibly small. With the possibility of collisions ruled out, science knows of only one explanation for the diffraction patterns observed: the electron is a wave phenomenon. Based on the experiments by Davisson and Germer and experiments made since by others, it is now generally conceded that the electron behaves like an electromagnetic wave.

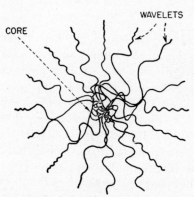

WAVELETS

CORE

Fig. 4-4. Artist's conception of the wave packet. Various frequency and amplitude and phase components synthesize to give a knot of waves having the characteristics both of a wave and a corpuscle.

36. WAVE-PACKET PICTURE OF THE ELECTRON

In the two preceding sections it has been indicated that the observed results are explainable in some experiments only by assuming that the electron is a particle and in others only by assuming that it is a wave. The concept of the "wave packet" has been developed to assist in reconciling the wave and particle dualism of the electron.[5]

The point of view to which the number of objections is minimum is the assumption that the electron, exhibiting as it does both wave and corpuscular properties, consists of a fortuitous conglomeration or concentration of waves of different frequency, as in Fig. 4-4. The common intersection of these waves produces a core or center which acts, it is thought, like the solid particle observed in the experiments mentioned in the opening paragraphs of this chapter, while the wavelets may account for the wave properties. This is clearly an *ad hoc* solution to the problem of reconciling the wave and particle dualism, but it is the best theory available.

Henceforth, though we shall speak of electrons, the reader is asked to bear in mind that we shall actually be referring to wave packets. Holes, which are similar to electrons in many ways, are also thought to be best represented by wave packets.

37. ELECTRON LOCATION—HEISENBERG'S PRINCIPLE

Having concluded that the electron may be regarded as a wave packet, consider next the problems associated with the location of the electron at any time. The location of electron position is limited in practice by a principle first enunciated by Heisenberg in 1927 and called the indeterminacy or uncertainty principle.[6]

Heisenberg's equation defines the limits of accuracy with which we can determine certain extrinsic parameters which describe microscopic particles:

$$\Delta(mv)\ \Delta x \geqq h \qquad (4\text{-}1)$$

The momentum p is defined as the product of mass times velocity, written

$$p = mv \qquad (4\text{-}2)$$

analogously to the way in which energy E is defined as the product of force F times distance x, or

$$E = Fx \qquad (4\text{-}3)$$

The mv in Eq. (4-1) may be the momentum of an electron, for example. This momentum is frequently useful in describing the behavior of particles.

Equation (4-1) states that the error in the determination or measurement of the momentum mv times the error in the determination or measurement of its position x from some reference point will always be equal to or greater than Planck's constant h in magnitude. For our purposes it is unnecessary to go into the derivation of this equation now, but it is important to note that this equation was derived from rigorous mathematical physics, and no experimental evidence has ever been found which contradicts it. Equation (4-1) sets a limit to the accuracy with which we may measure any two quantities that describe an electron when the product has the units of Planck's constant and when both quantities are being measured at the same time. Let us put some figures into this equation to get some idea of the orders of magnitude we are talking about.

The mass of the electron is approximately 9.1×10^{-28} g. The velocity of an electron when accelerated by a potential of approximately 1,000 volts is of the order of 2×10^9 cm per sec, and this velocity can be measured to within about 1,000 cm per sec, so that Δv, the error in v, is 1,000 cm per sec. In Eq. (4-1) three quantities are involved on the left-hand side: m, v, and x. Assume that in a given experiment, as is usually the case, only the velocity v and the displacement x would be measured. The mass is usually assumed to be known in experiments where the indeterminacy principle is applied. If we regard the Δ in Eq. (4-1) to have the same effect as the differential symbol of elementary calculus, Eq. (4-1) may be written, since $m = \text{constant}$,

$$m \, \Delta v \, \Delta x \geq h \qquad (4\text{-}4)$$

Using now the values mentioned,

$$9.1 \times 10^{-28} \times 10^3 \times \Delta x = 6.6 \times 10^{-27} \text{ erg-sec}$$

or

$$\Delta x = 0.73 \times 10^{-2} \text{ cm}$$

Since we are only interested in magnitudes, let us round this figure off and call the error in the determination of the distance one-hundredth of a centimeter. This is not too large an error, and it would seem that our ability to measure a distance to within 0.01 cm should be satisfactory for most applications. In measurements on a microscopic level, however, 0.01 cm is a tremendous error because it is so large compared to the dimensions of the particles. It has already been mentioned in connection with our discussion of the grating experiment that the diameter of the electron is of the order of 10^{-13} cm. If the error in determining the position of the electron from some reference point is of the order of 10^{-2} cm, it means that we can determine its position to within

$$\frac{10^{-2}}{10^{-13}} = 10^{11} = 100,000,000,000 \text{ diameters}$$

38. MACROSCOPIC EXAMPLE

Let us put it differently: the room in which the reader may find himself is probably under 20 ft long, but the actual dimension is not too important here. One hundred billion times the length of the room is approximately 400 million miles. Suppose you, the reader, commissioned a physicist to locate the room that you are in from some reference point, say the North Pole. What would be your reaction if the physicist said that he could locate your room from the North Pole with an error no less than 400 million miles?

But let us say that in the measurement of the velocity a larger error can be tolerated. Let us be quite liberal about it and agree that we will tolerate a 100 per cent error in the measurement of the velocity. Will this help us locate the electron more closely? To compute the new Δx, our Δv of Eq. (4-4) is now 2×10^9 and we have

$$9.1 \times 10^{-28} \times 2 \times 10^9 \, \Delta x = 6.6 \times 10^{-27}$$
$$\Delta x = 0.36 \times 10^{-8}$$

We now see, again rounding off this figure since only orders of magnitude are important, that the error in our determination of the position is now fully 100,000 times the electron diameter. From a physical experimental viewpoint such data have no important value, in spite of the fact that a 100 per cent error in our determination of the velocity or the momentum has been assumed.

39. MEANING OF THE UNCERTAINTY PRINCIPLE

What does this mean? It means that in a simultaneous measurement of momentum and position or of energy and time, or of any two parameters whose product has the dimensions of Planck's constant, our ability to obtain precise information is extremely limited because we are working on a microscopic level. To measure the position of an electron alone, having no knowledge at the same time of its momentum or energy, provides the physicist with rather useless data. When he tries to measure both at the same time, the uncertainty principle shows that if he wants to measure the momentum he has virtually no knowledge of where the electron may be. It is for this reason that the physicist does not attempt to specify the exact location of an electron at a given time. The reader will see a physical reason for the validity of the uncertainty principle from the following analysis.

40. LIGHT DISTURBS ELECTRON POSITION

The sight of an object indicates that light has struck the object, has been reflected into the eye, and has energized the nerve impulses that convey to the brain a specific intelligence. As pointed out in Chap. 3 the emission of electrons from a surface bombarded by light is a quantum effect. It is convenient to speak of particles called photons, with an energy hf, which do the bombarding.   When we say, therefore, that light strikes an object we see, we are saying that photons, each of energy hf, strike the object.   When these photons strike a large object, for instance a ball, the action of the photon on this very large mass produces no perceptible motion of the ball.

This is on a *macroscopic* level. If, however, the object we were trying to see were an electron, the photon striking the electron would cause a large and important displacement of the electron.[7]   When the photon bounces off the electron and into the eye of the observer, it appears to come from a point where the electron was before its displacement by the photon.   By the time the light information arrives at the eye, however, the electron is far removed from the point where the light information says it is.   Hence on a *microscopic* level the tools for observation so seriously disturb whatever is being observed that information is subject to the very large errors specified by the indeterminacy principle.

41. PROBABILITY OF LOCATING ELECTRONS

Inability to specify exactly or even within some reasonable error the position of an electron has led to an entirely new approach in the specification of the position of an electron when at the same time other useful information must be known.   In physics today, therefore, as an outgrowth of the uncertainty principle we do not say that an electron with a certain energy will be at a given point at a certain time, but we speak of the probability that the electron will be at a certain point. In picturing the electron, therefore, in our minds it is naive to the point of being incorrect to think of the electron as being represented by a point which is in motion about a nucleus.   In the case of the hydrogen atom with one electron, outside the nucleus, a more correct picture is as shown in Fig. 4-5, where we see the electron represented as a smeared-out or hazy region about the nucleus.   The light regions farther from the nucleus represent smaller orders of probability that the electron may be found there.

The probability of finding the electron is actually the highest in carefully defined mathematical orbits, which are of no particular interest to us at this time, but it is important that the reader realize that thinking about an electron as a point charge or even as a wave packet as in Fig. 4-4 is not strictly correct because of the impossibility of actually seeing such a picture in practice.   The smeared-out region of Fig. 4-5 is really all that can be pictured in the mind.   Consider a propeller blade spinning at high speed.   If the propeller never came to rest and you never saw it except spinning, the only picture of the system that you could permit yourself to visualize would be as a blur. By analogy, the electron, which can never be brought to rest and examined, can be visualized only as a blur or hazy region.

With these ideas in mind it is essential to remember that such pictures or sketches as the reader may see which show electrons as little dots or small dashes (for the negative sign) are symbolic only, much as a condenser represented by two parallel lines on a schematic diagram does not necessarily consist of two plates at all. Failure to remember

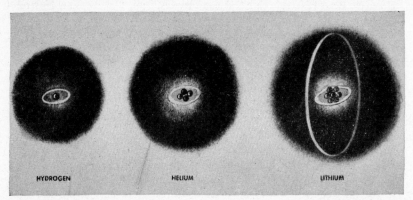

HYDROGEN   HELIUM   LITHIUM

Fig. 4-5. The diffused picture (artist's conception) of the electrons about the nucleus. The white elliptical curve indicates a typical orbit, not a fixed orbit. The very hazy fringes indicate regions where the probability of finding the electron is very small.

that these pictures are symbolic only will lead to confusion when in subsequent chapters we discuss the transistor action in the solid germanium material on a microscopic level.

42. SUMMARY

In summary, the reader should retain the following salient points from this chapter:

1. In certain phenomena, particularly when the surroundings in which the electron finds itself are very large compared to its diameter, the electron behaves like a minute bit of matter, or a corpuscle.

2. In certain phenomena where the surroundings are of the order of magnitude of its size, the electron behaves like an electromagnetic wave.

3. This wave-particle dualism of the electron is conveniently expressed by the concept that the electron is a wave packet, representing a fortuitous combination of waves of suitable frequency and amplitude into an entity having characteristics both of a particle and a wave.

4. In specifying the position of an electron, we speak of the proba-

bility of its being at a certain point, and because of this fact it is best to consider the electron as a smeared-out or diffused wave packet in the region about the nucleus.

5. The pictorial representation of the electron as a dot or dash is symbolic only.

REFERENCES

1. Hoag, J. B.: "Electron and Nuclear Physics," pp. 2–6, D. Van Nostrand Company, Inc., New York, 1949.
2. Hoag, J. B.: "Electron and Nuclear Physics," pp. 452–453, D. Van Nostrand Company, Inc., New York, 1949.
3. Brown, T. B.: "Foundations of Modern Physics," pp. 135–139, John Wiley & Sons, Inc., New York, 1949.
4. Richtmeyer, F. K., and E. H. Kennard: "Introduction to Modern Physics," pp. 252–253, McGraw-Hill Book Company, Inc., New York, 1947.
5. Stranathan, J. D.: "The Particles of Modern Physics," p. 554, The Blakiston Company, New York, 1948.
6. Slater, J. C., and N. H. Frank: "Introduction to Theoretical Physics," pp. 333–339, McGraw-Hill Book Company, Inc., New York, 1933.
7. Krauskopf, K. B.: "Fundamentals of Physical Science," pp. 327–329, McGraw-Hill Book Company, Inc., New York, 1953.

5 NATURE OF SEMICONDUCTORS

In the three preceding chapters concepts particularly appropriate to transistor theory and not normally encountered in the study of vacuum tubes have been discussed. A superficial view of transistor operation was given, and simplified principles of quantum mechanics were considered which will assist in a deeper understanding of transistor action. In addition, special aspects regarding the nature of the electron have been reviewed for use in the analysis of the microscopic structure of the solid materials used in transistors. In this chapter the reader will observe the application of these very general theorems to the study of germanium and silicon and will gain a better insight into the nature and structure of semiconductors.

43. ATOM STRUCTURE

In this section we shall be concerned primarily with the germanium and silicon atoms, as the general subject of atomic theory is beyond the scope of this book.[1] Mention has been made that the present theory of the structure of matter envisions a nucleus containing protons (+) about which are distributed electrons (−) in sufficient quantity so that the total charge of the atom is zero. It is essential to bear in mind that the *normal* atom, if not disturbed or ionized, is *neutral* or has zero charge.

The electrons outside the nucleus are arranged in shells or rings, as indicated diagrammatically in Fig. 5-1. The atomic number of germanium is 32, and this means that there are 32 electrons rotating around the nucleus, as indicated. But as the reader may recall from the previous discussion it is not to be inferred that these electrons are at any time physically distributed as shown—the positions of the electron shown may, for convenience in thinking, be regarded as the most probable locations. An electron shown in the sketch as being in the outer ring of four, for instance, has a fairly large probability at various times of being just outside the nucleus and even closer to it than the two electrons of the inner ring. Similar remarks apply to all the other electrons. Thus the reader sees immediately that for electrons we always speak of probability with regard to their position, and only for convenience in discussion do we draw ultrasimplified

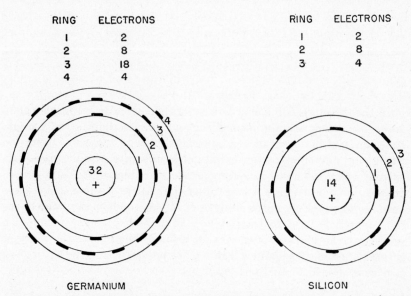

RING	ELECTRONS
1	2
2	8
3	18
4	4

RING	ELECTRONS
1	2
2	8
3	4

GERMANIUM   SILICON

Fig. 5-1. Schematic representation of germanium and silicon atoms to show electron rings surrounding the nucleus. Note the 2-8-18-4 arrangement for germanium and the 2-8-4 arrangement for silicon. The first three rings for germanium and the first two for silicon are complete rings. Note how the sum of the plus charges in the nucleus and the minus charges in the rings adds to zero.

sketches like Fig. 5-1. More correctly, we should show a smeared-out picture as in Fig. 4-5.

For purposes of discussion, we may consider that an atom consists of a nucleus surrounded by one or more concentric rings of electrons. A ring is regarded as *complete* if it has a particular number of electrons associated with it. The ring nearest the nucleus, or ring 1, requires *two* electrons to be complete. The next outer ring, ring 2, has *eight* electrons, and ring 3 has *eighteen* electrons (eight for argon) when complete. Note, therefore, that both the position of the ring and the number of electrons in it must be known to determine whether a particular ring is complete. The significance of the term "complete ring" will become more apparent from the following discussion.

44. IONIZATION ENERGY

It is possible to knock out one or more electrons from any of the rings about the nucleus.   In the case of the incomplete rings such as the outer rings of four electrons shown for the two elements in Fig. 5-1, it is possible to cause an additional electron or more to become attached to the atom in the incomplete ring.   In either case, whether the atom gains an electron or more or loses an electron or more, the atom is said to be *ionized*.   To knock out electrons from the various rings of the atom requires energy.   This energy may be obtained, for example, from heat in the form of thermal agitation, by bombardment by some other particle, or by subjecting the atom to electric fields, etc.

One of the ways of determining in which ring of an atom a given electron exists is by measurement of the amount of energy required to ionize the atom with respect to an electron in that particular ring. The study of ionization of atoms[2] is quite complex and actually need not concern us here to any great extent.   It is essential, however, to bear in mind: (1) The ionization energy for an electron in an inner ring is greater than that for an electron in an outer ring.   (2) For a given position of a ring with respect to the nucleus, let us say it is the second ring, more energy is required to remove an electron from a complete or full ring than from an incomplete or unfilled ring.

45. PROBABILITY OF TRANSITIONS

In general, when an electron is at a given energy level, there is a greater probability that it may move or jump to a lower level than to a higher level because, to jump to a higher level, energy from some outside source must be supplied.   On the other hand, because of random processes, there is a finite probability that an electron will jump to a lower level.   The point of interest here is that, in consequence of this simplified picture, electrons in the states of higher energy have a greater probability of change or transition to new levels than electrons in the lower energy levels.   If an electron changes its energy level frequently or the probability of such change of energy is large, we say that the electron is in an *unstable* state, and contrariwise, if the probability for an energy transition is small, the electron is in a *stable* state.

46. STABLE ELECTRONS

It has been pointed out in the preceding paragraphs that:

1. The amount of energy which must be supplied to an atom to remove an electron from a completed ring is greater than for an incom-

plete ring.   This is because the energy levels of the electrons in the completed rings are lower than for the incomplete rings.

2. Electrons in the lower energy levels have a smaller probability of transition to different levels than those in the higher energy levels; therefore, the lower energy level electrons tend to be more stable.

From these two statements it follows that the electrons in the completed rings are more stable than those in the incompleted rings.   This is actually the crux of the matter that will be of interest to us.   It may be further remarked that, if a certain state of a system is more stable than another, the probability will always be greater of finding this system in the stable state.   Because the stable condition is the one of highest probability, in certain substances, some natural and some artificial, the atoms tend to adjust themselves and their electrons into a state of stability.

Whereas the atoms of the elements are frequently found in an ionized condition, the ionization is restricted to the incomplete rings, the full rings seldom, if ever, being found in an ionized condition. As a result, simple chemical compounds involve interactions among the electrons in the incomplete rings only, and for this reason these electrons are called the "valence" electrons (Latin: *valeo*, to be worth, or to be strong).   Because only the valence electrons enter into chemical combinations under normal circumstances, diagrammatically only the valence electrons are usually shown and the complete rings are understood and omitted.   In subsequent diagrams for the germanium and silicon atoms, we shall therefore show only the four valence electrons.

47. VALENCE BONDS

In Fig. 5-2 are shown several atoms of carbon.   Carbon is tetravalent (four valence electrons), atomic number 6, and the two electrons of the inner ring are not shown, as per the convention mentioned. Note that for the inner ring two electrons constitute a completed ring. In the particular substance whose atomic structure is shown by this crude sketch, the valence electrons of atom 1 are shared, as it were, with the valence electrons of atoms 2, 3, 4, and 5.   With this arrangement atom 1 behaves as though its second or outer ring were now complete and had eight electrons in it.

Admittedly this is oversimplified, but the observed fact is that an electron in an incomplete ring, and having an energy level E_1, is actually found to occupy a lower energy level E_2 when it is part of an electron-sharing arrangement, such as shown in Fig. 5-2.[3]

Whatever is said about a single atom and its electrons in reality applies to the countless myriads of such atoms and electrons which constitute the semiconductor material. Each electron of an atom such as 1 is shared with a suitable nearby valence electron such as from atom 2, and this pair of electrons thus may be said to form a bond, which, because it involves valence electrons, is called a "valence bond." This term is part of the basic terminology in semiconductor theory and is frequently encountered in the analysis of transistor action.

The four valence bonds shown for the carbon atoms give rise to a type of substance which the reader knows as diamond. Of particular significance in transistor work is the fact that the atomic structure for pure germanium and silicon is exactly as shown for diamond in Fig. 5-2. One need merely write Ge and Si in the place of the C in the figure to have the correct picture.

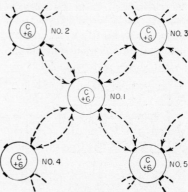

Fig. 5-2. Covalent bond structure in a tetravalent atom lattice. Such valence bonds may involve atoms of carbon (diamond form), germanium, or silicon, among others. Note how each electron is bound by the valence bond and is not free to take part in the conduction process.

48. SEMICONDUCTORS AND NUMBER OF ELECTRONS

Interesting and useful information about silicon and germanium can be deduced just from the simple picture of the valence-bond structure. First, let us state the axiom, well known to the reader, that in order to have electric current there must be carriers of electric current. Except for the special cases when the carriers may be holes, as discussed in Chap. 2, the carriers are electrons. As a corollary, if large numbers of electron carriers are available, the current may be large and, other things being equal, we say that the circuit involved has low resistance or high conductivity. Contrariwise, if the number of available or free electrons is small, the circuit has high resistance or low conductivity. When we say that an electron is free, we mean that it is not in the sphere of influence of the nucleus or that it is not in a circumnuclear ring. When an electron is in a valence bond, it is in a stable state of low energy, is considered to be bound in the valence bond, and is not free to take part in conduction.

From the preceding statements we may reason as follows:

1. Most of the electrons in a material whose structure involves valence bonds are bound.

2. Very few electrons are free to take part in the conduction process.

3. Since the number of electrons free to take part in conduction is small, the material is not a good conductor.

4. Since the three preceding statements are applicable to germanium and silicon, these materials fall into the category of part-conductors, or semiconductors.

49. FORBIDDEN BAND OR ENERGY GAP

Because energy must be imparted to the electron to get it out of its orbit about the nucleus, it is fairly clear that free electrons have, in

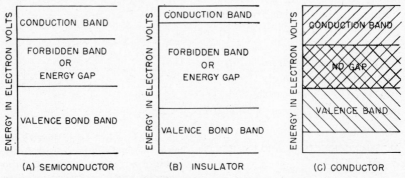

Fig. 5-3. Relation between conduction bands, forbidden bands, and valence-bond bands for conductors, semiconductors, and insulators. Note the overlapping bands for conductors, narrow forbidden band for semiconductors, and wide forbidden band for insulators.

general, a higher energy level than electrons in a ring whether the ring is completed or not.   As has already been defined in Chap. 3, a series or ensemble of adjacent energy levels is called an energy band.

In Fig. 5-3A is shown a sketch indicating a conduction band or the levels of energy of free electrons.   The ensemble of energy levels for the electrons in the valence bonds or "covalent bonds," as these are sometimes called, forms a band of energy levels which is called the "valence-bond band."   As indicated in Fig. 5-3A, the energy levels in the valence-bond band are lower than the energy levels in the conduction band.   The interesting point about this picture of the structure of germanium or silicon is that between these two bands is a series of energy levels which, for a given material, is never observed to exist.   These form an "energy gap" which is also called the "forbidden band."

An insight into the importance of this concept of forbidden bands, conduction bands, and valence-bond bands is obtained from the consideration that it is quite possible to classify the conductors, the semi-conductors, and the insulators by this means. In the case of conductors (see Fig. 5-3C), there is no forbidden band or energy gap at ordinary temperatures, there is an overlapping of the conduction and valence bands, and valence bonds may or may not exist. This implies that very large numbers of electrons whose energy falls in the conduction band are always present. In a given material if very large numbers of electrons with energies in the conduction band are always present, the material is a "conductor" by definition.

In the case of insulators the energy gap is very large, perhaps as high as 15 electron volts. The number of electrons which at room temperatures will acquire sufficient energy by thermal agitation alone to jump the gap and make the transition from the valence band to the conduction band will be small (see Fig. 5-3B). Bearing in mind from our previous discussions that the most probable state of the electron is in the lower energy levels or in the valence band, it may be seen that if the energy gap is large the number of electrons which will be found in the conduction band is small, and by definition the material is an "insulator."

50. SEMICONDUCTORS AND ENERGY GAPS

Semiconductors have a conductivity in the range between conductors and insulators and have an energy gap of the order of 1 electron volt. For the semiconductors germanium and silicon, the width of the forbidden band is 0.7 and 1.11[4] electron volts, respectively, and by comparison the energy to remove an electron when covalent bonds are not involved is of the order of 0.05 electron volt. Thus a useful criterion for classifying conductors, semiconductors, and insulators is on the basis of the width of the energy gap.

Because the energy gap for germanium and silicon is small, even at room temperatures some electrons are available for conduction, having broken from their valence bonds. While the number of electrons raised to the conduction level by thermal agitation is sufficient to place these two substances in the category of the semiconductors, it is insufficient to support a satisfactory degree of transistor action. Impurities such as arsenic (As), antimony (Sb), and boron (B) are frequently present in germanium and provide additional carriers to alter the conductivity. These and other impurities, gallium (Ga) and indium (In), for example, may be added in controlled amounts to produce a desired value of conductivity. Even the purest germanium now available contains sufficient impurities to provide free electrons or holes which materially increase the conductivity.

51. VALENCE BONDS OF PENTAVALENT IMPURITIES

In Fig. 5-4 is shown a basic arrangement consisting of an impurity atom, such as arsenic, in a matrix of germanium atoms. Arsenic is a pentavalent element, which means that its outermost and incomplete ring has five electrons. The closed rings of arsenic are three in number, consisting of two, eight, and eighteen electrons, respectively, and do not enter into the picture. As mentioned earlier in this chapter, these rings are not shown in the figure, but their presence must be understood.

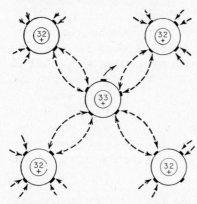

Fig. 5-4. Germanium crystal structure showing an atom of arsenic (center atom) replacing one of germanium to form its own valence bonds with adjacent atoms and leaving one electron to add to the possible current carriers. The fifth valence electron of the arsenic does not enter into a valence bond. A small amount of energy will bring this fifth electron up to the conduction band of energy levels where it can act as a carrier of current.

The atoms in a solid are arranged in a definite order or pattern and this specific arrangement of atoms is called a "lattice,"[5] (see Fig. 5-6). The positions of the atoms are called the "lattice sites," and when one atom displaces another from its normal lattice site, it is said to enter the lattice structure *substitutionally*. On the other hand, if an atom assumes a position within the volume generally enclosed by the lattice structure without being located at a lattice site, it is said to enter *interstitially*.

The important characteristic of certain types of pentavalent impurities such as arsenic or antimony is that they exhibit a greater affinity for certain lattice sites within the structure of the germanium than the germanium atoms normally at those sites. Arsenic may be added when the germanium is in a molten state, and upon solidification it is observed that arsenic atoms have entered the germanium lattice structure substitutionally. The electrons in the outer ring of the arsenic atom then form their own covalent bonds with adjacent neighbors, as Fig. 5-4 shows, and thereby form a stable structure for the electrons of both arsenic and germanium which are involved in the valence bonds. But arsenic is pentavalent, and there is one electron left over. There are no adjacent electrons for this excess electron to form covalent bonds with, and in accordance with the stability picture described, this electron is very easily ionized from the sphere of influence of the arsenic nucleus. It readily enters the conduction band to act as a free electron and a carrier. To remove such an electron from its ring, only about 0.05 volt is required, and this energy is readily available from thermal agitation at room temperature. By comparison, 0.72 volt would be required to remove this electron if it were in a covalent bond.

52. DONORS OF ELECTRONS

Thus the impurities provide additional carriers for this semiconductor at room temperature. Because these impurity atoms contribute an electron, they are called "doNors," and the reader will find it is a convenient mnemonic to note that we have capitalized the N to show that doNors give rise to N-type semiconductor material. The doNor is an important concept in the study of transistors, and it is essential that the reader understand its significance. N-type germanium is due to a "doNor impurity," and the majority carriers of electric current are Negative particles or electrons. The discussion here refers to a typical or prototype reorientation in the material, and in the actual germanium pellet used in the transistor, small as it is, there are myriads of such impurity atoms contributing corresponding numbers of electrons. In a sample of high-purity germanium, 1 impurity atom per 100 million germanium atoms is a typical ratio. Controlled amounts of impurities are added in the manufacture of transistors to obtain an optimum impurity concentration. In such purposely contaminated germanium samples, a comparable figure is 1 impurity atom per 10 million germanium atoms, or roughly ten times as many.

53. VALENCE BONDS AND TRIVALENT IMPURITIES

A trivalent impurity such as indium may be added to germanium when in the molten state, and upon solidification the atoms of indium, replace atoms of germanium in their lattice sites. Each indium atom robs an electron from a neighboring valence bond, bringing to four the number of electrons in its valence ring. Having robbed this electron, as shown in Fig. 5-5, the indium atom forms its own covalent bonds with adjacent germanium atoms and thereby enters into a stable arrangement in the lattice structure. The valence bond from which an electron has been taken now has a deficiency of one negative charge.

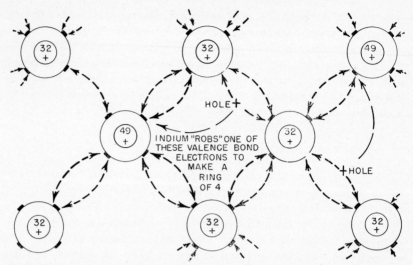

Fig. 5-5. Germanium crystal structure showing an atom of indium replacing one of germanium, adding an electron to its valence ring of three, then forming covalent bonds with its nearest neighbors. In the valence bond where the "robbed" electron had been, a hole is created.

54. MORE ACCURATE DEFINITION OF A HOLE

At this point it is suggested that the reader review the introductory definition of a hole which was given in Chap. 2. It was stated there that when an electron is removed from a neutral atom a positive charge is created and this is of the nature of a hole. However, it was pointed out that this is a preliminary definition and not the accurate one. Now we are prepared to give a more accurate definition of a hole. The particular net positive charge remaining when an electron is removed from a covalent bond is a hole; therefore, strictly speaking, holes are an attribute connected with atoms whose electrons enter into valence bonds. Merely removing an electron from a neutral atom does not create a true hole in the semiconductor sense of the word.

At this point it may be profitable to remind the reader that we are not talking about tiny balls of fire spinning about the nuclei, one of which has been removed to the indium atom. We are speaking of wave packets whose descriptive wave functions define the probability of finding these wave packets in the region of the germanium nucleus and whose quantum states are described by different quantum numbers when in a valence bond, compared to the quantum numbers when not in a valence bond.

The redistribution of the quantum states of the electrons in the system when one has been removed from a valence bond is for physico-mathematical purposes conveniently described in terms of the positive net charge remaining, and this convenient abstraction is called a "hole."[6]   When so regarded, the hole is endowed with a true positive mass, a true positive charge, a real velocity, and a real energy, and the system acts as if such a positive particle existed.   But as these few lines may indicate, the ball-of-fire picture is inadequate for such an analysis and if heedlessly applied on a microscopic level within the atomic structure of the solid will give inconsistent and inadequate explanations of observed phenomena.

55. P-TYPE GERMANIUM AND ACCEPTORS

Returning to our discussion of the action of the trivalent impurities, because the indium atom has taken on an additional electron, it is called an "accePtor" and the impurity which acts in this manner is called an "accePtor impurity."   The word accePtor is written with a capital P to serve as a mnemonic for the fact that the material thus created is said to be a P-type material because the majority carriers of current are the Positive charges or holes.   Holes are regarded as true carriers of electric current because observed conduction phenomena in semi-conductors can be explained only by the assumption that holes may play the same role in the conduction process as do electrons.   Nor-mally both electrons and holes are present in a semiconductor material, and both may act as current carriers in the conduction process.   In N-type germanium, electrons greatly outnumber the holes and are therefore referred to as the majority carriers; the holes are then called the minority carriers.   In P-type material where the holes outnumber the electrons, the holes are the majority carriers and the electrons are the minority carriers.

Normally N-type germanium is used in point contact transistors. Both N and P types are used in junction transistors.   These types of germanium plus I-type, intrinsic germanium, are the only ones that are known and used in transistors at present.   Information regarding the construction of transistors will be given in a later chapter.

56. LATTICE STRUCTURE AND CRYSTALS[7]

In Fig. 5-6 is shown the lattice structure or array for the germanium and silicon crystals.   A crystal may be regarded as the fundamental building block or iterative unit of which certain materials such as germanium and silicon are made.   When silicon and germanium freeze from their molten state, they invariably freeze as a series of small repeated units called "crystals." In Fig. 5-6 the lines which outline the cube show the fundamental unit to be a cubical solid or volume. It is not necessary for all the atoms which form the crystal to be entirely within this cubical volume. For instance, each of the corner atoms is shared by the eight crystals which have a common corner at that lattice site. The eight atoms which actually compose the crystal are arranged in a regular geometric pattern of three dimensions which is called the "lattice." For every such cubical unit or crystal all the atoms need not be at their lattice sites nor need the arrangement always be as regular as the figure implies. The existence of interstitial atoms has already been mentioned, but in addition irregularities in the form of dislocations of various kinds are the rule rather than the exception. References to order and disorder in the literature refer to the irregularities in the crystal structure.

Fig. 5-6. A three-dimensional representation of the crystal lattice of germanium. Note the hexagonal arrangement of the atoms. The corner atoms are considered as shared by eight similar cubic crystals with a common vertex, and the total contribution of all the corner atoms to a unit crystal is one atom. "Crystal" refers to the entire cubical structure; "lattice" refers to the arrangement of the atoms within the crystal volume.

57. MEANING OF SINGLE CRYSTAL

In speaking about crystals, it is particularly important to distinguish between the word crystal as used by the physicist and as used by the metallurgist. When the physicist says single crystal, he means the microscopic iterative unit consisting of atoms arranged as discussed previously. Regular and regularly arranged crystals as defined by the physicist which are formed without creating boundary planes or so-called grain boundaries compose a single crystal in the sense of the metallurgist. The crystal of the metallurgist is a large single piece of metal which may, in some cases, weigh several pounds. In examining a crystal, the polycrystalline structure is recognized by the presence of lines on the surface of the material. The single crystal is recognized by the complete absence of such boundary lines or grain lines on its surface. The use of single-crystal germanium has contributed materially to the development of uniform and reproducible transistors.

58. SUMMARY

In summary, the reader should retain the following salient points from this chapter:

1. The fundamental structure of germanium is crystalline, and the crystal is cubical in shape.

2. The electrons belonging to the atoms in the crystal enter into stable configurations known as valence bonds. The breaking of a valence bond produces a free electron and a hole.

3. Pentavalent impurities such as arsenic displace atoms of germanium in the lattice structure to form four covalent bonds with the nearest neighbors allowing the fifth valence electron to be readily removed. In this way the arsenic impurities act as doNors, giving rise to N-type material.

4. Trivalent impurities such as indium enter substitutionally into the lattice structure of germanium, acquire an additional electron into the valence ring, and form four covalent bonds with the nearest neighbors. In this way the indium impurity atoms act as accePtors, giving rise to P-type material.

REFERENCES

1. "Outline of Atomic Physics," Chap. VI, by members of the Staff, Physics Department, University of Pittsburgh, John Wiley & Sons, Inc., New York, 1936.
2. Slater, J. C.: "Introduction to Chemical Physics," pp. 338–344, McGraw-Hill Book Company, Inc., New York, 1939.
3. Hume-Rothery, W.: "Atomic Theory for Students of Metallurgy," pp. 86ff., The Institute of Metals, London, 1948.
4. Conwell, E. M.: Properties of Silicon and Germanium, *Proc. IRE*, Vol. 40, No. 11, p. 1327, November, 1952.
5. Seitz, F.: "The Physics of Metals," Chap. I, McGraw-Hill Book Company, Inc., New York, 1943.
6. Shockley, W.: "Electrons and Holes in Semiconductors," pp. 178ff., D. Van Nostrand Company, Inc., New York, 1950.
7. Bragg, W. H., and W. L. Bragg: "The Crystalline State," Chap. VI, George Bell & Sons, Ltd., London, 1933.

6 POINT CONTACT TRANSISTORS

The previous chapters have developed theoretical concepts associated with P- and N-type semiconductor materials. These principles will be applied to a detailed analysis of the theory of operation of the point contact transistor.

59. TEMPERATURE DEPENDENCE OF SEMICONDUCTORS

A great deal of information is obtainable from the covalent-bond picture of germanium and silicon. From this picture it is apparent on a qualitative basis that germanium and silicon transistors are temperature-dependent devices. An increase in temperature will be accompanied by disruption of some of the covalent bonds, thereby freeing electrons to act as carriers. By definition, the presence of these additional carriers will increase the conductivity. Many of the parameters which characterize a transistor are dependent on the conductivity, and these parameters will vary with temperature. If the temperature is increased sufficiently, enough covalent bonds are broken so that additional increases in temperature will have a negligible effect on the number of available carriers. Under such circumstances, the conductivity approaches an upper limit which is called the "intrinsic conductivity." The word "intrinsic" implies that the conductivity of the semiconductor is essentially dependent upon the properties of the material itself rather than upon the impurities which control its conductivity at lower temperatures.

For germanium normally suitable for transistor application, the intrinsic temperature is of the order of 100°C. Near the intrinsic temperature, control of the carriers is very difficult because of their very large number and their high thermal energy. Since this control is essential to efficient transistor action, it is evident that the intrinsic temperature sets an upper limit for satisfactory transistor operation.

In practice, other considerations further limit the maximum operating temperature so that it may be substantially less than the intrinsic temperature.

Present-day germanium transistors are not considered to be operable much above 100°C; a practical range is from 55°C to 75°C as maximum temperature limits. If the temperature is reduced to low values, it can be seen that thermal energy is insufficient to provide enough carriers, the resistivity rises, and transistor action is impeded. Satisfactory transistor action is still possible at temperatures as low as −55°C.

60. DONOR-ACCEPTOR ARRAYS

In Chap. 5 it was shown that impurity atoms occupy lattice sites and by their displacement of germanium atoms give rise to excess electrons or holes. In the conduction process the carriers are the holes or the electrons—ionized atoms at the lattice sites do not contribute to the conduction. Attention must be drawn to the fact that the process of conduction in a semiconductor is essentially an electronic rather than an ionic one. In an ionic conduction process, the conduction is by atoms which have gained or lost one or more electrons, i.e., by ions. If we could look just below the surface of a semiconductor such as germanium, at a given instant of time, we would see an array of countless germanium and impurity atoms vibrating because of thermal agitation about their mean lattice positions, with holes or electrons, which are mobile, moving among the atoms. In the case of a doNor material, the impurity atoms have a net positive charge, and it is convenient for analytical purposes to picture the situation as in Fig. 6-1A. Here is shown an array of doNors, hereafter indicated as plus signs enclosed in circles, near the surface of the N-type material; for the P-type material, an array of accePtors with their negative charge is shown in Fig. 6-1B. This picture will serve as a useful tool in our analysis of transistor action.

61. PN JUNCTION

Figure 6-2A shows a piece of P-type material adjacent to a piece of N-type material, such an arrangement producing a PN junction. It is not possible to make a satisfactory junction by simply taking a piece of N-type and a piece of P-type germanium and putting them together, regardless of the pressure used to hold them together or how carefully the interfaces are cleaned and polished.[1] Because an action occurring at a microscopic level among particles of atomic dimensions is involved, it is extremely difficult to get the orders of purity and cleanliness or smoothness at the surfaces that are required to obtain a satisfactory PN junction. It is therefore not considered feasible to make a PN junction mechanically. A process for making PN junctions will be described later. PN junctions have been used successfully in the construction of crystal diodes using either germanium or silicon as the semiconductor. Germanium PN-junction power rectifiers have extensive potential application because of their high efficiency and because they may be operated with unusually high current densities. Our particular concern with this structural arrangement, in addition to the fact that it is the basic combination of the junction-type transistor, stems from the fact that it is a convenient device for establishing a general rule for the polarities of applied potentials both for transistors and for diodes.

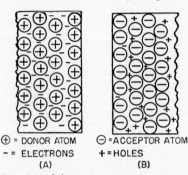

⊕ = DONOR ATOM   ⊖ =ACCEPTOR ATOM
– = ELECTRONS   + =HOLES
   (A)   (B)

Fig. 6-1. (A) Donor material. Note the symbol for donors. (B) Acceptor material. Note the symbol for acceptors. Note the array of positively charged atoms, or donors, and the array of negatively charged atoms, or acceptors, just below the surface of the germanium.

62. POTENTIAL HILLS

Consider Fig. 6-2A again and let us focus our attention on the holes and the electrons in the P and N regions. It might appear at first that, under the action of ordinary diffusion, the excess of holes would diffuse into the N region and the excess of electrons would diffuse into the P region so that, in time, the PN junction as such would cease to exist. Of course we know that this does not happen at ordinary temperatures, and a very simple analysis, but one which has some very far-reaching implications, will show why. In trying to diffuse into the N region, a hole in the P region encounters a barrier layer of positively charged atoms (doNors) just across the junction plane.[2] The positive electric field created by the doNors opposes the transgression of the holes.

Sketch B of Fig. 6-2 shows what the potential variation or distribution looks like to the hole trying to get across the junction. As it approaches the junction, the lines of electric flux extending out impede its motion, and if the hole does reach the junction, it must have had initially a large energy to overcome the opposition of the doNor electric field. The increase of energy which a hole must thus possess in order to move against the electric field is shown in Fig. 6-2B as a

small potential hill. The name is commonly applied to the effect at
the junction which prevents the holes from diffusing across it.   At
room temperature, the holes will not have sufficient energy from
thermal agitation to climb the potential hill, and therefore a significant number of holes do not, in general, diffuse from the P to

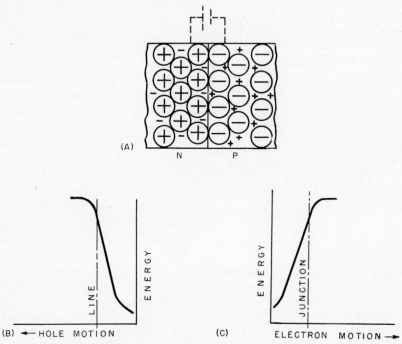

Fig. 6-2. (A) This arrangement of a donor and acceptor material constitutes a PN
junction.

   (B) Note how a hole, in trying to diffuse from the acceptor material to the donor
material, must climb a potential hill because of the array of donors near the surface
of the N germanium.

   (C) An electron, trying to diffuse from the N to the P material, must have an energy
indicated by the potential hill.   The electron can attain the required energy level due to
the application of an electric field, or from thermal agitation energy if the temperature
is raised.

the N region.   Electrons in the P region, however, will, because of the
electric field of the doNors mentioned above, diffuse easily into the N
region, "sliding" down a potential hill.   But then, not only are the
electrons minority carriers in the P region, but also their migration to
the N region will never annihilate the PN junction because there is
already an excess of electrons in the N region.

   In C of Fig. 6-2 is shown the corresponding condition for electrons in the N region which would, ordinarily, diffuse into the P region under normal kinetic vibration or motion. Analogously for the case of the holes, electrons which approach the junction come into the influence of the negative electric field because of the array of the accePtors and encounter the potential hill which turns most of them back.

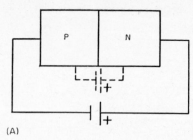

(A)

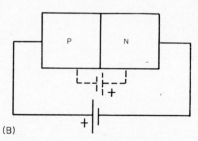

(B)

Fig. 6-3. (A) Here the potential hill, represented by the dashed-line battery, is reinforced or raised by the externally connected battery. This identifies the reverse-current connection (high resistance).

(B) Here the potential hill, represented by the dashed-line battery, is overcome or lowered by the externally connected battery. This is the forward-current connection (low resistance).

63. POLARITY AND POTENTIAL HILLS

The effect due to the array of accePtors and doNors is representable, as in Fig. 6-2A, by a small battery which is shown dashed in the figure. For the position shown it will introduce the same potential hills as do the arrays of acceptors and donors. This picture is extremely important because it provides instantly the answer to the polarity problem. If a battery is connected as in Fig. 6-3A, it aids the equivalent battery of Fig. 6-2A and increases the height of the potential hill. With this arrangement the number of carriers which can climb the potential hill is very small. Most of the conduction is actually due to the minority carriers since the polarity of bias enhances the flow of electrons from the P region to the N region and of holes from the N region to the P region. But, of course, the number of minority carriers is so small that the total current is small, and this polarity of bias gives rise to the reverse-current or high-resistance condition. In Fig. 6-3B, however, the external battery is connected so as to oppose or flatten out the potential hill or the equivalent battery of Fig. 6-2A. It must be evident, therefore, that now the flow of holes from the P to the N region and the flow of electrons from the N to the P region is enhanced. This is the low-resistance or forward-current polarity of bias. We shall have frequent occasion to establish the correct polarities for transistor work by application of this simple picture of potential hills.

64. BARRIER POTENTIAL

The order of magnitude of the potential difference across the junction in the absence of an external battery is in tenths of a volt,[3] and it may thus appear that a very small battery connected as in Fig. 6-3B would be sufficient to annihilate the potential hill completely. But this is not so, and a small amount of reflection will show the reason. We are dealing with a semiconductor which has approximately a hundred thousand times the resistance of a conductor such as copper. It is clear then that an important potential drop occurs in the P and N region without reference to the barrier at all, and, of course, as the current increases this drop increases. The more the barrier is broken down by using the polarity of Fig. 6-3B, the more readily do the carriers move across it, and in that sense the resistance of the barrier is decreasing. As the current increases, the net drop available across the barrier itself for counteracting this contact potential at the barrier decreases, and it is clear that the two actions are opposed in direction. Nevertheless, it is possible to make the potential hill quite small by the use of potentials of the order of 1 volt. If the battery potential is made too high in the reverse direction, voltage breakdown occurs (see Fig. 6-3A). In the case of the forward connection of Fig. 6-3B, the application of too high a voltage will permanently damage the junction because of the heating effects of excessively high currents.

65. STATE OF POINT CONTACT THEORY

Before proceeding to the discussion of the theory of the point contact transistor, it is necessary to make some precautionary remarks. The vacuum tube has been known for over 50 years, and vacuum-tube theory, considering the extraordinarily large number of contributors since its inception, is on relatively firm ground. In vacuum-tube theory, the reader is accustomed to seeing only the well-worked-out and thoroughly established theories in print, each such theory having had ample time to be checked and cross-checked by many workers in the field. This is in general not true of transistor theory because the entire field is barely six years old. In a way this is what makes the field so attractive—there is so much room for interesting research and development work and for important contributions to the field. But on the other hand, there is not the unanimity of opinion regarding the theoretical explanation of observed phenomena that is taken for granted in electrical engineering and vacuum-tube theory.

This unsettled condition is particularly evident with respect to point contact devices, including transistors and diodes. Authorities in the field today do not unanimously agree upon a theoretical explanation of point contact transistor operation. To the reader familiar with the calculus this will not appear particularly surprising. The mathematical analysis of physical phenomena occurring at a point such as the pointed tip of the fine wire used for the cat whisker is extremely difficult and involved. Theories which adequately explain all the known phenomena involved in point contact operation have not been completed. Many of the equations which have been developed are so complex and difficult to verify experimentally that physically significant solutions are not yet available. There is, therefore, no complete mathematically supported theory of point contact rectification or transistor action which may be used to interpret observed phenomena or predict future behavior.

The theoretical explanation of the action of a point contact transistor which will be given must be considered to be merely one of the many possible theories, and the reader should look upon it with a certain amount of critical reserve. The explanation to be given is, in the opinion of the authors, the best currently available, but because the art is so young it is well to bear in mind that it will probably be considerably modified in years to come. Finally, by thus being alerted to the rather unsatisfactory status of the present theory, the reader should keep his mind open to newer and improved explanations of the phenomena observed and should not consider the matter closed.

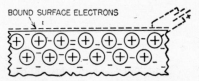

Fig. 6-4. Surface electrons in bound surface states. According to the surface states theory, a layer of electrons may be considered to exist in bound states at the surface. This layer, in conjunction with the array of donors just below the surface, produces in effect the potential hill represented by the dashed-line battery.

66. THEORY OF OPERATION OF POINT CONTACT TRANSISTORS[4]

In Fig. 6-5 is shown the essential arrangement for point contact transistor operation. The base or the pellet is a piece of germanium, N type, about 4 or 5 ohm-cm resistivity, approximately 20 mils thick, and about 50 mils in length and width. The cat whiskers are wires of some metal such as phosphor bronze approximately 5 mils in diameter, spaced approximately 2 mils apart, with some simple provision such as a bend in the wire to keep a few grams of pressure on the surface of the germanium. The cat whisker shown on the left is called the "emitter" for reasons which will appear shortly. The other cat whisker is the "collector." The base electrode on the underside of the germanium pellet consists of an ohmic soldered connection.

If the reader is concerned with possible deleterious effects of the heating involved in the soldering operation, it is necessary to remark that permanent harmful effects on the electrical properties of the germanium are not observed until temperatures considerably higher than those encountered in the soldering operation are reached. Further, to degrade the characteristics of the germanium appreciably, elevated temperatures must be maintained for times much in excess of those encountered in the soldering process.

It is known that electrons which find their way to the surface of the semiconductor become held or bound in certain conditions or states

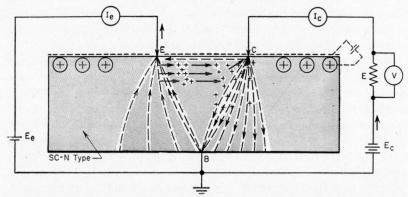

Fig. 6-5. The essential phenomena occurring in the point contact transistor which result in a gain in current and resistance. Note the role of the surface states and array of donors with the equivalent potential hill denoted by the dashed-line battery.

that are different from the quantum states of the electrons inside the bulk of the material.[5] When the electrons enter into these surface states or surface quantum states, they appear to be bound in them and do not readily return into the bulk of the material. The result is that a surface layer of such electrons in these surface states is built up on the material. For an N-type material, and mention has already been made that point contact transistors are usually made with N-type material, this surface layer of electrons, as shown in Fig. 6-4, combines with the array of donors just below the surface to form a small potential hill, as shown by the dashed battery. This arrangement produces an effect analogous to the PN junction discussed in connection with Fig. 6-2.

67. RULES FOR POLARITY OF APPLIED VOLTAGES

Two rules may be established for the polarities of connections of transistors which will apply to all the transistors, point contact and junction. The reasons for these rules will become apparent to the reader during this chapter and the next:

1. The emitter is always biased in the forward or low-resistance direction.

2. The collector is always biased in the reverse or high-resistance direction.

On the basis of these two rules and if we accept the surface states electron theory discussed above, it is apparent that the emitter bias or battery E_e of Fig. 6-5 will be connected to oppose the potential hill at the surface as shown and the collector battery E_c will be connected to aid the surface potential hill. It is thus seen that without knowing the theory of operation of the transistor the reader by the simple mnemonic outlined will nevertheless know exactly how to bias a point contact transistor or, as we shall see later, a junction-type transistor. Looking at the figure, the reader will observe that the surface electrons near the emitter have been removed because of the polarity of the connection, but those a little farther away are still present. This is intended to illustrate the concept of bound electrons. If a metal plate such as in a capacitor is given a charge, the charge will, in general, distribute itself evenly over the surface. If a battery terminal of suitable polarity is connected to the plate, all the charge on the plate can be drained off at once merely by connecting the battery at one point because the charges on a conductor plate are, in general, not bound. This is not true of an insulator or semiconductor. When the cat whisker at the emitter is applied as shown, only the electrons on the surface in the immediate vicinity are whisked away by the battery; the remaining surface electrons remain in their bound states as indicated.

68. NEED FOR THE CAT WHISKER

Questions which may have been troubling the reader regarding the operation of the transistor are: Why is it necessary to use a cat whisker? Why cannot a simple metal plate connection be used? To answer these questions we must first investigate the general characteristics of a point in electrical work. The reader is aware that lightning rods are pointed and that terminals between which large potentials must exist without an arc-over are made rounded or spherical. An electric field such as may exist between the two plates of a capacitor is usually considered to be made up of lines or rays called "flux lines." The number of such flux lines depends on the potential, not on the area. Thus, for a given potential, electric flux lines are extremely crowded at a point and the electric flux intensity (which by definition is flux lines per unit area) is very high. In a lightning rod, for instance, since the cloud must be discharged into the rod as soon as possible before the cloud accumulates enough charge to cause a lightning flash, the rod is made pointed. By crowding the electric flux lines from the cloud into a point, sufficient field intensity is developed to cause a current to flow down the electric rod and thus partially discharge the cloud.

Large potentials may not be applied to a transistor because of the possibility of very large currents which will cause heating or, for the case of reverse connection, voltage breakdown.[6] To break the covalent bonds in the germanium, a high-intensity electric field is needed at the emitter, but we cannot use a high voltage. The only way to get this high-intensity field is to use a point, and for that reason the emitter contact is a point contact.

69. HOLE INJECTION

When the emitter bias E_e is applied, even though this bias is of the order of 1 volt, a high-intensity electric field is created at the point which imparts sufficient energy to the electrons in the valence bonds nearby to raise them into the conduction band and to break these valence bonds. These electrons, under the influence of the applied potential, immediately flow out of the material and into the emitter. The breaking of the valence bonds creates holes in the immediate vicinity of the emitter, as shown in Fig. 6-5. The reader can see that, while the term is somewhat a misnomer, this process of creation of holes is called "injection" because the effect is the same as if holes had been "injected" by the emitter. As soon as the holes are created, they drift toward the collector under the influence of the electric field between emitter and collector and by ordinary electron diffusion.

Since we are dealing with an N-type material, with free or excess electrons, many of the holes on their way to the collector will recombine with the electrons and cease to exist. As these recombinations are taking place all the time, the number of holes which will combine with electrons increases with the transit time; since a large number of holes is necessary for maximum effectiveness in transistor action, it is desirable to place the emitter and collector close together. Point contact transistors of current design have emitter to collector spacings up to approximately 5 mils. If spaced too far apart, the gain and frequency response are adversely affected.

In the region of the collector the potential hill at the surface limits the current flow, and in the absence of holes the current will be of the order of 1 or 2 ma. Holes which arrive in the immediate vicinity of the collector are attracted by the negative charge there, and in moving to the collector point they tend to partially cancel out or nullify the potential hill at the surface. In this way more electrons are permitted to climb the potential hill, and the current at the collector is increased.

This increase in collector current as a result of hole injection is transistor action, and it is observed that small changes in the hole injection, such as may be due to a modulation of the emitter bias by an ac potential, result in amplification of the emitter current containing the modulation intelligence.

70. RESISTANCE GAIN

In transistor action the low-resistance connection is used in the emitter circuit and the high-resistance connection in the collector circuit, referring to the biasing potentials applied. Let us now extend this concept by setting down the following rules:

1. The internal resistance of the transistor between emitter and base, usually designated by r_{11}, is always a relatively low resistance; the internal resistance of the transistor between collector and base, usually designated by r_{22}, is usually a relatively high resistance.

2. Transistor action is accompanied by a resistance gain in that the ratio of r_{22} to r_{11} is greater than 1.

The low-resistance connection of the battery E_e in Fig. 6-5 satisfies the emitter circuit requirement of rule 1, but in the collector circuit the action of the holes nullifies the effect of the surface charge and thereby lowers the internal resistance between collector and base. Because point contact transistor action is always accompanied by this effect of the holes in decreasing the internal resistance of the germanium, it is seen that the collector to base resistance requirement of rule 1 cannot be met. If r_{22} is small, satisfactory voltage and power gains cannot be achieved. However, there is an additional factor involved which will now be described.

71. DEPARTURE FROM OHM'S LAW

Looking at Fig. 6-5 the reader will observe that some holes are shown which do not follow a straight-line path from emitter to collector but which, by the process of diffusion and random motion, travel in a more or less circuitous or indirect path to the collector. These holes form a positive space charge or cloud within the germanium in the region of the conducting path and thereby evoke or attract additional electrons from nearby sites, lowering the resistance of the path. The significant point here is that the advent of the holes causes a decrease in the collector to base resistance because of the positive space-charge effect and the effect of the holes in annihilating the surface charge. The result is that the resistance of the collector circuit is significantly decreased and a current flows that may be two to three times the emitter current. However, this clearly does not explain a resistance gain.

The condition of low resistance and high current is shown in section AB of Fig. 6-6. In the region from A to B the current is seen to be proportional to the voltage in accordance with Ohm's law; or stated somewhat differently, increase of voltage is accompanied by a proportionate increase in current.

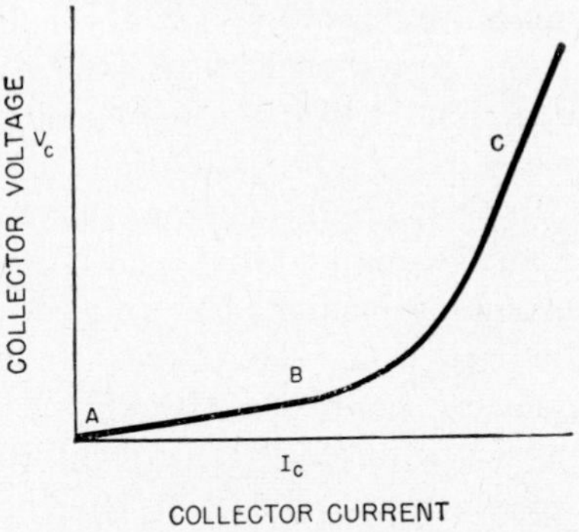

72. REASON FOR HIGH r_{22}

If the applied collector bias is increased beyond point B, the available supply of electrons soon becomes inadequate to sustain an Ohm's law current. The supply of electrons is controlled by:

1. The normal number of majority carriers at room temperature. This is a function of the impurity content.

2. The neutralizing action of the holes on the surface electrons.

Fig. 6-6. A typical collector characteristic curve indicating variation of collector current with applied bias voltage. After point B insufficient carriers are present to support a proportional current for the applied electric field, and the apparent resistance increases rapidly.

3. The positive space charge due to the diffused holes.

Above point B of the figure, for instance, increases of applied potential V_c are not followed by proportionate increases of the current because of this exhaustion of the available carriers or electrons, and the curve rises steeply, as shown in Fig. 6-6. Note that the slope of the curve in the figure is r_{22}, the collector to base resistance.

The transistor is normally operated approximately at point C of the figure, where it is obvious that the collector to base resistance is high. Summarizing, in the collector circuit the reason for the high resistance is not alone the reverse current connection of the bias, but also the exhaustion of the available current carriers beyond the Ohm's law limit.[7]

73. TYPICAL VALUES OF POINT CONTACT TRANSISTOR PARAMETERS

Let $i_e r_{11}$ represent the internal voltage drop from emitter to base and $i_c r_{22}$ the internal voltage drop from collector to base. Since i_c is greater than i_e because of the effect of the holes and r_{22} is greater than r_{11} because of the carrier exhaustion effect mentioned, the possible voltage gain of the transistor, which is the product of current gain and resistance gain, may be considerable. It is important to note that the contributions to the voltage and power gain in the point contact transistor are due both to the current gain and to the resistance gain.

The ratio of i_c to i_e is usually denoted by the Greek letter α (alpha), and for typical point contact transistors is of the order of 2.3. Typical values for r_{11} and r_{22} are approximately 300 and 15,000 ohms, respectively, representing a resistance gain of about 50. Thus it may be seen that typical voltage gains are of the order of 115 and typical power gains are of the order of 250.

In their migration from the emitter to the collector the holes move in an N-type material, and it must have occurred to the reader that recombinations of holes and electrons should be the rule rather than the exception. This is so. In fact, the discussion regarding recombination should explain why a very important effort in solid state physics is directed toward improving and controlling the lifetime of these carriers. Single crystals of germanium which are to be used in the manufacture of transistors are compared and evaluated for their lifetimes as a production control. Lifetime of carriers in single-crystal germanium is an important design parameter. Typical values of lifetime vary from a few microseconds to two or three thousand microseconds.[8]

74. MOBILITY

The velocity of the holes and the electrons in semiconductors is not the same as the velocity of electrons in conductors. The reader accustomed to thinking of electron velocities in orders of hundreds of thousands of centimeters per second may be surprised to learn that in semiconductors the velocities are of the order of a few thousand centimeters per second. Typical values for germanium are: for electrons, about 3,600 cm per sec, for each volt per centimeter of potential difference or, as is sometimes said, of potential gradient; for holes, about 1,700 cm per sec per volt per cm of gradient.[9]

Some very important effects in the transistor ensue as a result of this relatively slow movement of holes and electrons in semiconductors. For instance, in a wire, information in the form of modulated waves piling up when fed into one end is not a matter of concern. The extremely high velocity of the electrons in the wire which carry the intelligence makes it almost certain that for any reasonable frequency the information fed in will move out of the way before the next bit is fed in. In semiconductors, however, because the velocity is so low this piling up presents a serious limitation. At relatively low frequencies serious modulation distortion results because of the piling up of intelligence connected with the long transit time of electrons and holes.

75. $f_{\alpha co}$—FREQUENCY OF ALPHA CUTOFF

Another consequence of the large transit time in transistors is evident in the decrease of the current gain alpha with frequency. When the period of one cycle is equal to the transit time, the positive half of a sinusoid may still be within the emitter-collector region when the negative half of the same cycle enters. Under these conditions, the effect on the flow of holes due to the positive and negative halves of the cycle cancel and the current gain is zero. This is for the extreme case when frequency is the reciprocal of the transit time; for lower frequencies, the effects are in proportion and the observed fact is that the current gain decreases with frequency.

The decrease of alpha with frequency is also due to the fact that all the flow lines of the holes from emitter to collector are by no means straight lines. In fact, these flow paths resemble more closely the flux lines observed in pictures of the magnetic field between two poles. Since the transit time for these circuitous paths is greater than for the straight paths, neutralizations of the effects of the holes occur, particularly at the higher frequencies (lower periods). While figures of frequency cutoff as high as 300 Mc have been reported in the literature,[10] these must be regarded as development laboratory values rather than representative limits obtainable from transistors now on the market. For most point contact transistors currently being produced, upper frequency limits are in the neighborhood of 10 Mc, typical values around 5 Mc. Some remarkable progress is being made in new types, both junction and point contact, in the matter of frequency response. The reader can confidently expect commercially available units with importantly extended frequency limits to appear on the market in the near future. This frequency limitation does point out, however, the desirability of having the emitter and collector as close together as possible because the frequency response increases rapidly as the spacing is decreased. Mechanical and electrical counterindications set a lower limit on this spacing (see Fig. 13-9).

76. SUMMARY

1. The point contact transistor is capable of current gain because of the action of holes in enhancing the collector current for a given amplitude of emitter current.

2. Voltage and power gain of the point contact transistor are due to a combination of current and resistance gain.

3. The theory of operation of point contact devices in general is, as yet, not completely understood, and it is essential to keep abreast of the literature in order to observe the progress in this field.

4. The concept of potential hills is essential for the discussion of transistor action and is useful as a convenient mnemonic by which the polarity of applied biases may be remembered.

5. The frequency response of point contact transistors is a function of the transit time and the distribution of the flow lines of the carriers from emitter to collector.

REFERENCES

1. Shulman, G. C., and D. M. Van Winkle: Pressure Welded PN Junctions in Germanium, *J. Appl. Phys.*, Vol. 24, p. 224, February, 1953.

2. Shockley, W.: "Electrons and Holes in Semiconductors," pp. 86ff., D. Van Nostrand Company, Inc., New York, 1950. Further references given.

3. Shockley, W.: The Theory of PN Junctions in Semiconductors and PN Junction Transistors, *Bell System Tech. J.*, Vol. 28, No. 3, pp. 441–444, July, 1949.

4. Shockley, W., G. L. Pearson, and J. R. Haynes: Hole Injection in Germanium, Quantitative Studies and Filamentary Transistors, *Bell System Tech. J.*, Vol. 28, No. 3, pp. 344–366, July, 1949. Further references given.

5. Bardeen, John: Surface States and Rectification at a Metal-Semiconductor Contact, *Phys. Rev.*, Vol. 71, pp. 717–727, May 15, 1947.

6. Torrey, H. C., and C. A. Whitmer: "Crystal Rectifiers," Chap. 8, McGraw-Hill Book Company, Inc., New York, 1948.

7. Bardeen, John, and Walter H. Brattain: Physical Principles Involved in Transistor Action, *Phys. Rev.*, Vol. 75, pp. 208–225, Apr. 15, 1949.

8. Haynes, J. R., and W. Shockley: The Mobility and Life of Injected Holes and Electrons in Germanium, *Phys. Rev.*, Vol. 81, No. 5, pp. 835–843, Mar. 1, 1951.

9. Prince, M. B.: Drift Mobilities in Semiconductors. I. Germanium, *Phys. Rev.*, Vol. 92, No. 3, pp. 681–687, Nov. 1, 1953.

10. Slade, B. N.: The Control of Frequency Response and Stability of Point Contact Transistors, *Proc. IRE*, Vol. 40, pp. 1382–1384, November, 1952.

7 JUNCTION TRANSISTORS

In the preceding chapter the theory of operation of the point contact transistor was discussed. In this chapter the theory of operation of junction transistors will be presented, and a brief description will be given of the method of manufacture of these units.

77. BIAS POLARITIES

In considering the problem of the application of bias to the point contact transistor, a mnemonic was introduced to assist in the establishment of the polarities of the applied voltages. We shall apply this mnemonic to show how one can establish the polarities of the applied biases for junction type transistors even without full knowledge of the theory of operation. In Fig. 7-1 an equivalent sketch is shown which represents a PNP-type junction transistor. The name is based on the fact that it is physically made of three alternate layers of P-, N-, and P-type materials, respectively, as shown in the figure. Reading from left to right the connections are emitter (E), base (B), and collector (C), as shown. We may now reason as follows to determine the polarity of the emitter bias:

1. Since the emitter is a P material, the impurity atoms are acceptors. In the P material, near the PN junction, it is convenient to consider an array of fixed negative charges shown by the encircled negative signs in Fig. 7-1. Together with the corresponding positive array on the other side of the junction due to the donors in the N material, the acceptors form a small potential hill pictorially indicated by the dotted battery across the emitter junction.

2. The emitter is always biased in the forward or low-resistance direction.

3. To connect the bias battery in the low-resistance direction, it is

73

necessary to overcome or flatten the potential hill mentioned in 1; hence the polarity is as shown, positive to emitter, negative to base.

An entirely analogous process of reasoning, recalling that the collector is always biased in the high-resistance direction, yields a polarity in the collector circuit as shown, positive to base, negative to collector.

The theory of operation of the PNP transistor is rather straightforward, once the fundamental concepts discussed in previous chapters

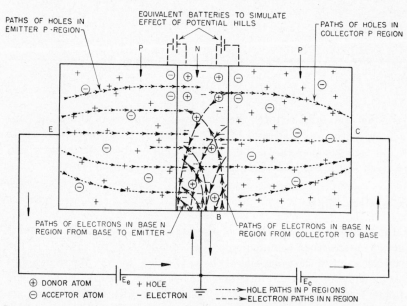

Fig. 7-1. Flow paths of holes and electrons in operation of PNP junction transistor. Note how conduction in P regions is principally by holes while the electrical circuit externally is principally by electrons. Note also how holes from the emitter P region pass through the base N region, suffer recombinations, and complete the circuit through the collector P region. Base current is small because I_e and I_c flow in opposite directions as shown.

are mastered. While very learned treatises may be written to describe in complex mathematical language the *modus operandi*, this is not only unnecessary for a satisfactory understanding of the theory of operation, but it also complicates unnecessarily the fundamentals the reader must first absorb before proceeding to a more advanced treatment of the subject.

78. THEORY OF OPERATION OF PNP TRANSISTOR[1]

The P material in the emitter region contains an excess of holes which are the majority carriers. Under the influence of the electric

field as supplied by the battery E_e, holes will acquire sufficient energy
to move into a conduction band, become carriers of electric current,
and be transported into the N region.   The N region is of the order of
1 mil in width.   Holes drift toward the collector primarily by diffusion
and also under the influence of the electric field due to the battery E_c,
with recombinations taking place all the time. With respect to these,
the reader should note carefully that holes which emanate from the N
region actually slide down a potential hill in terms of the donor and
acceptor picture.   The fact that the holes, which are the current
carriers in the PNP transistor, slide down a potential hill means that
many of them will get across; many holes mean many carriers, and
many carriers mean low resistance.

The high resistance in the collector circuit is not due to the resistance
across the collector junction or the P material at the collector.   In
the PNP transistor, initially, the collector circuit resistance is low
because of the effect of the holes sliding downhill from the N to the P
region, as discussed above.   This effect is shown in Fig. 7-2 as a very
low resistance in the region AB of the V_c-I_c or collector characteristic.
As the collector voltage is increased, more current carriers are needed
to sustain this low resistance than are available from the supply of
holes, and there is an apparent sharp increase in the circuit resistance
as the voltage keeps rising but the current remains quite small.

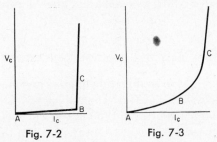

Fig. 7-2.   Fig. 7-3.

Fig. 7-2. Collector characteristic for a junction-type transistor.   Note the very steep
operating region at C, indicating high collector to base resistance, and compare point
contact Fig. 7-3.
Fig. 7-3. Collector characteristic for point contact type transistor.   The operating
point is approximately at C for a collector resistance of about 15,000 ohms; compare
1 megohm for junction types.

79. COMPARISON OF PC AND JUNCTION TRANSISTORS

Collector circuit resistances of the order of megohms are possible,
and in general the V_c-I_c curve for the junction transistor is steeper in
the operating region at C than for the corresponding region for the
point contact transistor.   This can be seen by comparing Fig. 7-2

and 7-3. Another interesting aspect of the comparison between Figs. 7-2 and 7-3 is that the high-resistance region of the collector characteristic is approached relatively slowly for the point contact transistor and the high-resistance region is approached rather abruptly for the junction type.

In the case of the point contact transistor, we are dealing with an N-type material and, while the main streamlines of current carriers are in an approximate straight line from the collector to the base, there are, of course, secondary streamlines which follow curved paths. Therefore, a relatively large volume of material from which electrons may be supplied is made available. Even when the current carriers necessary to sustain the low resistance are nearly exhausted, enough electrons can be drawn in from adjacent regions with the help of the positive space charge to prevent a very abrupt change in the voltage-current relationship. In the junction transistor, when the holes which act as carriers are exhausted beyond the point where they maintain the low-resistance characteristic, there is no further way in which to augment the carriers except to increase the emitter current. It turns out, however, that increasing the emitter current leads to thermal difficulties which limit the permissible emitter current. Thus the available carriers are limited in number to those which can be supplied from the narrow N region; after a critical voltage is attained, no additional carriers are available and the collector resistance rises sharply.

80. ALPHA LESS THAN UNITY FOR JUNCTION TRANSISTORS

A certain amount of recombination of holes and electrons is unavoidable when the holes transfuse into the N region. This means that not all the carriers which represent the emitter current I_e will reach the collector where these carriers contribute to I_c. On this basis the reader will understand that, except for very special arrangements which will be touched upon later, it is impossible for the current gain, or alpha, of a junction transistor to be unity or greater than unity. The current gain, or alpha, of a junction transistor is always less than unity. Further, it should be evident that the wider the N region, the longer the holes will reside in a material whose excess carriers are electrons. For a wider N region the number of recombinations will be increased, and therefore the alpha, or current gain, of the transistor will decrease.

As an illustration, a barrier region width of 15 mils or more does not produce a usable transistor, and the width of the region is usually kept in the neighborhood of 1 mil. It will appear presently why widths of much less than a mil are usually impractical. In addition to the reason of current gain, it is undesirable to make the N region too wide because this increases the over-all transit time and would tend to make the frequency response poorer.

81. PREPARATION OF GERMANIUM[2]

Probably one of the most interesting aspects of the junction transistor is its method of manufacture. Germanium is usually obtained as a by-product in the extraction of zinc from its ore, and is available commercially as germanium dioxide (GeO_2), a white powder. The oxide is heated at 650°C in a reducing atmosphere of hydrogen for several hours and is thereby reduced to germanium powder. This powder is heated in a graphite boat to a temperature of about 1000°C, at which temperature the powder becomes a liquid, resembling molten lead in appearance. The process is carried out with a gas, like argon or hydrogen, surrounding the melt to prevent what would otherwise be a very rapid and undesirable union of the germanium with the oxygen in the air. The molten mass is then slowly cooled, and the solid germanium is obtained in the form of bars usually several inches long and about a square inch in cross-sectional area. In this state the purity may not be satisfactory for optimum transistor performance; in addition, the germanium is polycrystalline, whereas for transistor work single-crystal material is desirable. Next, the material is purified by a process called "zone melting." In this process a short section of the germanium ingot is melted and the molten region moved slowly from left to right along the bar. Most impurities in germanium prefer to remain in the liquid phase rather than freeze into the solid state and will be swept along with the molten zone. The impurities will thus be concentrated toward the right end. Except for this portion of the bar, germanium with a resistivity as high as 60 ohm-cm may be obtained from the process of zone purification. The maximum theoretical resistivity of germanium has been computed to be approximately 65 ohm-cm. Since impurities add to the available carriers of electric current, the observed resistivity increases with the purity.

The single-crystal germanium necessary for transistors is obtained by a process called "pulling." In this process the purified germanium is melted in a crucible, and into this melt, in a noninteracting atmosphere, a germanium seed is dipped. The seed is a small piece of single-crystal germanium. As the seed is slowly withdrawn from the melt, the molten material adheres to it and solidifies; from this process large ingots of single-crystal germanium may be obtained. Since the germanium obtained from zone purification usually has a greater purity (higher resistivity) than is optimum for use in transistors, impurities in controlled amounts and of the desired type are added during the pulling step to decrease the resistivity to the desired value. From the resulting single crystal, suitable pieces of germanium are cut for use in transistors.*

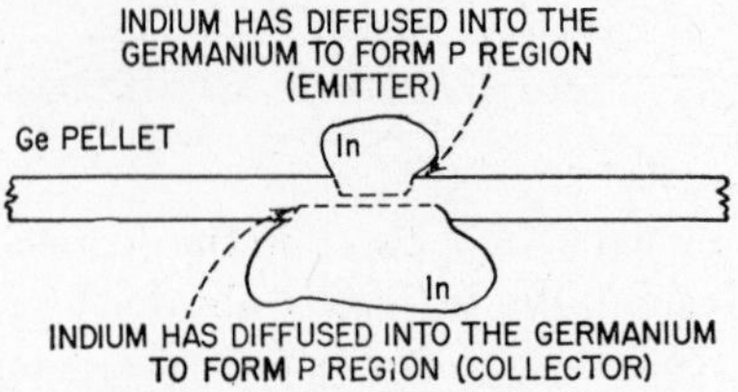

INDIUM HAS DIFFUSED INTO THE
GERMANIUM TO FORM P REGION
(EMITTER)

Ge PELLET   In

INDIUM HAS DIFFUSED INTO THE GERMANIUM
TO FORM P REGION (COLLECTOR)

Fig. 7-4. Essentials of the diffusion process for the manufacture of PNP transistors. The undiffused portion of the indium (or gallium) blob is used to make the appropriate connection.

82. PNP TRANSISTOR CONSTRUCTION

PNP transistors are usually made by a diffusion or alloy process.[3] Starting with a pellet or die of N-type germanium about 50 mils square and 10 mils thick, a bead of a P-forming element such as indium or gallium is placed on top of the germanium slab approximately in the center. The entire assembly is heated in an oven to a temperature below the melting point of germanium but above the melting point of the indium. The result is that the indium or gallium diffuses into the germanium slab, approximately as shown in Fig. 7-4 by the top blob in solid lines. The process is then repeated on the other side, as shown by the lower blob. In diffusing into the germanium during the heating process the trivalent P-forming impurity, gallium or indium, forms a P-type germanium on either side of the central and unaffected N-type layer with the result that a PNP type of structure is obtained. While close temperature and purity control can be maintained in such a process, the diffusion of the P-forming material into the germanium is not really amenable to extremely close control. The edge of the diffusing region which becomes the barrier

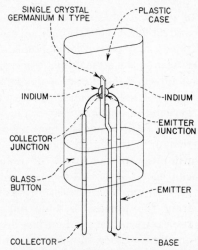

Fig. 7-5. A phantom view of the diffusion type of junction transistor, showing a possible method of assembly and mounting. Pin spacing and diameter is now standard, see Fig. 13-11. (*Courtesy of RCA.*)

between the P- and N-type material probably does not have ideal evenness and parallelism. Where the barrier region is uneven in width, hole paths are of different lengths and the holes take unequal times to

* A more detailed description will be found in Chap. 13.

get across.   Also, such irregularities in the border region may lead to trapping centers.   These are microscopic volumes within the material wherein particular arrangements of donors and acceptors form unintended potential hills where holes or electrons are trapped, *i.e.*, their normal itineraries are prevented.   One of the external results of these irregularities is that they contribute to the noise.   Typical noise figures for these transistors vary from 20 to 35 db above thermal noise.[4]   The reader can see from the nature of the process that it is inherently not capable of the very fine control one might like, and the transistor industry is at present very much in need of an ingenious scheme for making PNP transistors which would be inherently susceptible of extreme degrees of control[5] (see Fig. 7-5).

83. THEORY OF OPERATION OF NPN TRANSISTOR

In Fig. 7-6 the construction and method of biasing of another important transistor type called the "NPN transistor" are shown picto-

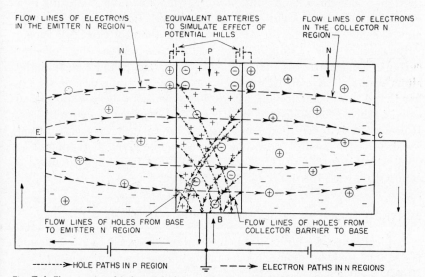

Fig. 7-6. Flow paths of holes and electrons in operation of the NPN type of transistor. Note that conduction in the N regions is principally by electrons.   The external circuit is completed in the base region by hole conduction.   Compare Fig. 7-1.

rially.   As the figure shows, the unit consists of alternate layers of N and P material, the center or barrier layer being P type.   The mnemonic for the determination of the polarities of the applied biases which has been discussed for the point contact and PNP transistors is directly applicable to this case also.   Recalling (1) the positive charge of donors in the N region and negative charge of acceptors in the P region, (2) the low resistance necessary in the emitter circuit and the high resistance in the collector circuit, and (3) how the applied battery overcomes the potential hill in one case and accentuates it in the other, the reader should have no difficulty in verifying the polarity shown.

The theory of operation as in the case of PNP transistors is extremely simple. Under the influence of the applied electric field, electrons cross the barrier from the emitter N region to the base P region where some of them recombine with the holes which are the majority carriers of the P region. Thereafter, under the influence of the applied collector battery, the electrons move toward the collector terminal to establish the collector circuit. Analogously to the case for the PNP transistor, the electrons initially slide downhill from the base region into the collector N region and the collector circuit resistance is low. Figure 7-2 is entirely applicable for this case also. When the supply of electrons necessary to maintain this low-resistance region has been exhausted, further increases in collector potential do not yield proportionate increases in the number of carriers available, resulting in a very high resistance of the order of megohms. In general, this resistance is somewhat higher in NPN transistors than for the PNP type.

Because of the recombinations in the base region, the collector current changes are less than the emitter current changes so that the alpha of the NPN transistor, as for any junction transistor, is always less than 1. This failure of i_c, the ac component of collector current, to equal i_e, the ac component of emitter current, represents a current loss. However, it is more than compensated for by the very substantial resistance gain possible, and some figures can be given at this point to illustrate this fact both for the PNP and NPN types and to afford a comparison with the point contact transistor.

84. TYPICAL PARAMETER VALUES FOR JUNCTION TRANSISTORS

Typical ranges for alpha are: point contact types, 2.0 to 2.5; junction types, 0.95 to 0.99. These figures indicate how the point contact type affords a current gain and the junction type a current loss. Typical values of emitter to base resistance r_{11} and collector to base resistance r_{22} for the point contact type have already been given as 300 and 15,000 ohms, respectively, and these values should be compared with the corresponding values of 500 ohms and 1,000,000 ohms for the junction types, respectively.

Mention has already been made that the voltage gain of the transistor is the product of the current gain by the resistance gain. It follows that, at least on a theoretical basis, the voltage gain of

$$2.3 \times \frac{15{,}000}{300} = 115$$

for the point contact type must be compared with

$$0.95 \times \frac{1{,}000{,}000}{500} = 1{,}900$$

for the junction types.   It is thus seen that substantial voltage gains are feasible with the junction type of transistor, and the reader will appreciate this fact more fully when informed that junction type transistors of the NPN type have been made which showed a collector to base resistance of 10 megohms.   Certainly the potentialities for large voltage and power gains appear to rest more with the junction types than with the point contact types.   At the present time the point contact types enjoy a superiority over the junction types mostly in the matter of frequency response and in their suitability for switching applications.

85. GROWN-JUNCTION METHOD OF CONSTRUCTION OF NPN TRANSISTOR

As with the PNP transistor, one of the most interesting aspects of the NPN unit is the method of manufacture.   Recalling from our previous remarks that the purely mechanical method of assembly just will not work, we may proceed directly to a description of the junction method[6] for making NPN units in contradistinction to the diffusion method used for the PNP units.

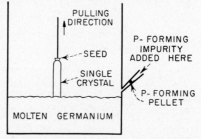

Fig. 7-7. Essentials of the grown-junction method of construction of NPN junction transistors.   The P-forming pellet melts and spreads through the molten germanium.

The preparation of the germanium up to the pulling stage is common to the construction of the PNP and NPN units.   For NPN units, in the pulling process, a P layer is formed perpendicular to the long or pulling axis of the single crystal.   This is done by dropping into the melt a small bit of P-forming trivalent impurity such as gallium or indium (refer to Fig. 7-7).   The P-forming impurity rapidly diffuses throughout the melt because of thermal effects and the agitation of the bath resulting from the rotational motion superimposed on the vertical pulling motion.   As the crystal is pulled up, a P layer adheres to the crystal.   After a carefully controlled time, an N-forming pentavalent impurity such as arsenic is added in a controlled amount, returning the bath to its predominantly N-type character.

An interesting phenomenon which occurs in this process is that, in the conversion from N to P and P to N types, the melt goes through what may be described as a net zero-hole–electron-pair stage, where the effect of the trivalent and pentavalent impurities cancel and at one instant the net number of carriers may be zero. Because of the decrease of resistivity with increased impurity concentration, more than one NPN sandwich may not be feasible in a single crystal.

While this process may not appear to provide particularly close control of the width of the P layer, nonetheless excellent NPN junctions can be formed. In general, the grown junction method produces PN junctions which have electrical characteristics comparable to those produced by the diffusion method. By careful control, as the single crystal is slowly pulled upward, a suitably thin region of the crystal is obtained as P type, and the proper NPN sandwich is formed, with a barrier layer about 1 mil wide. A process inherently capable of providing even more precise control is very much desired at present by metallurgists working in this field.

The ingot resulting from this process is then cut into slabs at right angles to the long axis of the crystal. Each slab is about the size of a half dollar and about a fourth as thin. Thereafter, the slabs are diced into suitable sizes for the transistor with each pellet about 0.100 in. in length, and with a cross-sectional dimension about 30 mils on a side. Each pellet is a true germanium sandwich of N material on the outside and P material between. Considerable skill and craftsmanship are needed to locate the actual P region and to weld a fine connecting wire to it.

Generally speaking, the junction transistors are inferior to the point contact transistors in the matter of frequency response because of the larger inherent capacity of the junction units and of the longer transit time. Nonetheless, junction units have been made which exhibit frequency response comparable with point contact units.

86. THE TWO PRINCIPAL METHODS OF CONSTRUCTION

Two principal methods for the construction of junction transistors have been discussed: the diffusion method used to make PNP transistors and the grown junction method used to make NPN transistors. It must not be inferred that these are the only methods presently known for the construction of these two types. The diffused junction technique is quite feasible for the construction of NPN units. At present, the most common techniques are the ones first described—diffusion for PNP and grown junction for the NPN. The metallurgy of the techniques for both processes, as applied to both transistor junction types, must still be considered to be in a state of development, and there is room for important improvements in this very fascinating field.

87. RATE-GROWN JUNCTIONS

A new technique for the manufacture of junction transistors is the so-called rate-grown junction[7] method. It is based on the following three significant aspects of the metallurgy of germanium:

1. Most impurities in germanium, except boron and silicon, prefer to remain in the liquid phase rather than freeze into the solid state. Stated differently, at the border between a solid and molten region, the atoms of most of the impurities tend toward the molten region as they are more soluble in the melt than in the solid.

2. The extent to which the impurities are soluble in the solid, or the solubility, varies with the rate at which the germanium crystal grows during the crystal-pulling or creation process. Solid-phase solubility of impurities in monocrystalline germanium increases with the rate of growth of the germanium crystal. This is particularly true for antimony, although it is not true for trivalent impurities such as gallium and indium.

3. For gallium or indium, which are trivalent, P-forming impurities, the solubility in the solid phase is very nearly independent of the rate of growth of the crystal.

These unusual characteristics of the crystal-growth process are utilized to make alternate P and N regions in the rate-grown junction method. When the crystal growth rate is small, the solubility of the N-forming impurities, such as antimony, is small, but the solubility of the P-forming impurities, gallium and indium, is constant and relatively large. Hence, more P-forming impurities enter the solid phase and a P region results. When the crystal growth rate is large, the solubility of the pentavalent, N-forming impurity antimony in the solid phase is large compared to the constant solubility of the gallium or indium, and the majority carriers will be N type. By cycling the crystal growth rate, alternate regions of N- and P-type germanium can be formed. Excellent NPN and PNP units have been made in this way; however, the method is at an early stage, and considerable improvement in this technique must be effected before this process becomes an established art in the manufacture of junction transistors.

88. TRANSISTOR TETRODE[8]

A four-terminal transistor has been developed, which represents a modification of the NPN-junction unit. While complete information on this new addition to the transistor family is still not available, the essentials of the modification can be described. A second ohmic contact is made to the base region on the face of the bar opposite to that used for the normal base contact, as shown in Fig.

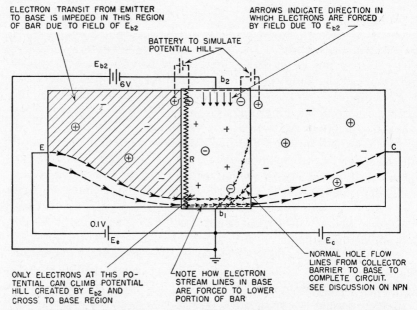

ELECTRON TRANSIT FROM EMITTER
TO BASE IS IMPEDED IN THIS REGION
OF BAR DUE TO FIELD OF E_{b2}

ARROWS INDICATE DIRECTION IN
WHICH ELECTRONS ARE FORCED
BY FIELD DUE TO E_{b2}

BATTERY TO SIMULATE
POTENTIAL HILL

E_{b2} 6V b_2

E   R   C

b_1

0.1 V E_e E_c

ONLY ELECTRONS AT THIS PO-
TENTIAL CAN CLIMB POTENTIAL
HILL CREATED BY E_{b2} AND
CROSS TO BASE REGION

NOTE HOW ELECTRON
STREAM LINES IN BASE
ARE FORCED TO LOWER
PORTION OF BAR

NORMAL HOLE FLOW
LINES FROM COLLECTOR
BARRIER TO BASE TO
COMPLETE CIRCUIT.
SEE DISCUSSION ON NPN

Fig. 7-8. Essentials of operation of the transistor tetrode. R is an imaginary resistor to represent the voltage drop (assumed uniform) within the base region, from top to bottom of the germanium bar. The usual base connection is at b_1. The drop in the emitter region is usually negligible compared to the drop at the barrier and is neglected in the analysis.

7-8.   A bias is applied to the second base terminal b_2, making it negative with respect to the base terminal b_1. This bias is large compared to the emitter-to-b_1 bias. It will be recalled from the theory of operation of the NPN transistor that electrons from the emitter N region cross over into the center P region because of the flattening of the potential hill between the emitter N and base P regions. To make the discussion concrete, assume that the applied forward bias potential is approximately 0.1 volt, battery E_e. As the figure shows, a bias of approximately 6 volts is applied to the upper base terminal b_2, and we may consider that along the edge of the P region, near the emitter side, a potential gradient from -6 to 0 volts exists, from top to bottom. The P region may be considered a continuous resistor, and along this resistor will exist an (assumed) uniform drop.

Electrons from the base will arrive at the emitter-base barrier at a pressure or potential of approximately -0.1 volt. Only those electrons which arrive at the emitter-base junction far enough down so that their -0.1 potential is negative with respect to the potential level of the gradient, as determined by resistor R, will get across. For such electrons, the effective potential hill is flattened. Electrons near the top of the bar, arriving at the barrier with a potential of -0.1 volt, encounter a gradient level of almost -6 volts, and for them the potential hill is, in essence, raised—therefore few, if any, will get across. The net effect is to render impassable the portion of the barrier shaded in the figure and to restrict the lines of current flow through the P layer to the region near b_1 as shown. The same effect is obtained by imagining that the negative electric field effectively forces the current streamlines of electrons down toward the lower region as indicated.

89. CHARACTERISTICS OF TETRODE TRANSISTOR

The circuit effects obtained by this technique include improved voltage gain at higher frequencies and a lower collector capacitance. In practice, the P region for these units is also made somewhat narrower than is the practice for NPN units, and this further improves the frequency response by reducing the transit time. A parameter to be introduced in a subsequent chapter, the base resistance r_b, is greatly decreased by the tetrode principle; the decrease in base resistance produces the improved voltage-gain frequency response and reduced positive feedback. The base resistance, for the junction units, may be thought of as the equivalent resistance introduced into the external circuit by virtue of the motion of carriers through the base region on their way to and from the emitter and collector barriers.

90. PN HOOK TRANSISTOR[9]

Another special type of transistor which promises important current gains and efficient amplification is the PNPN type of junction transistor. A conventional PNP transistor, with the collector region replaced by a PN junction, may be operated in such a way that a hook-shaped potential hill is created at the final junction; hence the name PN hook. The essentials of the mechanical construction are illustrated in Fig. 7-9, but it is to be noted that the central

N and P regions are quite narrow. The device will not operate satisfactorily if the central P region is too wide.

The theory of operation is based on the fact that holes which are the carriers in the left-hand PNP region, on arriving at potential hill 3, encounter the positive field of the right-hand N-region donors and are "trapped," *i.e.*, their further travel is impeded. The accumulation of holes at the barrier creates a positive space charge which tends to annihilate the effect of potential hill 3. Electrons from the collector, passing through the right-hand N region, would ordinarily find a high resistance path because of the array of acceptors in the central P region at the right-hand barrier. The effect of the holes

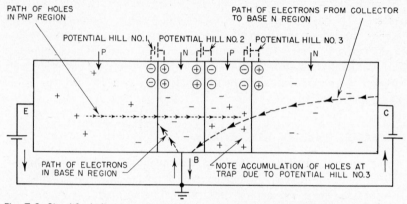

Fig. 7-9. Simplified diagram showing operation of the PN hook type, or PNPN, transistor. This junction type of transistor can produce current gains well over 20.

accumulating at potential hill 3 is to decrease this negative field at the barrier, and electrons from the collector are enabled to cross this barrier into the central P region. Since these electrons must travel through the P region mainly by diffusion, it must be made very thin or narrow to prevent excessive recombinations. Note that in the over-all system one recombination process is already going on as the holes from the left-hand P region move through the central N region, and this recombination introduces its own loss. Electrons which survive the trip through the central P region easily slide down potential hill 2, enter the central region which is the N base, and complete the circuit.

Thus the holes allowed to take part in the left-hand PNP arrangement, and as modulated by an ac input signal, control a much-enhanced electron current because of the positive space charge, and very appreciable current gains are possible. It has been stated repeatedly that junction transistors have a current gain, or alpha, less than unity. The current gain of junction transistors employing the hook principle may be greater than unity; in fact, current gains of 20 and greater have been reported. The difficulty of making satisfactory units, the relatively high noise level, and lack of reproducibility render it unlikely that such units will be commercially available in the near future. With the advancements being made in transistor fabrication, it appears virtually certain that in time units employing this principle will be obtainable.

91. PHOTOTRANSISTOR[10]

An important member of the transistor family is the phototransistor, variously called photodiode or photocell, see Fig. 7-10. While the

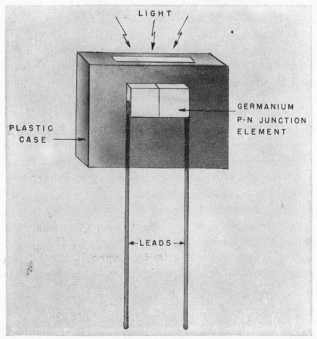

Fig. 7-10. A junction diode type of phototransistor. (See Chap. 15 for NPN type, and Ref. 15, Chap. 15.) Similar junction units are made with the light impinging on either end, instead of upon the junction. Phototransistors may also be of the point contact type. (*Courtesy of the Western Electric Co.*)

physical construction is that of a PN diode, the device is considered to belong to the transistor category because the light performs a function analogous to the emitter.

The theory of operation is based on the ability of light to impart enough energy to electrons in valence bonds to raise them to the conduction band. The disruption of the valence bonds increases the available supply of electrons and holes, and these act as current carriers to decrease the resistivity.   Thus, when light shines on the junction, a marked decrease in the resistance is observed, or for constant impressed voltage, a marked increase in current.

Phototransistors are commercially available at present.   They are extremely practical in that large voltage swings are attainable and they are small in size and weight.   A number of interesting aspects of the phototransistor will be given to assist readers considering possible applications: (1) A phototransistor need not be a junction unit—practical phototransistors may be made using point contact principles. (2) It is not necessary to shine the light directly on the junction, as indicated in Fig. 7-10.   An entirely feasible unit may be made with the light focused on either end of the PN assembly, provided the P or N region is made reasonably thin.   A marked advantage of making the P and N regions quite thin is observed in the speed of response —the thicker units obviously require a longer transit time for the carriers, and this clearly will decrease the speed of response.   (3) As has been mentioned in an earlier chapter, the energy contained in a light ray depends not on the intensity, but on the frequency: energy equals Planck's constant times frequency, for each photon or unit corpuscle of light.   Accordingly, to impart the required energy, quite short wavelengths or high frequencies must be used, and the efficiency of most of these cells falls off rapidly in the infrared region, beyond 2μ.   The cells give good efficiency well into the infrared region.   (4) When the frequency is too high, the electrons are not only removed from their valence bonds, but acquire enough energy to actually leave the germanium—photoemission is observed.   Since the photoemission effect for germanium is unimportant compared to other materials, phototransistors are not used beyond blue or the ultraviolet.

92. SUMMARY

The salient points of this chapter are:

1. Holes are the current carriers in the PNP transistor; in the NPN transistor electrons are the carriers.

2. Junction transistors are capable of high orders of voltage and power gain compared to the point contact units.

3. The transistor industry is at present in need of improved metallurgical processes for the construction of PN junctions and the processing of germanium (and silicon) in general.

4. Special transistors such as the PNPN and phototransistor are examples of the steadily growing list of semiconductor devices with properties unusually attractive for commercial applications.

REFERENCES

1. Shockley, W.: The Theory of PN Junctions in Semiconductors and PN Junction Transistors, *Bell System Tech. J.*, Vol. 28, pp. 435–489, July, 1949.
2. Rugare, A. S.: The Metal Germanium and Its Use in the Electronics Industry, *Metal Progress*, Vol. 62, No. 2, pp. 97–103, August, 1952.
3. Saby, J. S.: Fused Impurity PNP Junction Transistors, *Proc. IRE*, Vol. 40, No. 11, pp. 1358–1360, November, 1952.
4. Montgomery, H. C.: Transistor Noise in Circuit Applications, *Proc. IRE*, Vol. 40, pp. 1461–1471, November, 1952; and Bess, L.: A Possible Mechanism for 1/f Noise Generation in Semiconductor Filaments, *Phys. Rev.*, Vol. 91, No. 6, Sept. 15, 1953.
5. Technical Staff of Philco Research Division: The Surface Barrier Transistor, *Proc. IRE*, Vol. 41, No. 12, pp. 1702–1720, December, 1953.
6. Teal, G. K., M. Sparks, and E. Buehler: Growth of Germanium Single Crystals Containing PN Junctions, *Phys. Rev.*, Vol. 81, p. 637, Feb. 15, 1951.
7. Hall, R. N.: PN Junctions Produced by Rate Growth Variation, *Phys. Rev.*, Vol. 88, p. 139, Oct. 1, 1952.
8. Wallace, Jr., R. L., L. G. Schimpf, and E. Dickten: A Junction Transistor Tetrode for High Frequency Use, *Proc. IRE*, Vol. 40, pp. 1395–1400, November, 1952.
9. Shockley, W.: "Electrons and Holes in Semiconductors," pp. 112ff., D. Van Nostrand Company, Inc., New York, 1950.
10. Shive, J. N.: Properties of M-1740 Photocell, *Proc. IRE*, Vol. 40, No. 11, pp. 1410–1413, November, 1952.

8 ELECTRONICS OF TRANSISTORS

In the previous chapters the physics of the transistor was discussed to establish a theoretical foundation for a full understanding of transistor electronics. Subsequent chapters will discuss the circuit behavior of the transistor and show how the physical principles can be used to explain the operation of existing circuits and assist in the design of new circuits.

93. BLACK BOX

In electrical engineering, and more particularly in electronic engineering, it is frequently convenient to analyze the performance of an unfamiliar circuit or electronic device in terms of an assembly or combination of commonly used fundamental circuit elements.[1] For purposes of analysis, the unfamiliar device is regarded as a "black box," from which emerge, for our purposes, two input and two output terminals. The challenge is to determine what is in the black box, electrically speaking, without opening it up; frequently, having access to the inside of the device does not provide the equivalent electrical circuit that is desired. This is true, as the reader may know, for quartz crystals and is particularly true in the case of transistors. Further, it is assumed that we cannot use the box in our work but must find an equivalent four-terminal circuit whose performance, when put into a given electrical circuit, will be identical to that of the black box. To this end we make certain tests

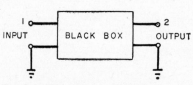

Fig. 8-1. Elementary generalized electrical network known as the black box, with a pair of input and output terminals. Applied to the transistor in the grounded- or common-base connection, terminal 1 is the emitter, terminal 2 the collector, and the ground corresponds to the base terminal of the transistor.

on the black box, having access only to its four terminals with the objective of determining an equivalent circuit and parameter values. The transistor is essentially a four-pole or four-terminal electrical device, the base acting as the common terminal for both input and output.

The analysis of such four-pole black boxes is fairly standard but will be discussed in some detail to show its application to the transistor.

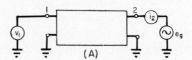

Fig. 8-2A. Circuit hookup to measure r_{12} (or Z_{12} since a ratio of alternating voltage and current is involved). Terminal 1 corresponds to the emitter, terminal 2 to the collector, and the ground to the base of a transistor, when connected in the grounded-base arrangement.

The process essentially consists of applying an input to either the left- or right-hand pair of terminals and measuring voltages and currents in the manner to be described below. Essentials of the arrangement are shown in Fig. 8-1, and in all cases the voltages are measured with a very high-impedance voltmeter which may be considered for all practical purposes as an open circuit. Let us agree to call the input or left-hand terminal 1 as marked and the output terminal 2 as shown; the other terminals are understood to be at ground potential.

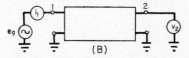

Fig. 8-2B. Circuit hookup to measure r_{21} (or Z_{21}). See comments under Fig. 8-2A.

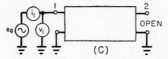

Fig. 8-2C. Circuit hookup to measure r_{11} (or Z_{11}). See comments under Fig. 8-2A.

94. CONVENTIONS REGARDING NOTATION

The resistance obtained by measuring a voltage and a current is denoted by two numbers in its subscript, the first referring to voltage and the second to current. For instance, r_{12} will mean the resistance obtained by measuring the voltage across terminal 1 or in circuit 1

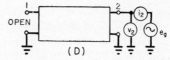

Fig. 8-2D. Circuit hookup to measure r_{22} (or Z_{22}). See comments under Fig. 8-2A.

and the current in circuit 2, see Fig. 8-2A. This implies that the test voltage e_g is applied to terminal 2 since the current in circuit 1 is only that drawn by the voltmeter and can be ignored. Similarly, r_{21} is the resistance obtained by applying the test voltage e_g to circuit 1, since the current is measured in 1, and measuring the open-circuit voltage in circuit 2, see Fig. 8-2B. These are important conventions for transistor work, and the reader is urged to become acquainted with them by studying for himself to determine what r_{11} and r_{22} mean, see Fig. 8-2C and 8-2D. We shall also adopt the convention finding much favor in transistor work which states that small letters refer to parameters which characterize the device itself or are intrinsic in the device, whereas capital letters refer to externally added components. Thus, the internal resistance associated with e_g would be designated by R_g. With these simple conventions let us now consider four tests, the data from which will assist in completely characterizing the four-terminal device.

95. ASSUMPTIONS REGARDING IMPEDANCE

It is necessary to point out that, with respect to the transistor, the ratios obtained by dividing the observed voltages by the observed currents are truly in the nature of impedances and not resistances. However, because in many instances, the reactive component of the impedance is negligible compared with the resistive component and because using the resistance notation simplifies the introductory presentation of the essential points, we shall use the resistance notation and ignore the reactive component. It is anticipated that the reader who will ultimately do design work in the field of transistors will run across this particular problem, and it is well to bear in mind that the transistor parameters are intrinsically frequency dependent. The error introduced by treating them as purely resistive components is tolerable in many cases.[2]

96. MEASUREMENTS TO OBTAIN THE r's

Because the following four tests are actually the ones used in evaluating and comparing many types of transistors, the reader should make a special point of understanding the procedures and the significance of the results. The measurements are quite straightforward and proceed as follows:

1. Apply the signal to terminal 1 which corresponds to the emitter, read i_1 and v_1, and obtain

$$\frac{v_1}{i_1} = r_{11} \quad \text{(see Fig. 8-2C)} \tag{8-1}$$

For both point contact and junction transistors this value will usually be of the order of 500 ohms.

2. Apply the signal to terminal 1, read i_1 and v_2, and obtain

$$\frac{v_2}{i_1} = r_{21} \quad \text{(see Fig. 8-2B)} \tag{8-2}$$

For point contact transistors this may be of the order of 30 kilohms and for junction types 1 megohm and higher.

3. Apply the signal to terminal 2 which corresponds to the collector, read i_2 and v_2, and obtain

$$\frac{v_2}{i_2} = r_{22} \quad \text{(see Fig. 8-2}D\text{)} \tag{8-3}$$

For point contact types this may be of the order of 20 kilohms and for junction types of the order of 1 megohm and higher.

4. Apply the signal to terminal 2, read i_2 and v_1 and obtain

$$\frac{v_1}{i_2} = r_{12} \quad \text{(see Fig. 8-2}A\text{)} \tag{8-4}$$

For point contact types and junction types this is usually of the order of 300 ohms.

97. ACTIVE NETWORK VERSUS PASSIVE NETWORK

To obtain a black-box equivalent, it is necessary to find a combination of basic components that will give the same meter indications as a transistor in these tests. Actually there are many possible arrangements, but the simplest of them all is the T arrangement of resistors shown in Fig. 8-3. It is not difficult to see that, if we applied the voltage to terminal 1, for instance, and read the current in circuit 1 or the emitter circuit and the voltage across it, it is conceivable that we could get the r_{11} of Eq. (8-1), and similarly for all the other resistances. In reviewing this process to see how the equivalent T fulfills the requirements we have set forth, the reader will find a very important discrepancy.

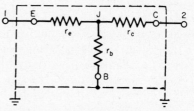

Fig. 8-3. A possible equivalent circuit one might construct to simulate the results obtained by taking the measurements 1 through 4 on a transistor. As explained in the text, this equivalent circuit suffers from a very severe limitation, and a more satisfactory approximation is given in Fig. 8-4.

Consider tests 2 and 4: In test 2 the signal is applied to the emitter, the emitter current recorded, and the voltage from terminal 2 to ground measured. It has already been mentioned that we are using a very high-impedance voltmeter to make these measurements and for all practical purposes can consider that it draws no current. If that is the case, the voltage drop across r_c can be ignored, and to all intents and purposes v_2 is essentially the voltage from point J of Fig. 8-3 to ground.   Then v_2 and i_1 measure the voltage and current, respectively, for r_b and the r_{21} of Eq. (8-2) is r_b.   In test 4 the voltage is applied to terminal 2 and the current in the collector circuit measured.   The high-resistance voltmeter which records v_1 is, as before, actually recording the voltage from point J to ground; so the voltage across r_b and the current through it are being measured.   The quotient is the r_{12} of Eq. (8-4) and is again seen to be r_b.   Looking at the comments made under 2 and 4 above, it is seen that r_{12} is very significantly different from r_{21}, whereas for the simple equivalent T of transistors it should be the same.   Where is the discrepancy?

The answer to this question raises a very important point regarding circuits and networks in general, *viz.*, the differentiation between an active and a passive network.   If a network is passive, it contains no generators or sources of voltage or current and a signal passing through it can suffer attenuation but no amplification because the circuit does not contribute from within itself to the amplitude of the signal. For a passive network the r_{21} or forward transfer resistance is always equal to the r_{12} or feedback resistance.   Since, in the case of the transistor, the forward and feedback resistances are very definitely unequal, we may properly infer that the transistor is not representable by a passive network.

An active network, on the other hand, has a power source or generator which is capable of amplifying the input signal or contributing from within itself to the amplitude of the input.   An excellent example is the vacuum tube for which the active aspect of its behavior is represented on its equivalent diagram by a generator of voltage output μE_g.   For a vacuum tube, for instance, the forward and feedback characteristics are very definitely unequal also, but, of course, such parameters are of limited usefulness only for the characterization of the behavior of vacuum tubes.

98. $r_m i_e$

The preceding discussion shows that an equivalent circuit for the transistor consisting solely of passive elements like resistors is inadequate. A generator or voltage source of some kind must be shown in the equivalent diagram to indicate (1) that we are dealing with an active network and (2) that the forward and feedback resistances will be unequal when tests 2 and 4 are performed.   This equivalent generator is indicated by $r_m i_e$ in the equivalent circuit of Fig. 8-4.   The r_m is called the mutual resistance for the network; the reader will gain further familiarity with the significance of this term in subsequent discussions.   Attention is drawn to the fact that the current indicated by i_e is the current through the emitter resistance r_e and is not necessarily the loop current in circuit 1. The parameters r_e, r_b, and r_c shown are called emitter resistance, base resistance, and collector resistance, respectively, and play a very important role in the circuit electronics of transistors. The reader should verify to his own satisfaction from Eqs. (8-1) to (8-4) and Fig. 8-4 the following basic relationships:

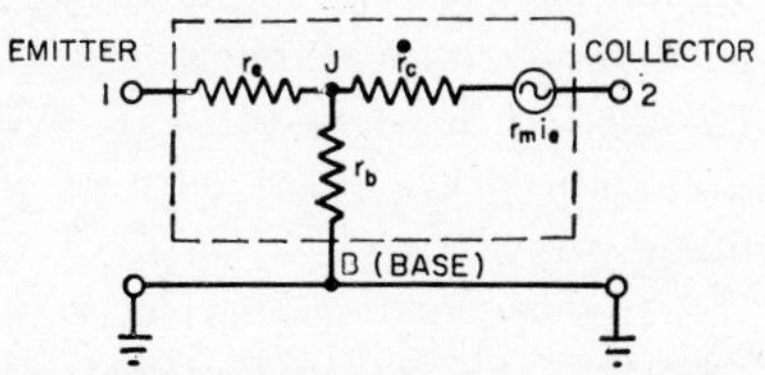

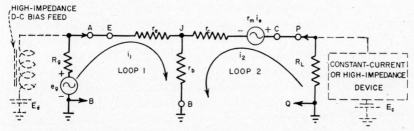

Fig. 8-4. A more accurate equivalent circuit representation of the transistor, both point contact and junction, with a generator $r_m i_e$ to indicate the active nature of the network. It is called the equivalent *T* network. Note that point *J* is NOT accessible; connections can be made only to emitter, collector, and base.

$$r_{11} = r_e + r_b \qquad (8\text{-}5)$$
$$r_{12} = r_b \qquad (8\text{-}6)$$
$$r_{21} = r_m + r_b \qquad (8\text{-}7)$$
$$r_{22} = r_c + r_b \qquad (8\text{-}8)$$

Equation (8-7) is not immediately apparent until one writes the circuit equations involving these parameters; these equations will be developed subsequently.

99. TRANSISTOR EQUIVALENT CIRCUIT

In Fig. 8-5 the equivalent circuit is shown and the transistor terminals which are available for connection are marked E, C, B. For

Fig. 8-5. The equivalent *T* circuit of the transistor, with suitable load and generator. Bias supplies are shown dotted to indicate that the shunting effect of the voltage source is considered negligible, or already lumped into parameters R_g and R_L shown. Connections to transistor are made at *E*, *C*, and *B*. Typical parameter values are shown in Table 8-1.

completeness a generator is shown in loop 1 whose output voltage is e_g and whose internal resistance is R_g, and a load is shown R_L.

Before proceeding to a more detailed analysis of this circuit, a number of preliminary comments of a general nature should be noted. Without the following precautionary notes the reader will be confused by the analysis of Fig. 8-5.

1. The resistances indicated as r_e, r_b, r_c, and r_m in the figure, if it were desired to be quite accurate, would really be shown as impedances. In the tests for the four-pole parameters, ac is used and the ratio of an ac voltage to an ac current is an impedance so that actually the tests outlined in Eqs. (8-1) to (8-4) do give impedances. However, these impedances are valid only at the test frequency. Usually this frequency is 270 cps.

2. As the reader may have realized from his understanding of the theory of operation of the transistors we have been discussing, the transistor is a biased device. Just as the vacuum tube is biased to a definite operating point the transistor must be biased to a suitable operating point by appropriate emitter and collector biasing potentials. The transistor has an optimum operating point with respect to these bias voltages just as a vacuum tube has an optimum operating point with respect to its plate and grid voltages. A glance at Fig. 8-5, however, shows that these bias voltages are omitted. To be strictly accurate, they should be included because they may represent important shunt or series resistances with respect to the circuit shown. These are omitted for convenience in the circuit analysis. A shunt-feed bias arrangement such as shown by the dotted circuit in Fig. 8-5 may be used if desired. To obtain the equivalent of several megohms in the shunt circuit a constant-current arrangement such as a pentode may be used, with an internal resistance of the order desired. For junction types with a collector resistance of several megohms, it may be necessary to cascade two such pentode circuits to get the high internal resistance required.[3] Certainly in the emitter circuit such a shunt impedance will have almost no effect. Refer to typical values of the four-pole parameters given in Table 8-1. In cases where the shunting effect of the dc biasing arrangement is not negligible, a simple series feed arrangement may be used and the effect of the series resistance introduced by the battery considered already lumped into the values of R_L and R_g shown.

3. It is important to observe the i_e shown for the equivalent generator. This i_e will in all cases in our future discussion refer to the current flowing through the emitter resistance r_e. In Fig. 8-5 i_e and i_1 are identical, but this is not always the case. In some circuits, emitter current is not the same as the current through loop 1, and care must be taken not to substitute the loop current for i_e in all cases.

4. A consistent convention must be adopted regarding the polarities of the generators in Fig. 8-5. The polarity convention to be used in these chapters is that at a given instant of time the negative end of the equivalent generator $r_m i_e$ is toward the junction point J. In consonance with this, the negative terminal of the generator e_g goes to

ground, as shown in the figure. This convention will assist materially in obtaining consistent results in the analysis of this and future circuits.

5. In Fig. 8-1 the base of the transistor is grounded and common to the input and output loops. This particular connection for obvious reasons is called the grounded-base connection and sometimes the common-base connection. But it must be clear that it is possible to work out a circuit arrangement wherein the emitter is grounded and the signal is fed into the base. Such an arrangement is called the grounded-emitter connection or, alternatively, the common-emitter connection. Finally, the signal may be fed into the base and the collector grounded, in which case the output is taken from the emitter. Such a connection is called the grounded-collector or common-collector circuit. These two latter types of connection will be discussed more fully later on, but for the time being our discussion in this chapter will be limited to the grounded-base connection unless one of the other connections is specifically indicated. In particular, Eqs. (8-5) to (8-8) are valid only for the grounded-base connection and will lead to incorrect results if applied to the grounded-emitter or grounded-collector connection. This point cannot be emphasized too strongly, and we shall return to it subsequently.

6. In writing the mesh or Kirchhoff-law equations for the analysis of Fig. 8-5, the reader will find it convenient to consistently apply the following rules regarding current direction and polarities, in so far as they affect the signs of the terms in the equations.

100. RULES FOR APPLYING KIRCHHOFF'S LAWS

1. Current direction is taken as the direction of the flow of electrons. The so-called conventional current flow which adopts the point of view that the flow of current is opposite to the direction of electron flow will not be used in this book, but sometimes, for convenience, arbitrary directions may be assumed.

2. If an arrow is used to indicate the direction of current flow, the head of the arrow is taken as positive and the tail of the arrow negative when considering the voltage drop.

3. When writing the terms for an equation which expresses Kirchhoff's law that the sum of the voltage drops and rises around a closed loop is zero, all the terms of the expression are to be considered for purposes of determining polarity as being written on one side of the equation. See, for example, Eq. (8-9).

4. By convention, voltage drops are assigned a plus sign; a generator or voltage source, referred to as a voltage rise, is given a minus sign.

5. The currents considered in Fig. 8-5 are loop currents, which

means that the currents i_1 and i_2 as in Fig. 8-5 are considered to flow separately in their respective loops. In circuit elements where both flow, the principle of superposition is applied; that is, the currents are considered to add algebraically.

6. Consider the current i_e in the equivalent transistor generator shown as $r_m i_e$. This current i_e is defined as the current through the emitter resistance r_e *when this current flows toward the junction J.* For instance, in Fig. 8-5 the current through r_e is clearly i_1 and i_1 flows toward J. We may then say $i_e = i_1$. Occasionally the direction of i_1 which is really chosen arbitrarily may be taken opposite to that shown in Fig. 8-5, in which case i_e would be the negative of i_1. This concept will be found particularly useful for writing equations for the grounded-emitter circuit.

101. PARAMETERS NEEDED FOR EVALUATION OF PERFORMANCE

Before proceeding to the analysis of the circuit it is certainly proper to ask ourselves: What information are we trying to obtain as a result of the analysis? To begin with, for a given transistor the r's are assumed to be known, R_g is also known, and the load resistance R_L is either known or assigned according to design requirements. A suitable voltage e_g is applied to the transistor, and we would then like to know without actually hooking up each transistor under a variety of different conditions how the circuit will perform. By performance of the circuit, we usually mean the following: the input resistance, the output resistance, the voltage gain, and the power gain. To obtain this information it is necessary first to find currents i_1 and i_2. The problem reduces itself to finding the loop currents and obtaining from the currents the information of interest.

102. LOOP EQUATIONS FOR EQUIVALENT CIRCUIT OF GB TRANSISTOR

To obtain the currents knowing the other parameters in Fig. 8-5, the procedure is to write down for each loop an expression of the fact that the sum of the voltage rises and voltage drops in a closed loop is zero. Beginning at the ground point at the extreme left of loop 1 and proceeding clockwise in the direction of the arrow, we may consider the voltage drops and rises as follows:

Since e_g is a generator or voltage rise and since the current flows through it from minus to plus, by rule 4 above, e_g will be assigned a minus sign. Across R_g and r_e are two simple voltage drops which are given a positive sign, also according to rule 4. Both i_1 and i_2 flow through r_b in the same direction. We infer that the voltage drops due to i_1 and i_2 are additive. Based on this analysis we may now write as follows:

$$i_1(R_g + r_e + r_b) + i_2 r_b - e_g = 0 \qquad (8\text{-}9)$$

In loop 2, starting at the ground point on the extreme right and proceeding around the loop in the direction of the current, we have first the $i_2 R_L$ drop which is given a positive sign. Since i_2 flows from *plus to minus* through $r_m i_e$, we assign a positive sign to this generator voltage or voltage rise (rule 4). By rule 6, $i_e = i_1$ and the transistor generator can now be written $r_m i_1$ instead of $r_m i_e$. Across r_c the voltage drop is clearly $r_c i_2$; since both i_1 and i_2 flow through r_b, the drop across it is $r_b(i_1 + i_2)$. We may now write the expression which shows that the sum of the voltage drops and voltage rises in loop 2 is zero:

$$i_1(r_b + r_m) + i_2(R_L + r_b + r_c) = 0 \qquad (8\text{-}10)[4]$$

Equations (8-9) and (8-10) completely define or describe the circuit of Fig. 8-5 in so far as the ac voltages and currents are concerned. It must be evident from the fact that the equations do not contain the appropriate parameters that this analysis cannot possibly give information regarding such matters as noise, distributed capacity, frequency response, or any of the parameters such as lifetime and density of carriers which describe the transistor material itself. The equations will, however, provide information regarding resistances, voltage and current gains, power gain, and the stability of the circuit.

The solution of linear simultaneous Eqs. (8-9) and (8-10) for the currents reveals the following:

$$i_1 = \frac{e_g(R_L + r_b + r_c)}{(R_g + r_b + r_e)(R_L + r_b + r_c) - r_b(r_b + r_m)} \qquad (8\text{-}11)$$

$$i_2 = \frac{-e_g(r_b + r_m)}{(R_g + r_b + r_e)(R_L + r_b + r_c) - r_b(r_b + r_m)} \qquad (8\text{-}12)$$

These expressions give currents i_1 and i_2 in terms of the circuit parameters which, for a given transistor and circuit, are known. Henceforth, in our discussion, we may therefore treat i_1 and i_2 as known quantities and express the circuit characteristics desired in terms of the currents as well as the circuit parameters.

103. TYPICAL VALUES OF TRANSISTOR PARAMETERS

Because it is helpful in discussing this material to talk about specific numbers, a typical working set of transistor and circuit parameters is given in Table 8-1 for use in all future numerical computations.

Although the values given may be regarded as typical for point contact and junction transistors now on the market, transistors with widely different parameter values may be encountered. The values of R_g, R_L, and e_g have been selected as representing practical orders of

TABLE 8-1

Parameter	Point contact transistor	Junction transistor*
r_e	150 ohms	25 ohms
r_b	120 ohms	500 ohms
r_m	35 kilohms	0.96 megohms
r_c	15 kilohms	1.0 megohm
R_g	500 ohms	500 ohms
R_L	20 kilohms	100 kilohms
α	2.3	0.96
e_g	0.01 volt	.001 volt

* Average includes NPN and PNP units.

magnitude in common use; accordingly, the numbers to be given for comparison may be looked upon as practical, working values.

104. INPUT RESISTANCE—GB CONNECTION

In Fig. 8-5 the arrows at A and B indicate the circuit condition seen by a generator such as e_g when the generator is connected from emitter to ground. The effect of the transistor and the rest of the circuit to the right of points A and B might, if desired, be replaced by a single resistance whose effect, in so far as the generator is concerned, will be the same as the system now shown. The reader familiar with radio circuits will recognize this equivalent resistance seen by the generator as the input resistance, sometimes called the driving point resistance.[5] Figure 8-6 indicates how R_i, the internal resistance, replaces the effect of the circuit to the right of points AB while current i_1 remains the same. The useful information to be obtained from Fig. 8-6 is that if we taken e_g and divide by i_1 the result is the total resistance in the circuit of Fig. 8-6. If from this total resistance you subtract R_g, the internal resistance of the generator, the result is the input resistance R_i. That is,

$$R_i = \frac{e_g}{i_1} - R_g \tag{8-13}$$

Studying this equation we observe that i_1 is defined by Eq. (8-11) so that it is possible to obtain the input resistance as a function of the circuit parameters. Making the substitution from Eq. (8-11) into

Eq. (8-13), we obtain

$$R_i = r_b + r_e - \frac{r_b(r_b + r_m)}{R_L + r_b + r_c} \qquad (8\text{-}14)$$

This equation expresses the input resistance of a grounded-base transistor in terms of the circuit parameters, and by studying this expression, a number of useful bits of information will become apparent. Note first the negative sign before the third term on the right-hand side. In general, the circuit parameters of a transistor or its equivalent active T parameters are always positive numbers; therefore, a combination of parameters may occur in Eq. (8-14) which will make R_i negative. This circumstance leads to the particular application of transistors in electronic switching arrangements where the negative input resistance is intentional. Where it is unintentional, instability and parasitic oscillations occur. These points will be covered more fully in a subsequent chapter.

Fig. 8-6. All that portion of Fig. 8-5 to the right of points AB causes a current i_1 to flow from generator e_g and is replaced by R_i in this figure to reproduce the same result.

Using the typical values given in Table 8-1, the reader can quickly verify that the input resistance for a point contact unit will be in the order of 150 ohms and for a junction unit, approximately 90 ohms. This brings to light immediately the important fact that the transistor in the grounded-base connection is a low input impedance device. The reader acquainted with vacuum-tube practice where, for class A operation, the input resistance at ordinary frequencies may be of the order of a megohm or more will note the sharp contrast between transistors in the grounded-base connection and vacuum tubes in so far as their input resistance is concerned.

105. SIMPLIFICATION FOR R_i FORMULA

Looking at Table 8-1 and Eq. (8-14), a useful simplification of Eq. (8-14) is obtained by reasoning as follows: in general, in electronics great precision in the specification of component parts is rarely necessary. For instance, the reader familiar with radio circuits will verify that, if a coupling resistor is specified as 100,000 ohms, a resistor from 85 to 120 kilohms will usually do just as well without any apparent change in circuit performance. Applying this principle to Eq. (8-14), we may ignore r_b whose value is 120 ohms for the point contact unit compared to r_m which is 35,000 ohms. This is doubly true for the junction unit, where we can ignore 500 ohms compared to 0.96

megohm. Similarly, in the denominator of the third term on the right-hand side we can ignore r_b compared to $R_L + r_c$ both for the point contact and junction units. A simplified but practical form of Eq. (8-14) which will be used in subsequent analyses is

$$R_i \cong r_b + r_e - \frac{r_b r_m}{R_L + r_c} \tag{8-15}$$

106. SHORT-CIRCUIT STABILITY

The grounded-base transistor is operated sometimes intentionally, and sometimes not, with the output shorted. As an illustration, consider the operation of a transistor in a circuit where a frequency of 20 mc is present, although the operating point may be at a much lower frequency. For purposes of the illustration, we shall assume that the transistor still has a useful current gain at 20 mc. It is, therefore, useful to consider the case when R_L of Fig. 8-5 is virtually shorted as, for instance, by C_c, the collector capacity. If we put R_L equal to zero, Eq. (8-15) becomes

$$R_i = r_b + r_e - \frac{r_b r_m}{r_c} \tag{8-16}$$

In transistor practice a parameter somewhat analogous to the g_m of a vacuum tube is α. A formal definition for α will be given later, but in equation form it is defined by

$$\alpha = \frac{r_b + r_m}{r_b + r_c} = \frac{r_{21}}{r_{22}} = -\frac{i_c}{i_e} \tag{8-17}[6]$$

In keeping with the approach enunciated above that great orders of precision are normally not required in electronics, we may ignore r_b compared to r_m in the numerator and r_b compared to r_c in the denominator, both in point contact and junction transistors. Refer to Table 8-1. When this is done, the expression for α becomes

$$\alpha \cong \frac{r_m}{r_c} \tag{8-18}$$

If we substitute α for r_m/r_c Eq. (8-16) becomes

$$R_i \cong r_b + r_e - r_b \alpha \tag{8-19}$$

As Table 8-1 shows, α of point contact transistors averages 2.3 and r_b is of the same order of magnitude as r_e. It is apparent that the input resistance may be negative for a point contact transistor connected grounded base if the output is shorted. Recalling the remarks made regarding instability when the input resistance is negative, it is obvious that the point contact transistor is in general short circuit unstable.[7] However, it must not be inferred that all point contact transistors are always short circuit unstable. Point contact transistors with very low values of r_b have been developed which are short circuit stable.

For the junction transistor where α is always less than unity, a glance at Eq. (8-19) will show that R_i is always positive. The possibility of short-circuit instability in the point contact unit contrasts sharply therefore with the uniform stability of the junction unit under comparable conditions. This consideration of short-circuit stability will frequently decide unequivocally which type of transistor to use in a given application.

107. OUTPUT RESISTANCE GB CONNECTION

To obtain the output resistance, which is the resistance presented at points P and Q of Fig. 8-5 to a load R_L, we make use of an artifice which

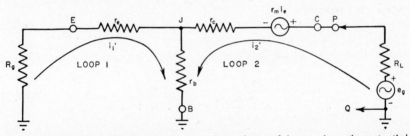

Fig. 8-7. For purposes of finding R_o, the output impedance of the transistor, the potential of the generator e_g is moved into loop 2, as shown; all other aspects of Fig. 8-5 remain invariant. Currents i_1' and i_2' then flow in loops 1 and 2, respectively, instead of the currents i_1 and i_2 of Fig. 8-5.

the reader will find useful in many other applications. In Fig. 8-7 observe how the generator e_g has been placed in series with R_L and the generator resistance retained where it had been before, in the input circuit. We are now in a position to determine what type of impedance a theoretical generator e_g placed in the circuit, as shown, would encounter. Note that this theoretical generator is considered to have zero internal resistance. It should be clear that the resistance seen by the generator e_g, connected as in Fig. 8-7, less R_L, will be the output resistance. The circuit equations which describe Fig. 8-7 are identical with Eqs. (8-9) and (8-10) except that now e_g will appear in loop 2. The equations are given below, and note that we have now written i_1'

and i_2' because clearly these currents will differ from i_1 and i_2 of Eqs. (8-9) and (8-10).

$$i_1'(R_g + r_e + r_b) + i_2'r_b = 0 \qquad (8\text{-}20)$$
$$i_1'(r_b + r_m) + i_2'(R_L + r_b + r_c) - e_g = 0 \qquad (8\text{-}21)$$

We need to solve these two equations for i_2' only as can be seen from the equivalent circuit, Fig. 8-8, where the effect of all that portion of the circuit of Fig. 8-7 which is to the left of points PQ has been replaced by a single resistance R_o which is the output resistance of the circuit. When this is done, it is found that i_2' is given by

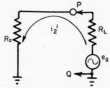

$$i_2' = \frac{e_g(R_g + r_e + r_b)}{(R_g + r_b + r_e)(R_L + r_b + r_c) - r_b(r_b + r_m)} \qquad (8\text{-}22)$$

Fig. 8-8. All that por-
tion of Fig. 8-7 to the
left of points PQ causes
a current i_2' to be drawn
from generator e_g and
is replaced by R_o in this
figure to reproduce
the same result.

The output resistance R_o in Fig. 8-8 is the total resistance of the circuit less the load resistance R_L, or

$$R_o = \frac{e_g}{i_2'} - R_L \qquad (8\text{-}23)$$

Using the value of i_2' from Eq. (8-22)

$$R_o = r_b + r_c - \frac{r_b(r_b + r_m)}{R_g + r_b + r_e} \qquad (8\text{-}24)$$

Again ignoring r_b as negligible compared to r_m or r_c, a simplified form of Eq. (8-24) is

$$R_o \cong r_c - \frac{r_b r_m}{R_g + r_b + r_e} \qquad (8\text{-}25)$$

108. TYPICAL VALUES OF R_o—GB CONNECTION

Using the values from Table 8-1 to obtain orders of magnitude, it can be verified that the output of resistance of the grounded-base transistor is approximately 9,500 ohms for the point contact and 530,000 ohms for the junction types. Collating this information with the data previously obtained for the value of the input resistance, we may infer that the transistor in the grounded-base connection has a low input resistance, usually under 1,000 ohms, and an output resistance anywhere from a few thousand ohms to approximately a half megohm. Impedance-wise, the grounded-base transistor resembles a step-up transformer.

The negative sign in Eq. (8-24) suggests, as for the case of the input resistance, that a combination of parameters may be found for which R_o is negative. A negative output resistance will lead to instability or parasitic oscillations just as will a negative input resistance. The reader will observe from Eq. (8-24) that very low values of input generator resistance R_g generally tend toward instability in transistor operation. In preparation for what is to follow, it is noted that the input and output resistance levels given for the grounded-base connection do not apply to the grounded-emitter and grounded-collector connections.

109. VOLTAGE GAIN—GB

In general, voltage gain is defined for any device as the ratio of output voltage to input voltage. In keeping with the rules regarding the polarity of voltage rises and voltage drops formulated in the first part of this chapter, if the input voltage, which is a voltage rise, is given a negative sign, the output voltage, which is a voltage drop across R_L, should be assigned a plus sign. In practice it is not so important to observe whether we assign a plus or minus sign to a voltage rise or voltage drop so long as opposite signs are assigned to voltage drops and voltage rises. Observing that the effective voltage output is that available across the load resistance, we may write for the voltage gain

$$VG = \frac{i_2 R_L}{-e_g} \qquad (8\text{-}26)$$

Knowing i_2 from Eq. (8-12), substitute in Eq. (8-26) and obtain

$$VG = \frac{(r_b + r_m)R_L}{(R_g + r_b + r_e)(R_L + r_b + r_c) - r_b(r_b + r_m)} \qquad (8\text{-}27)$$

As has been done previously, we may ignore r_b compared to r_c or r_m and thereby obtain a simplified form of the expression for the voltage gain as follows:

$$VG \cong \frac{r_m R_L}{(R_g + r_b + r_e)(R_L + r_c) - r_b r_m} \qquad (8\text{-}28)$$

Substituting numbers for the parameters from Table 8-1, it is easily verified that the voltage gain for a point contact transistor is of the order of 30 and that for a junction type approximately 150.

The voltage gain depends directly on the value of R_L selected. It will be observed from Table 8-1 that, in selecting a load resistance, we have actually favored the point contact unit in selecting R_L greater than r_c for the point contact and only one-tenth of r_c for the junction. The reader familiar with radio circuits will realize that in general too high a value of load resistance is not practical because of stray capacities. In any event, having favored the point contact unit in selecting the value of R_L, it should be evident that in general the junction transistor is capable of giving higher voltage gains than is the point contact type. This is particularly well illustrated by the maximum-voltage-gain analysis which follows.

110. MAXIMUM VOLTAGE GAIN—THEORETICAL[8]

It is useful for many applications to know what is the maximum theoretically possible voltage gain that may be obtained from a point contact or junction transistor. To obtain these numbers, it is necessary to idealize the circuit arrangement by assuming an ideal generator, of zero internal resistance, and an ideal load, of infinite resistance. If the internal generator resistance is zero, no voltage drop can occur across it; also, if the load resistance is infinite, all the available generator voltage will be developed across it.

Using Eq. (8-5) to (8-8) in Eq. (8-27), there is obtained

$$VG = \frac{r_{21}R_L}{(R_g + r_{11})(R_L + r_{22}) - r_{12}r_{21}} \tag{8-29}$$

Divide the numerator and denominator by R_L

$$VG = \frac{r_{21}}{(R_g + r_{11})[1 + (r_{22}/R_L)] - (r_{12}r_{21}/R_L)} \tag{8-30}$$

If we put R_g equal to zero in Eq. (8-30) and allow R_L to approach infinity, we obtain the maximum theoretically possible voltage gain

$$VG_m = \frac{r_{21}}{(0 + r_{11})(1 + 0) - 0} = \frac{r_{21}}{r_{11}} \tag{8-31}$$

Now multiply the numerator by $r_{22}/r_{22} = 1$:

$$VG_m = \frac{r_{21}}{r_{22}} \frac{r_{22}}{r_{11}} \tag{8-32}$$

Looking now at Eq. (8-17) we see that r_{21}/r_{22} is α, and making this substitution in Eq. (8-32) we have the very interesting relation that

$$VG_{(\text{max theoretical})} = \alpha \frac{r_{22}}{r_{11}} \tag{8-33}$$

In considering the theory of operation of the point contact transistor it was pointed out that the voltage gain of the point contact transistor is due both to a current gain and a resistance gain. In a previous analysis it has been mentioned that α, which is defined by Eq. (8-17), is also the ratio of collector current to emitter current. Equation (8-33) clearly shows that the maximum possible voltage gain from a transistor is the product of the current gain and the ratio of the collector circuit resistance to the emitter circuit resistance

$$VG_{(\text{max theoretical})} = -\frac{i_c r_{22}}{i_e r_{11}} \tag{8-34}$$

From this equation we may deduce that the maximum theoretical voltage gain for the point contact unit using the average values from Table 8-1 is

$$VG_{(\text{max})} = 2.3 \times \frac{15,000}{270}$$
$$= 128$$

For the junction-type transistor, using the values of Table 8-1, the maximum theoretical voltage gain is 1,830. Thus the junction transistor is inherently capable of a much larger voltage gain than is the point contact unit. The less-than-unity current gain of the junction type contrasted with the 2.3 for the point contact is more than compensated for by the very large ratio of collector to emitter resistance in the junction type. This fact leads to a preference for junction units as amplifiers at frequencies where junction transistor operation is feasible.

111. SUMMARY

In summary, the following are the salient points of this chapter:

1. Important information regarding the behavior of a transistor in a practical circuit is obtainable from a solution of the Kirchhoff equations describing the equivalent circuit of a transistor.

2. A consistent set of rules must be used in applying the Kirchhoff laws, and these are given in paragraphs 1 through 6 of Sec. 100.

3. A great deal of information about the behavior of the circuit which represents a transistor is obtainable by finding: the input resistance, output resistance, voltage gain, and power gain. (The power gain will be discussed in the next chapter.)

4. In the grounded-base connection the transistor has an input resistance usually less than 1,000 ohms and an output impedance from 5,000 to 500,000 ohms approximately.

5. The junction transistor is inherently capable of a higher voltage gain than is the point contact type transistor.

REFERENCES

1. Guillemin, E. A.: "Communication Networks," John Wiley & Sons, Inc., New York, 1935.

2. Giacoletto, L. J.: Equipments for Measuring Junction Transistor Admittance Parameters for a Wide Range of Frequencies, *RCA Rev.*, Vol. 14, No. 2, pp. 269–296, June, 1953.
3. Second Quarterly Progress Report, Contr. DA 36-039 sc-30237, Raytheon Mfg. Co., Newton, Mass., Oct. 1, 1952 to Jan. 1, 1953.
4. Ryder, R. M., and R. J. Kircher: Some Circuit Aspects of the Transistor, *Bell System Tech. J.*, Vol. 28, No. 3, pp. 367–400, July, 1949.
5. Bode, H. W.: "Network Analysis and Feedback Amplifier Design," D. Van Nostrand Company, Inc., New York, 1945.
6. Shockley, W.: "Electrons and Holes in Semiconductors," p. 40, D. Van Nostrand Company, Inc., New York, 1950.
7. Morton, J. A.: Present Status of Transistor Development, *Bell System Tech. J.*, Vol. 31, pp. 441–442, May, 1952.
8. Wallace, Jr., R. L., and W. J. Pietenpol: Some Circuit Properties and Applications of NPN Transistors, *Proc. IRE*, Vol. 39, pp. 753–767, July, 1951.

9 SMALL-SIGNAL PARAMETERS

In this chapter we shall consider the power gain of a transistor in the grounded-base connection and show the analytical process which leads to the conclusion that the parameters discussed thus far and which characterize the transistor are essentially small-signal parameters. The importance of the small-signal parameter concept stems from the fact that test equipment designed for the evaluation of transistors must conform to this requirement, and disregard of the small-signal considerations can lead to large errors in prediction of circuit performance.[1]

112. POWER GAIN FOR GB CONNECTION

In Chap. 8, equations were developed which express the input and output resistance and the voltage gain of point contact and junction transistors. Typical numerical values were given for orientation with regard to orders of magnitude (see Table 8-1). The power gain of an electrical device is, obviously, an important concept to the design engineer, and equations will be developed for computation of this parameter of a transistor.

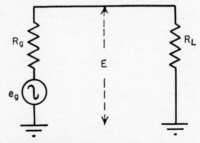

In Fig. 9-1 we show the familiar circuit of a generator with voltage e_g and internal resistance R_g supplying a load whose resistance is R_L. For a given generator, under what conditions will the power

Fig. 9-1. Equivalent circuit to illustrate conditions for obtaining maximum power from a given generator or source.

output or the power developed across R_L be a maximum? If we recall that the power across a resistance R when a voltage E is impressed

109

across it is E^2/R, the problem is tantamount to asking what value of R_L will make E^2/R_L of Fig. 9-1 a maximum. The reader should verify that, in general,

$$E = \frac{e_g R_L}{R_g + R_L} \tag{9-1}$$

and therefore $E^2/R_L = P$, the power across R_L, will be given by

$$P_o = \frac{e_g^2 R_L^2}{(R_g + R_L)^2 R_L} = \frac{e_g^2 R_L}{(R_g + R_L)^2} \tag{9-2}$$

It can be shown by a simple differentiation with respect to R_L, that P_o, the power delivered across the load, will be maximum if R_g is made equal to R_L. In vacuum-tube practice it is common to match the plate load resistance to the internal plate resistance in order to obtain maximum power output. This practice is an outgrowth of the principle that to obtain maximum power across a given load the internal resistance of the generator must be matched to the load resistance. If we make R_g equal to R_L in Eq. (9-2), the maximum possible power we can draw from the generator e_g under any circumstances will be given by

$$P_m = \frac{e_g^2}{4R_g} \tag{9-3}$$

This is a general principle and is not restricted to transistor theory. Returning to the problem of the transistor, see Fig. 9-2, the power output is given by $i_2^2 R_L$, where

$$i_2 = \frac{-e_g(r_b + r_m)}{(R_g + r_b + r_e)(R_L + r_b + r_c) - r_b(r_b + r_m)} \tag{9-4}$$

The power gain of the transistor is the ratio of $i_2^2 R_L$ to P_m, the maximum power which may possibly be drawn from the generator. It is worthwhile to note that if we use Eq. (9-3) for P_m we are assuming that the generator internal resistance will be exactly matched by the input resistance of the transistor. It should be realized that, in general, this will not be the case, and therefore we shall draw from the generator less power than is indicated by Eq. (9-3). The power gain is given by

$$PG = \frac{i_2^2 R_L}{e_g^2/4R_g} = \frac{4R_L R_g i_2^2}{e_g^2} \tag{9-5}$$

The power gain so determined for a given value of i_2 and R_L will be a lower limit or a minimum value since the power expression in the denominator is the maximum possible.

Substituting the value of i_2 from Eq. (9-4) into the expression for the power gain in Eq. (9-4)

$$PG = \frac{4R_L R_g (r_b + r_m)^2}{[(R_g + r_b + r_e)(R_L + r_b + r_c) - r_b(r_b + r_m)]^2} \qquad (9\text{-}6)$$

This expression can be simplified somewhat if we observe from Table 8-1 that r_b can be neglected compared to r_c or r_m, and we obtain a practical form of Eq. (9-6)

$$PG \cong \frac{4R_L R_g r_m^2}{[(R_g + r_b + r_e)(R_L + r_c) - r_b r_m]^2} \qquad (9\text{-}7)$$

113. TYPICAL VALUES OF POWER GAIN—GB

Using the typical values of the parameters as given in Table 8-1, for the point contact transistor a typical power gain is very nearly 100, representing 20 db, whereas for the junction type a typical power gain is 440, representing approximately 26 db. Again the reader will observe the superiority of the junction-type transistor compared to the point contact in power gain; in the previous chapter we have noted the superiority of the junction type in voltage gain as well. As has been mentioned elsewhere in this book, except for frequency response, the junction type of unit holds promise of preference over the point contact.[2,3]

114. IMPORTANCE OF α

It is often desirable to know the power gain as a function of the α of the circuit. Divide numerator and denominator of Eq. (9-6) by $(r_c + r_b)^2$:

$$PG = \frac{4R_L R_g \alpha^2}{\left[(R_g + r_b + r_e)\left(1 + \dfrac{R_L}{r_c + r_b}\right) - r_b\alpha\right]^2} \qquad (9\text{-}8)$$

Similarly, the power gain may be expressed as a function of the VG and α:

$$PG = \frac{4\bar{R}_g \alpha(VG)}{(R_g + r_e + r_b)\left(1 + \dfrac{R_L}{r_b + r_c}\right) - r_b\alpha} \qquad (9\text{-}9)$$

Also, the expression for the VG obtained in the previous chapter may be written as a function of α:

$$VG = \frac{\alpha R_L}{(R_g + r_e + r_b)\left(\dfrac{R_L}{r_b + r_c} + 1\right) - r_b\alpha} \qquad (9\text{-}10)$$

By inspection of Eqs. (9-8) to (9-10), the reader can see the reason for the inclusion of α as one of the important parameters which is useful for evaluation and comparison of transistors. Also, the relation $\alpha = -i_c/i_e$ shows the further usefulness of α as a comparison number for current gain.[4]

115. GROUNDED-BASE EQUATIONS

In the previous chapter, Eqs. (9-11) and (9-12) were derived for the grounded-base transistor arrangement.

$$i_1(R_g + r_e + r_b) + i_2r_b - e_g = 0 \tag{9-11}$$
$$i_1(r_b + r_m) + i_2(R_L + r_b + r_c) = 0 \tag{9-12}$$

We shall have occasion to refer to Eqs. (9-11) and (9-12) in a somewhat modified form:

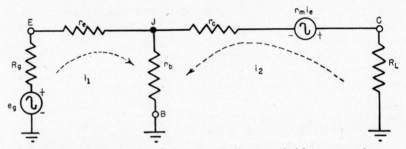

Fig. 9-2. Equivalent circuit of a transistor in the grounded-base connection.

In Eq. (9-11) let us put $r_e + r_b = r_{11}$ and $r_{12} = r_b$ according to the definitions laid down in the previous chapter. Finally, let us put $v_1 = e_g - i_1R_g$, which is the net voltage acting at the transistor terminals. Eq. (9-11) now becomes

$$v_1 = r_{11}i_1 + r_{12}i_2 \tag{9-13}$$

In deriving Eq. (9-12) we had assumed that there was no generator voltage acting in loop 2, see Fig. 9-2. If there were, we could write Eq. (9-12) thus:

$$r_{21}i_1 + i_2R_L + i_2r_{22} = e_{g2} \tag{9-14}$$

where we have used the relations $r_m + r_b = r_{21}$ and $r_c + r_b = r_{22}$. As before, if $v_2 = e_{g2} - i_2R_L$, to obtain the net effective voltage after the i_2R_L drop, Eq. (9-14) becomes

$$v_2 = r_{21}i_1 + r_{22}i_2 \tag{9-15}$$

116. SMALL-SIGNAL PARAMETERS

Consider a dependent variable y which varies with or is a function of an independent variable x. Mathematically we write

$$y = y(x) \tag{9-16}$$

Differentiate both sides with respect to x:

$$\frac{dy}{dx} = \frac{dy(x)}{dx} \tag{9-17}$$

Essentially, Eq. (9-17) is a tautology, or self-evident identity, and does not provide any particularly useful information. But if we write Eq. (9-17) in the form

$$dy = \frac{dy(x)}{dx}\,dx$$
$$= y'\,dx \tag{9-18}$$

the equation states a very important and useful fact. Equation (9-16) will, in general, avoiding special curves, give a graph like the one shown in Fig. 9-3.

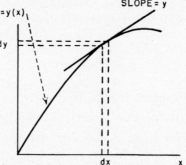

Fig. 9-3. Typical curve showing y as a function of x. The slope is

$$y' = dy(x)/dx.$$

Equation (9-18) says that if, for a given or selected change in x, say of dx, you want to find the corresponding change in the value of y, when y depends on x in the manner shown in Fig. 9-3 and symbolized in mathematics shorthand by Eq. (9-16), you need merely take the slope of the curve at the point in question and multiply by the given value of dx. Or, Eq. (9-18) may be interpreted to say: if, in measuring a distance x, you know that an unavoidable error dx is made, then to find the corresponding error in y, take the rate of change of y with x at the point in question, and multiply by the error dx. All these things are true if y depends on x only.

Suppose that y is a dependent variable which varies with either or both of two parameters x and z. Analogous to Eq. (9-16) is the following:

$$y = y(x,z) \tag{9-19}$$

Since a change in y, dy, may now be due to a change in either or both x and z, an equation entirely which is analogous to Eq. (9-17) would be Eq. (9-20):

$$dy = \frac{dy}{dx}\bigg]_{z=k} dx + \frac{dy}{dz}\bigg]_{x=k} dz^* \qquad (9\text{-}20)\dagger$$

Let us study Eq. (9-20) closely. First, note that the "dimensions" of each term on the right-hand side of Eq. (9-20) is dy, since dx and dz "cancel" at least dimensionally. This must be so for any physically valid interpretation. Second, note that now dy/dx, first term on the right-hand side, is not quite the same as in Eq. (9-17) because the change of dy in y corresponding to a change in x of dx is measured while z is kept constant. A similar remark applies to dy/dz for x constant. Finally, in words, Eq. (9-20) says:

If y is a function of x and z, a small increment dy in y will be given by adding the increment in x, i.e., the rate of change of y with x, holding z constant, times the increment in y (first term on the right-hand side) to the increment in z, i.e., the rate of change of y with z, holding x constant, times the increment in z (second term).

A practical application of Eq. (9-20) is in the determination of total errors. Say that y is a distance, which is a function of speed and time. If, in measuring the speed (x) you make an error dx and in measuring the time (z) you make an error dz, the total error is as given by Eq. (9-20). In this illustration, $dy/dx\big]_{z=k}$ would be the rate of change of distance with speed, as the time is held constant, and $dy/dz\big]_{x=k}$ would be the rate of change of distance with time, which is the speed.

Now let us return to our transistor circuit. In general, V_e, the dc emitter voltage, will depend on the emitter and collector currents or on the operating point. We write

$$V_e = V_e(I_e, I_c) \qquad (9\text{-}21)$$

and compare Eq. (9-19), $y \approx V_e$, $I_e \approx x$, $I_c \approx z$. Note from Eq. (9-21) that the dependent variable is the voltage V_e and that the independent variables are I_e and I_c. This shows immediately that the transistor is a current-operated device as the currents are the independent variables. In transistor work you usually adjust the currents to the correct operating point, and the voltages appearing are then fixed by the current values. To illustrate further the effect of this concept in practice, the static characteristics of transistors are plotted, by

* This is usually written

$$dy = \frac{\partial y}{\partial x}\bigg]_z dx + \frac{\partial y}{\partial z}\bigg]_x dz$$

† See any text on the elements of the differential and integral calculus.

common consent, with current as abscissa and voltage as ordinate, in keeping with the mathematical convention of plotting the independent variable along the x direction. This convention for transistors may be compared to the convention in vacuum-tube practice where currents are plotted as ordinates and voltages as abscissas, as in plate characteristics (see any vacuum-tube handbook).

Analogous to Eq. (9-20), obtained from (9-19), is Eq. (9-22) for Eq. (9-21):

$$dV_e = \frac{dV_e}{dI_e}\Bigg]_{Ic=k} dI_e + \frac{dV_e}{dI_c}\Bigg]_{Ie=k} dI_c \qquad (9\text{-}22)$$

For the dc collector voltage, we may also say that it depends on emitter and collector currents and get a relation comparable to Eq. (9-21):

$$V_c = V_c(I_e, I_c) \qquad (9\text{-}23)$$

And again on differentiating:

$$dV_c = \frac{dV_c}{dI_e}\Bigg]_{Ic=k} dI_e + \frac{dV_c}{dI_c}\Bigg]_{Ie=k} dI_c \qquad (9\text{-}24)$$

Equations (9-22) and (9-24) are extremely important in transistor analysis, and we shall discuss them in some detail for further applications.

117. SMALL CHANGES

Suppose it were desired to perform a physical experiment which would illustrate Eq. (9-24). A simple explanation might be based on an ac voltage and current wave. In Fig. 9-4 consider the sinusoidal voltage wave $v = v_m \sin wt = dv \sin wt$, where $v_m = dv$.

In an interval, $wt = \pi/2$, the amplitude changes from 0 to dv, and in the next quarter interval of time, from dv to 0, so that, disregarding the sign, the amplitude changes by dv for each quarter cycle. In general, Eqs. (9-22) and (9-24) apply properly if dv is actually infinitesimal, or extremely small, but in actual application a practical value of dv may be used.

In Fig. 9-5 is shown a possible plot of voltage versus current, say, of the emitter voltage V_e versus emitter current I_e, dc values, for a transistor. Assume that the operating point of the transistor is at V'_e, I'_e: If the emitter current is modulated sinusoidally by a small signal, i.e., so that I_e varies at most by dI_e, then I_e will vary from I'_e to $I'_e + dI_e$, from $I'_e + dI_e$ to I'_e, from I'_e to $I'_e - dI_e$, etc. What is the quantitative relation between the change dI_e in I_e and the change dV_e

in V_e? If we imagine for a moment that V_e depends on I_e alone, i.e., $V_e = V_e(I_e)$, then

$$dV_e = \frac{dV_e}{dI_e} dI_e$$

as in Eq. (9-18).

It should be clear that just as $dy/dx = y'$ is the slope of the $y = y(x)$ curve, dV_e/dI_e is the slope of the characteristic curve of Fig. 9-5.

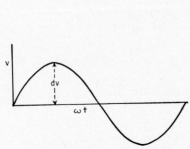

Fig. 9-4. Sinusoidal voltage (or current) used to simulate differential increments as in Eq. (9-24). Note small amplitude dv.

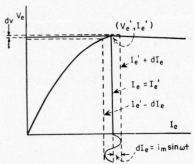

Fig. 9-5. A plot of the input or V_e-I_e characteristic to illustrate how a small-signal variation in I_e is used to compute the corresponding change in V_e.

(Note that dV_e/dI_e has the dimensions of a resistance, so that in this case the slope is a resistance, hence designated by R.) But as the reader can see, the slope of the curve must be taken virtually at a point if the relation

$$dV_e = R\, dI_e \qquad (9\text{-}25)$$

is to be true.

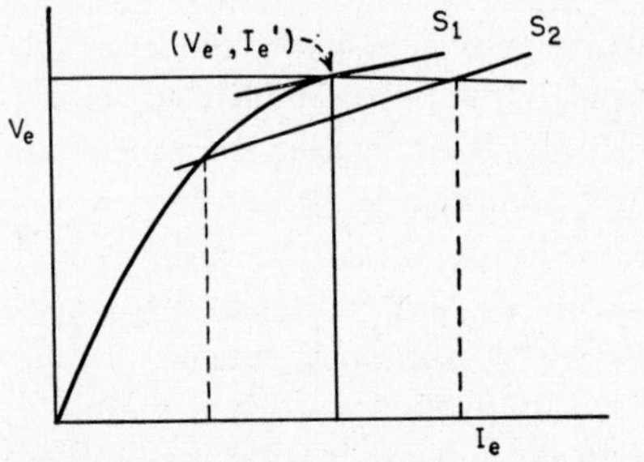

118. EFFECT OF LARGE SIGNALS

Suppose that in the Eq. (9-25) one were to use not the slope at the point (V_e', I_e') where the increment dV_e is to be computed, but instead the slope over a large region. This condition is shown by Fig. 9-6. The slope at the point (V_e', I_e') is actually S_1 as shown, but using a large swing about (V_e', I_e') gives a slope S_2 which is in general not equal to S_1. Thus, using a large distance about the point in question to compute the slope may introduce large errors, and the reader can see that the

Fig. 9-6. A plot of the V_e-I_e characteristic indicating how the use of a large signal, between dotted ordinates, would give an incorrect slope S_2 at the point (V_e', I_e'). The correct slope is S_1.

larger the distance used, the larger may be the error, particularly as the curve departs more and more from a straight line. We infer, then, that if a sinusoidal current is used to simulate dI_e, it must be a very small current or signal, or else large errors may be introduced. In view of these remarks, the differential quantity dV_e is representable, for purposes of a laboratory experiment, by an ac voltage and dI_e by an ac current, provided that they are suitably small. Later we shall mention a test which can be performed readily, which determines experimentally whether a signal is really a small signal.

Regardless of whether V_e is a function of one or two variables, the remarks about the size of the signal are still valid.

We may write Eq. (9-22) and (9-24) in terms of small ac v's and i's by applying the foregoing principles:

$$v_e = \frac{v_e}{i_e}\bigg]_{I_c=k} i_e + \frac{v_e}{i_c}\bigg]_{I_e=k} i_c \tag{9-26}$$

[This corresponds to Eq. (9-22).]

$$v_c = \frac{v_c}{i_e}\bigg]_{I_c=k} i_e + \frac{v_c}{i_c}\bigg]_{I_e=k} i_c \tag{9-27}$$

[This corresponds to Eq. (9-24).]

There are several comments which must be made about these two equations:

1. Note the use of small letters for ac values, and capitals for dc values, in keeping with the convention adopted by the authors for this book, and which is a proposed standard.

2. Consider the $I_c = k$, $I_e = k$ factors of Eqs. (9-26) and (9-27). If a change dI is representable by a small ac current, $i \sin wt$, as has been shown, of amplitude i, then zero change in dc current, i.e., $I_e = k$, or $I_c = k$, will be represented by an ac current of 0 amplitude. Using this fact we may properly write Eqs. (9-26) and (9-27) thus:

$$v_e = \frac{v_e}{i_e}\bigg]_{i_c=0} i_e + \frac{v_e}{i_c}\bigg]_{i_e=0} i_c \tag{9-28}$$

$$v_c = \frac{v_c}{i_e}\bigg]_{i_c=0} i_e + \frac{v_c}{i_c}\bigg]_{i_e=0} i_c \tag{9-29}$$

3. What is v_e/i_e at $i_c = 0$? It is the ratio of ac input voltage to ac current when the collector is open-circuited. By the definitions laid down in Chap. 8, this quantity is r_{11}, i.e.,

$$r_{11} = \frac{v_e}{i_e}\bigg]_{i_c=0} \tag{9-30}$$

Reasoning analogously, and using the definitions laid down in Chap. 8, we obtain directly

$$\left. \frac{v_e}{i_c} \right]_{i_e = 0} = r_{12}$$

$$\left. \frac{v_c}{i_e} \right]_{i_c = 0} = r_{21}$$

$$\left. \frac{v_c}{i_c} \right]_{i_e = 0} = r_{22}$$

Hence Eqs. (9-28) and (9-29) can be rewritten:

$$v_e = r_{11}i_e + r_{12}i_c \qquad (9\text{-}31)$$
$$v_c = r_{21}i_e + r_{22}i_c \qquad (9\text{-}32)$$

Equation (9-31) states that a potential v_e is acting in a circuit and produces the two potential drops $r_{11}i_e$ and $r_{12}i_c$ which together make up v_e. Similar remarks apply to Eq. (9-32). Replacing subscript e, in the emitter circuit, by the subscript 1, and the subscript c by 2, Eqs. (9-31) and (9-32) become

$$v_1 = r_{11}i_1 + r_{12}i_2 \qquad (9\text{-}33)$$
$$v_2 = r_{21}i_1 + r_{22}i_2 \qquad (9\text{-}34)$$

Now consider Eqs. (9-13) and (9-15). They are obviously identical to Eqs. (9-33) and (9-34), respectively, but were arrived at by entirely different methods of reasoning. Equations (9-13) and (9-15) were obtained from a circuit analysis using Kirchhoff's law for the voltage loops. Equations (9-33) and (9-34) were derived on a mathematical basis from the simple concept that V_e and V_c depend on both I_c and I_e, and the small-signal idea. What is the significance of the fact that, starting with radically different assumptions, identical equations were obtained?

As has been mentioned, the ultimate fact mathematically expressed by these equations is that, given all the other data, it is possible to find two numbers i_1 and i_2 that satisfy these equations. The fact that they happen to represent a current, in milliamperes perhaps, does not influence the mathematical description of how to determine these two numbers. There is a law of mathematics which says that for equations such as (9-33) and (9-34), which are linear (*i.e.*, contain no products like i_1i_2, or i raised to some power), the delineation is unique, *i.e.*, the equations will define only one pair of values i_1 and i_2 and no other. This means that regardless of how the equations were obtained, if they are linear, they must define the same two quantities. Since this is so, whatever assumptions were made to find Eqs. (9-33) and (9-34) *are also binding on Eqs.* (9-13) *and* (9-15) because they represent the same numbers.

119. ASSUMPTIONS IN DERIVING EQUATIONS

What are these assumptions? First, from the discussion in connection with Eqs. (9-31) and (9-32), the parameters are *open-circuit* values, i.e., $i_c = 0$, when measuring r_{11} and r_{21} and $i_e = 0$ when measuring r_{12} and r_{22}. This condition has already been met for Eqs. (9-13) and (9-15), see Chap. 8.

Second, from the discussion in connection with Eqs. (9-26) and (9-27), the parameters are measured using ratios of ac values. This condition has also been met, see Chap. 8.

Third, the symbol convention that

$$v_1 = e_{g1} - i_1 R_g$$
$$v_2 = e_{g2} - i_2 R_L$$

which was assumed to obtain Eqs. (9-13) and (9-15) is binding on Eqs. (9-33) and (9-34).

Last, and probably most important, from the discussion in connection with Eqs. (9-26) and (9-27), *the use of small signals* is assumed. This means that the four-pole parameters r_{11}, r_{12}, r_{21}, and r_{22} are *small-signal* parameters.

120. DETERMINATION OF SMALL SIGNALS

Since this is a very important concept, we may profitably dwell on this subject for a moment.

1. In selecting an amplitude for the measurement of the four-pole parameters, how does one know when the signal used is *de facto* a small signal?

The answer is based on the fact that, if the signal is not truly small, different amplitudes of the signal will give different values of parameters. The reason is contained in Eq. (9-22), and the reader can verify by drawing several curves that different slopes are obtained, depending on the size of signal used. In practice, a signal of some convenient size is selected and the parameter, say r_{11}, measured. Then the signal is increased slightly and the parameter measured again. If the value of r_{11} obtained in the second trial is close to the r_{11} originally obtained, within the accuracy desired, the signal is a small signal and conversely.[5]

2. It might appear that there is no objection to using a very small-amplitude signal originally, so that there is no question about the

signal being small. First, if the V-I characteristic is very curved, it is difficult to guess what constitutes a truly small signal. The test suggested above should therefore always be made. Second, too small a signal introduces measuring problems such as noise and the general difficulty of measuring fractions of a microvolt at ac.

3. Sometimes, when feasible, the parameter may be measured by the volt-ammeter method tacitly assumed here, and the resulting value compared to that obtained by using an entirely different measuring scheme. Other possible measurement methods include the bridge method,[6] scope presentation,[7,8] as well as variations and combinations of these. The results must compare within the accuracy desired if the signal is truly small.

121. DEFINITION OF AN OPEN CIRCUIT

Let us now review in a general way the data that have been assembled regarding r_{11}, r_{12}, r_{21}, and r_{22}. Because such parameters are so important in the specification of transistor characteristics, much experimental and theoretical work has been done and is continuing regarding these and other suitable parameters we shall now discuss.

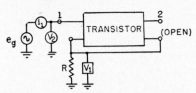

Fig. 9-7. Sketch indicating connections for measurement of r_{11}.

From the analysis made thus far, it can be understood why the parameters r_{11}, r_{12}, r_{21}, and r_{22} are called "small-signal open-circuit grounded-base four-pole parameters." In this and previous chapters the terms small-signal, grounded-base, and four-pole parameters have been explained. Let us now consider what constitutes an open circuit. Consider Fig. 9-7 which shows the circuit arrangement for measurement of r_{11}.

Both V_1 and V_2 are vacuum-tube voltmeters, and R is a small resistance of known value placed in the signal-generator returns to measure the current: $i_1 = V_1/R$. Voltmeter V_2 measures the voltage across the input of the transistor, and $r_{11} = V_2/i_1$. The output or collector circuit is not a true open circuit because:

1. Whatever scheme is used to bias the collector, a dc return path to the base is essential, and thus a dc path is always present to act as a closed circuit across the collector. Even if we made the internal resistance of the dc bias supply very high by using a choke of several hundred henrys—note dc current is small and $f = 270$ cps—we could still not maintain a virtual open circuit because

2. There is an ac shunting path always present because of the

internal transistor capacity and the stray capacity. Clearly, the impedance of this shunting path decreases as the frequency increases. A rough computation to determine orders of magnitude at the usual test frequency, 270 cps, will be made.

To give such a computation meaning, we should treat the worst case, all other cases presumably being covered if we can circumvent the difficulties of that one. The problem of establishing an open circuit in the collector, where, for junction types, r_{22} may be of the order of megohms, is usually the greatest difficulty.

A typical value of C_c, the collector capacitance, is 50 $\mu\mu$f, and a typical circuit may have an additional stray capacity of 10 $\mu\mu$f.

$$x_c = \frac{1}{2\pi f C_c} = \frac{10^{12}}{6.28 \times 270 \times 60}$$
$$= 9.81 \text{ megohms}$$

If r_{22} were 3 megohms, at 270 cps the 9.8 megohms would represent a shunt path of some importance, and the ideal open-circuit conditions desired are not satisfied.

Two principal approaches to this problem have been adopted:

1. By arbitrary convention the circuit is considered open if the shunt resistance is fifty times the internal transistor resistance. Thus, when measuring r_{11} and r_{21}, where the collector circuit must be open, the shunt path shall be $50 \times r_{22}$; and when measuring r_{12} or r_{22} the shunt path shall be $50 \times r_{11}$. See also paragraph 4.2.11 of Appendix III.

2. Measurements of other parameters such as the g's and h's described below have been used to characterize transistor operation. These measurements do not require the use of an open circuit across high-impedance elements. Then, if desired, parameters such as the r's may be derived mathematically from the quantities measured. Or, the performance of the transistor may be expressed in terms of these new parameters directly, it being assumed that with experience engineers will readily compare transistor performance in terms of these parameters. Refer to Appendix I.

122. CONDUCTANCES (g's)

It has already been mentioned that the equivalent T as characterized by Eqs. (9-13) and (9-15) is not the only equivalent circuit for the specification of the allegorical black box. The black box or transistor is equally well represented by an equivalent circuit which is a π network,[9] see Fig. 9-8. This circuit is analyzed by means of Eqs. (9-35) and (9-36), using the concept of conductances. A conductance is the reciprocal of a resistance. When multiplied by a voltage, a conductance represents a current, dimensionally.

$$i_1 = g_{11}v_1 + g_{12}v_2 \qquad (9\text{-}35)$$
$$i_2 = g_{21}v_1 + g_{22}v_2 \qquad (9\text{-}36)$$

Using Eqs. (9-35) and (9-36), all the four g's can be measured. For illustration, setting $v_2 = 0$, $g_{11} = i_1/v_1$ and similarly one can find g_{12}, g_{21}, and g_{22}, see Fig. 9-9. These g's are sometimes called the short-circuit conductances.

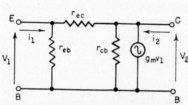

While it is true that resistances and conductances are reciprocals, the r_{11} which appears in Eq. (9-13) is not the reciprocal of g_{11}. It will be recalled that r_{11} in Eq. (9-13) was obtained using an open-circuited collector, but we have just seen that g_{11} is obtained by using a short-circuited collector. Hence, r_{11} is not $1/g_{11}$ and is, in fact, given by

Fig. 9-8. Equivalent π circuit to represent a transistor. This circuit, in conjunction with Eqs. (9-35) and (9-36), may be used to describe electrical conditions in a transistor instead of the equivalent T.

$$r_{11} = \frac{g_{22}}{g_{11}g_{22} - g_{12}g_{21}} \qquad (9\text{-}37)^{*9}$$

As stated, to obtain g_{11} we put $v_2 = 0$. But what does setting $v_2 = 0$ mean? It means that to find g_{11} we *short-circuit* the output. This

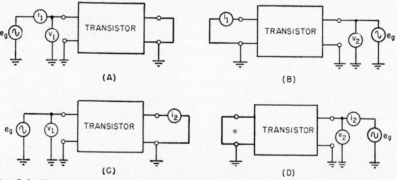

Fig. 9-9. Sketches to indicate connections in measuring the g's, or short-circuit conductances: (A) Measurement of g_{11} (or y_{11}, input admittance). (B) Measurement of g_{12}. (C) Measurement of g_{21}. (D) Measurement of g_{22}. Note that in every case one pair of terminals is shorted. The fact that the short may have to be through a milliammeter, since small currents are involved, may render it difficult at times to obtain a true short circuit.

* See Appendix I for interparameter transformation equations.

does away with the need for establishing an open circuit. Like any other good idea in engineering, it has its drawbacks. Note first that, similarly, to find g_{12} the emitter circuit is shorted, making $v_1 = 0$, and so on for all the other parameters.

The disadvantage of the g method is that some point contact transistors are short circuit unstable. This means that if the input or the output is ac short-circuited, the units may break into parasitic oscillations. Fortunately, the applicability of this method is greatest for junction types, where this instability is not normally encountered. The inference is that for point contact units the r's may be suitable, and with junction units the g's may be preferable.

123. HYBRID PARAMETERS (h's)

Because the use of the g's suggests that two different parameters are needed to take care of point contact and junction units, an entirely different set has been suggested.[10] These are the hybrid parameters, or h's, and the reason for the name will appear presently. The transistor may be characterized by means of the following two equations:

$$v_1 = h_{11}i_1 + h_{12}v_2 \qquad (9\text{-}38)$$
$$i_2 = h_{21}i_1 + h_{22}v_2 \qquad (9\text{-}39)$$

To find h_{11}, short the output, $v_2 = 0$, and

$$h_{11} = \frac{v_1}{i_1} \qquad \text{(see Fig. 9-10)} \qquad (9\text{-}40)$$

The r_{11} of Eq. (9-13) was obtained with open-circuited output; hence it is clear that h_{11} is not the same as r_{11}. As g_{11} was obtained with $v_2 = 0$, $h_{11} = 1/g_{11}$, so that the g_{11} of Eq. (9-35) *is* the reciprocal of h_{11} in Eq. (9-35); and since the reciprocal of a conductance is a resistance, h_{11} is of the nature of a resistance, dimensionally.

To find h_{12}, i_1 is made zero, by making the input an open circuit, placing the generator in the collector circuit, and measuring v_1 and v_2. Then

$$h_{12} = \frac{v_1}{v_2} \qquad (9\text{-}41)$$

As this is the ratio of two voltages, h_{12} has no dimensions, *i.e.*, it is a pure numeric like π. A similar analysis will show, for Eq. (9-39), that $h_{21} = i_2/i_1$ for a short-circuited collector. This is minus α by definition. $h_{22} = i_2/v_2$ is a conductance but is not identical with the g_{22} of Eq. (9-36) since all the parameters of Eq. (9-36) are obtained under short-circuit conditions. Note that h_{22} is obtained under open-circuit conditions.

Thus the hybrid parameters contain two pure numerics h_{12} and h_{21}, a resistance (h_{11}) and a conductance (h_{22}); from this enumeration, the reader can see why these parameters are called "hybrid." They possess, however, some of the advantages of both the r's and the g's.

1. In the matter of avoiding the necessity for maintaining an open circuit in the high-resistance collector, the h method shares the advantage of the g system in that h_{11} and h_{21} are made with the collector shorted.

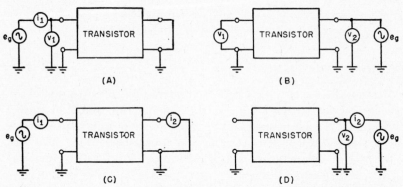

Fig. 9-10. Sketches to indicate connections in measuring the h's, or hybrid parameters: (A) Measurement of h_{11}. Note the shorted output, and compare g_{11}, Fig. 9-9(A). (B) Measurement of h_{12}. Note that the input is open and that voltage measurements only are made. (C) Measurement of h_{21}. Note that the output is shorted through a milliammeter and that current measurements only are made. (D) Measurement of h_{22}. Note that the input is open, and compare measurement of r_{22}. Because the h's represent a resistance, a conductance, and pure numerics, they have been called the hybrid parameters.

In the matter of avoiding the necessity for maintaining a short circuit in the low-resistance emitter circuit, the h system shares the advantage of the r system, since both h_{12} and h_{22} are made with the emitter open-circuited. Since the input resistance of some transistors may be quite low, of the order of tens of ohms, difficulties are encountered in effectively ac short-circuiting such impedances. In the h system, the input is open-circuited for such measurements (h_{12} and h_{22}).

2. Measurements for α in the g and r methods are indirect. In the r method r_{21} and r_{22} are found, their ratio is $\alpha = r_{21}/r_{22}$; in the g method, $\alpha = g_{21}/g_{22}$; but in the hybrid-parameter method, $\alpha = -h_{21}$ directly.

The principal disadvantages of the h's are that they are hybrid parameters and not directly amenable to circuit analysis. Whereas most engineers are acquainted with resistances and conductances and use them readily in circuit analysis, few are prepared to use the h's directly. If transformations are necessary, and these are quite cumbersome (see Appendix I), the advantages mentioned above may well be over-shadowed. The transistor industry and circuit-design engineers are currently studying the relative merits of each set of parameters. The indications are that considerable additional experience is needed before a single set of parameters to characterize transistors will be generally adopted. Definitions for the h's are given in Appendix III.

124. SUMMARY

In summary of this chapter:

1. Typical power gains possible with the grounded-base transistor connection are: point contact, 20 db; junction, 26 db.

2. In transistor terminology, r_{11}, r_{12}, r_{21}, and r_{22} are called the small-signal grounded-base open-circuit four-pole equivalent-circuit parameters. Attention is drawn to the fact that each part of the name has significance.

3. A test to determine whether a signal is truly a "small" signal is to measure the parameters, using a selected amplitude of signal, increase the signal by approximately 50 per cent, and remeasure the parameters. The measured values must compare within the orders of accuracy required, usually approximately 10 per cent. Repeat if necessary.

4. The r's, or the g's, or h's may be used to characterize the transistor equivalent circuit. Considerations such as common usage, short-circuit stability, and effective open and short circuits are involved in selecting the parameters for a given analysis.

REFERENCES

1. Knight, Jr., G., R. A. Johnson, and R. B. Holt: Measurement of Small Signal Parameters of Transistors, *Proc. IRE*, Vol. 41, pp. 983–989, August, 1953.
2. Sziklai, G. C., R. D. Lohman, and G. B. Herzog: A Study of Transistor Circuits for Television, *Proc. IRE*, Vol. 41, pp. 708–717, June, 1953; and for complementary symmetry using junction transistors: Sziklai, G. C.: Symmetrical Properties of Transistors and Their Applications, *Proc. IRE*, Vol. 41, pp. 717–724, June, 1953.
3. Sulzer, P. G.: Junction Transistor Circuit Applications, *Electronics*, Vol. 26, pp. 170–173, August, 1953.
4. For transistor equations expressing performance parameters as a function of alpha: Stansel, F. R.: Transistor Equations, *Electronics*, Vol. 26, pp. 156–158, March, 1953.

5. Tentative Recommendations of the 7.7.2 Joint IRE-AIEE Task Force on Methods of Test for Circuit Functional Components using Semiconductor Devices.

6. Giacoletto, L. J.: Equipments for Measuring Junction Transistor Admittance Parameters for a Wide Range of Frequencies, *RCA Rev.*, Vol. 14, No. 2, pp. 269–296, June, 1953.

7. O'Neill, B. J., and A. Gutterman: Methods and Equipment for Transistor Testing, *Electronics*, Vol. 26, pp. 172–175, July, 1953.

8. Golden, N., and R. Nielsen: Oscilloscopic Display of Transistor Static Electrical Characteristics, *Proc. IRE*, Vol. 40, pp. 1437–1439, November, 1952.

9. Giacoletto, L. J.: Terminology and Equations for Linear Active–Four Terminal Networks Including Transistors, *RCA Rev.*, Vol. 14, No. 1, pp. 28–46, March, 1953.

10. Discussed by D. A. Alsberg, BTL, before IRE, March, 1953: Transistor Metrology. See also Appendixes I and III.

10 GROUNDED-EMITTER AND

GROUNDED-COLLECTOR CONNECTIONS

In previous chapters, discussions have been restricted to the grounded-base connection for transistors. One of the main reasons for introduction of the grounded-base connection first is because it appears that in the testing and evaluation of transistors this connection will be used. In general, the values of parameters obtained and the interpretation to be placed on the measurements depend on the method of connection. The significance of the method of connection will become more apparent from the ensuing discussion.

The two other connections for transistors are the grounded-emitter and grounded-collector connections. It will become apparent from what follows that each method has both advantages and disadvantages.

125. GROUNDED-EMITTER CONNECTION

The parameters which describe the common-emitter connection most adequately for design and analysis purposes are the input and output resistances and the voltage and power gains. To find these, we shall need the loop currents. Following the rules given in Chap. 8, we set up the Kirchhoff-law equations for the two loops in Fig. 10-1, from which the currents may be found as a function of the transistor parameters which are known.

In Fig. 10-1 are shown the essentials of the grounded-emitter connection. Note that dc biases are omitted, that r's are shown instead of z's for simplicity, and that arbitrary current directions, toward the imaginary junction point J, are assumed.

Following the rules in Chap. 8, the loop equations are

$$(R_g + r_b + r_e)i_1 + r_e i_2 = e_g \qquad (10\text{-}1)$$
$$-r_m(i_1 + i_2) + r_e i_1 + (R_L + r_c + r_e)i_2 = 0 \qquad (10\text{-}2)$$

Note that $(i_1 + i_2) = -i_e$ and that i_e = current through r_e toward J. Ordinarily, with the direction of currents as selected, $r_m i_e$ would have a minus sign since it is a generator; since i_2 flows from plus to minus with respect to it, it requires another minus sign, so that $r_m i_e$ is now plus. However, $i_e = -(i_1 + i_2)$, and therefore the term appears as $-r_m(i_1 + i_2)$ in the equation. Rewritten in standard form, Eqs.

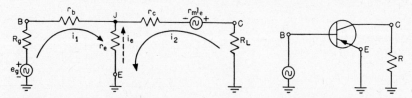

Fig. 10-1. Equivalent circuit diagram for the grounded- or common-emitter connection. Current directions are chosen arbitrarily. At the extreme right is shown how this connection appears on a schematic diagram.

(10-1) and (10-2) become

$$(R_g + r_b + r_e)i_1 + r_e i_2 = e_g \qquad (10\text{-}3)$$
$$(r_e - r_m)i_1 + (R_L + r_e + r_c - r_m)i_2 = 0 \qquad (10\text{-}4)$$

Solving for i_1:

$$i_1 = \frac{e_g(R_L + r_c - r_m + r_e)}{(R_g + r_e + r_b)(R_L + r_e + r_c - r_m) + r_e(r_m - r_e)} \qquad (10\text{-}5)$$

126. INPUT RESISTANCE OF GE CONNECTION

R_{i_e} = input resistance for grounded-emitter connection

$$= \frac{e_g}{i_1} - R_g$$

$$= r_e + r_b + \frac{r_e(r_m - r_e)}{R_L + r_e + r_c - r_m} \qquad (10\text{-}6)$$

Since one can normally neglect r_e compared to r_m,

$$R_{i_e} \cong r_e + r_b + \frac{r_e r_m}{R_L + r_e + r_c - r_m} \qquad (10\text{-}7)$$

For comparison, the equivalent relation for the grounded-base connection is

$$R_i \cong r_e + r_b - \frac{r_b r_m}{R_L + r_c} \qquad (10\text{-}8)$$

Studying these equations:

1. Note the convention adopted here: If no additional subscript is used (for example, R_i), the value refers to the grounded-base connec-

tion. R_{i_e} refers to grounded-emitter connection, and similarly R_{i_c} refers to the grounded-collector connection.

2. In Eq. (10-8), since r_b, r_m, r_c, and R_L are in general positive numbers, R_i will always be less than $r_e + r_b$ by the quantity $r_b r_m/(R_L + r_c)$.

3. In contrast, note that in Eq. (10-7) the input resistance will in general be greater than $r_e + r_b$ by the quantity $r_e r_m/(R_L + r_c + r_e - r_m)$. As this latter quantity may be negative, we distinguish two cases:

a. Junction transistors: As α is less than unity, and as $\alpha = r_m/r_c$, it is clear that $r_c - r_m$ is always positive. Hence,

$$\frac{r_e r_m}{R_L + r_e + r_c - r_m}$$

is always positive and R_{i_e} is always greater than $r_e + r_b$.

b. Point contact transistors: In this case α is greater than 1; therefore, r_m is greater than r_c, so that $r_c - r_m$ is negative. However, by making R_L greater than $r_c - r_m$, one can still make

$$\frac{r_e r_m}{R_L + r_e + r_c - r_m}$$

positive and the input resistance may be greater than $r_e + r_b$.

127. TYPICAL VALUES FOR R_i OF GE CONNECTION

Using the typical values from Table 8-1 we find:

$$R_{i_e} = 35,000 \text{ ohms for point contact units}$$
$$R_{i_e} = 700 \text{ ohms for junction units}$$

These values should be compared with 150 and 90 ohms, respectively, obtained for the grounded-base connection.

128. HIGH INPUT RESISTANCE POSSIBLE

As can be seen from Eq. (10-6), it is possible, in the grounded-emitter circuit, to make the input resistance quite high by proper choice of R_L. This is not, in general, possible with the grounded-base connection [see Eq. (10-8)]. When $R_L + r_c + r_e = r_m$, the denominator of the second term of the right-hand side, Eq. (10-6), becomes zero, and the input resistance becomes, theoretically, infinite. It is profitable to consider two cases:

a. Junction: As α is less than 1, and r_c is greater than r_m, the second term of the right-hand side can be made very large only if R_L is very small, and α is very near unity, say 0.997. Such α's are generally the exception in present-day transistors, and not the rule. Further, if R_L is made small, the possible voltage and power gain will be small.

b. Point contact: Here, making $R_L + r_e + r_c = r_m$ is entirely feasible, and high input resistances are readily achievable in practice.

It may have occurred to the reader that in Eq. (10-6) it is very possible that r_m is greater than $(R_L + r_e + r_b)$ if R_L is sufficiently small, and this may easily lead to a negative value of R_{i_e}. This is actually possible, and leads to a condition of instability wherein the circuit "sings," or oscillates parasitically. The subject of instability will be treated later in this book.

129. VOLTAGE GAIN OF GE CONNECTION

Returning to Eqs. (10-3) and (10-4) and solving for i_2

$$i_2 = \frac{e_g(r_m - r_e)}{(R_g + r_e + r_b)(R_L + r_e + r_c - r_m) + r_e(r_m - r_e)} \quad (10\text{-}9)$$

The voltage gain VG_e is given by

$$VG_e = \frac{-i_2 R_L}{e_g}$$

$$= \frac{-(r_m - r_e)R_L}{(R_g + r_e + r_b)(R_L + r_e + r_c - r_m) + r_e(r_m - r_e)} \quad (10\text{-}10)$$

Using typical values:

$$VG_e = -130 \text{ for point contact units}$$
$$VG_e = -575 \text{ for junction units}$$

These values should be compared with 30 and 150, respectively, for the grounded-base connection. The negative sign shows that the voltage across the load R_L and the input voltage e_g are 180° out of phase. Thus it is seen that the grounded- or common-emitter connection produces a phase change of 180°. It will be recalled that the grounded-base connection does not produce phase inversion.[1]

To find the theoretically maximum value of VG_e, one assumes, as was done for the grounded-base connection, that $R_L = \infty$ and $R_g = 0$. Divide the numerator and denominator of Eq. (10-10) by R_L, then multiply and divide the numerator by r_c.

$$VG_e \text{ (max)} = -\left(\alpha - \frac{r_e}{r_c}\right)\frac{r_{22}}{r_{11}} \quad (10\text{-}11)$$

Equation (10-11) should be compared with Eq. (10-12), which is the corresponding expression for the grounded-base connection of a transistor.

$$VG \text{ (max)} = \alpha \frac{r_{22}}{r_{11}} \tag{10-12}$$

The maximum theoretical voltage gain for the grounded-emitter connection is somewhat less than that for the grounded-base connection; however, since for most transistors r_e/r_c is negligible compared to α, there is, in practice, no appreciable difference between these two gains. As the numerical values obtained indicate, the grounded emitter connection need not always show a smaller gain than the grounded-base connection. The reason follows from the difference in the way the voltage gain varies with R_L and r_c in the two expressions for voltage gain.

130. POWER GAIN FOR GE CONNECTION

The power gain is obtained from the formula

$$PG_e = \frac{i_2^2 R_L}{e_g^2/4R_g} = \frac{4R_g R_L i_2^2}{e_g^2} \tag{10-13}$$

$$PG_e = \frac{4R_g R_L (r_m - r_e)^2}{[(R_g + r_e + r_b)(R_L + r_c + r_e - r_m) + r_e(r_m - r_e)]^2} \tag{10-14}$$

Using typical values:

$$PG = 1,700 \text{ for point contact units}$$
$$PG = 6,600 \text{ for junction units}$$

By comparison, for the grounded-base connection, corresponding values are 100 and 440, respectively. It is seen that the grounded-emitter connection is inherently capable of power gains greater than those for the grounded-base connection.

131. OUTPUT IMPEDANCE

To find the output impedance, e_g is set equal to zero in Eq. (10-3), and Eq. (10-4) is set equal to e_g instead of to zero. This is equivalent to removing the signal from loop 1 of Fig. 10-1 and inserting it in loop 2.

The resulting equations are

$$(R_g + r_b + r_e)i_1' + r_e i_2' = 0 \tag{10-15}$$
$$(r_e - r_m)i_1' + (R_L + r_e + r_c - r_m)i_2' = e_g \tag{10-16}$$

Solving for i_2'

$$i_2' = \frac{(R_g + r_b + r_e)e_g}{(R_g + r_b + r_e)(R_L + r_e + r_c - r_m) - r_e(r_e - r_m)} \qquad (10\text{-}17)$$

$$R_{o_e} = \frac{e_g}{i_2'} - R_L$$

$$= r_c + r_e - r_m + \frac{r_e r_m - r_e^2}{R_g + r_e + r_b} \qquad (10\text{-}18)$$

Using typical values:

$$R_{o_e} = -13{,}000 \text{ ohms for point contact units}$$
$$R_{o_e} = 63{,}000 \text{ ohms for junction units}$$

The fact that the output resistance is negative for the point contact transistor indicates that, under average operating conditions, the point contact consistor tends to be unstable when used in the grounded-emitter connection.[2]   Because this type of connection has some very worthwhile features, however, it is sometimes profitable to alter the circuit slightly to make it stable.   For a given transistor, r_m, r_c, r_b, and r_e are fixed, so that we can only add series resistance to r_e to bring the value of the output resistance into the range of positive values. A resistance of approximately 750 ohms placed in series with the emitter will make R_o positive for the point contact transistor.   This is a common artifice to stabilize a transistor circuit.   The reader who is studying this book in order to apply the transistor in his work should recompute the values of R_o, VG, R_i, and PG to determine the effect of adding 750 ohms to r_e on the parameters already computed for the point contact unit.[3]

On the other hand, because r_c is greater than r_m for the junction types, the output resistance is always positive for the junction transistor and we may infer that, collating Eq. (10-18) with Eq. (10-7), the grounded-emitter connection is *unconditionally stable* for this type. The advantages of the grounded-emitter connection, noted below, are completely realizable in the junction types, and the reader will observe in the literature that this connection is preferred for many applications.

Regarding magnitudes, an inspection of Eq. (10-18) will show that the very high values of resistance possible for R_i, Eq. (10-7), are not even theoretically feasible for R_o.   Since adding a high resistance to r_e to make R_o positive introduces prohibitive losses, just enough resistance is usually added to make R_o slightly positive, for the point contact unit.   Accordingly, the grounded-emitter connection for this type usually results in a high-input low-output impedance arrangement.   For the junction transistors, low-input high-output impedance arrangements are possible; but, with the proper α_{ce} and R_L, both high input and output impedances are attainable.

132. ADVANTAGES OF GE CONNECTION

The grounded-emitter circuit is apparently gaining favor because of the desirable gain and impedance relations mentioned. In addition, the grounded emitter has a particular advantage over the grounded base, from a biasing standpoint.

The elementary biasing arrangement for the grounded-base connection is shown in Fig. 10-2.

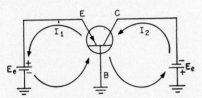

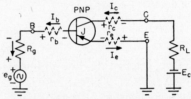

Fig. 10-2. Biasing connections for the grounded-base connection. Electron current flow directions are shown. Note that two batteries are usually needed.

Fig. 10-3. Biasing arrangement for the grounded-emitter connection. Dotted resistors are those of the equivalent diagram in Fig. 10-1, indicated to assist in establishing polarities of internal voltage drops. Note that one battery only is needed. The connection shown is for point contact and PNP units.

Speaking generally, since the emitter and collector currents in the base are in opposite directions, it would be difficult to use a single battery, in the base, to bias emitter and collector simultaneously. The reader should observe that directions of current shown in Fig. 10-2 are electronic; those in Fig. 10-1 are arbitrary, directed toward the junction J and selected for conformance with much of the literature on this subject.

In Fig. 10-3 a possible biasing arrangement for the grounded-emitter connection is shown. Note the use of a *single* battery for the bias supply. The dc collector-to-emitter path biases the emitter with respect to the junction point J shown by an amount $I_e r_e$. Point B is negative with respect to point E by an amount $I_b R_g$, and the correct bias polarities are achievable using only one power supply. The polarity in Fig. 10-3 is for the point contact and PNP transistors.

The sketch in Fig. 10-4 shows the same type of connection for the NPN type of transistor. Here, point B is positive with respect to point E by an amount $I_b R_g$, and the correct polarities are observed.

The possibility of using a single power supply is another of the important reasons why, for circuit applications, many design engineers favor the grounded-emitter connection.[4]

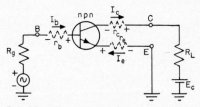

Fig. 10-4. Same comment as in Fig. 10-3, for the NPN junction units.

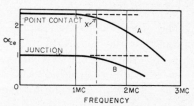

Fig. 10-5. Curves of α_{ce} versus frequency for point contact and junction units. Here the transistors were connected in the grounded-base arrangement.

One interesting but unfortunate aspect of the grounded-emitter connection is its poor frequency response compared with the grounded-base connection. In transistor work, when we speak of frequency response we usually mean α versus frequency. In Fig. 10-5 are shown two typical curves for α versus frequency, curve A for a point contact unit and curve B for the junction unit, both measurements having been made using a grounded-base connection. In Fig. 10-6 are shown the frequency-response curves for the *same* units, connected grounded emitter.[5] The reason for the poor frequency response of these units when connected grounded emitter compared with grounded base may be understood from what follows.

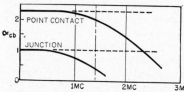

Fig. 10-6. Curves of α_{cb} versus frequency for the same transistors which yielded the data of Fig. 10-5. Here the units were connected in the grounded-emitter connection. Note the markedly poorer frequency response, particularly for the junction units, compared to the grounded-base connection.

133. CURRENT GAIN—GE

In specifying α, it is convenient to use the letters c, b, and e as subscripts and by their sequence to indicate the method of connection. In practice, the letters in the subscript state first the output-current terminal and then the input-current terminal—the letter omitted implies the common or grounded terminal. Thus, α_{ce} is the grounded base α, α_{cb} the grounded emitter α, and α_{eb} the grounded collector α. When we speak of the frequency-response curves, we mean the ratio of output to input current versus frequency, not the ratio of collector current to emitter current versus frequency.

In general, α is a measure of the current gain in the transistor and is defined as $-i_c/i_e$. For the grounded-base connection, it can be verified from Fig. 10-7 that $i_c = i_2$ and $i_e = i_1$, so that for this connection only we can write

$$\alpha = -\frac{i_c}{i_e} = -\frac{i_2}{i_1} \quad (10\text{-}19)$$

A notation that is frequently used in the literature is the small letter a for the ratio of output to input current, i.e.,

$$a = \frac{i_2}{i_1} \quad (10\text{-}20)$$

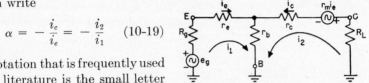

Fig. 10-7. An equivalent circuit diagram of the grounded-base connection to illustrate how i_e is identical to the loop 1 current and i_c to the loop 2 current. This is true for this connection only.

and from Eq. (10-19) it is seen that for the *grounded-base connection*

$$\alpha = -a \quad (10\text{-}21)$$

When we come to the grounded-emitter connection, it is not so much the ratio of collector current to emitter current that is of interest, as the ratio of output to input current a. The ratio of collector to emitter current is invariant with the method of connection. Except for stray capacitance, the transistor does not know how it is hooked up; but the ratio of output to input current differs quite widely for the three possible connections. We shall show presently how the grounded-emitter current gain varies with the value of α_{ce}. In practical transistor measurements it is common to measure the grounded-base α, α_{ce}, and to compute the grounded-emitter current gain from these data. Later, we shall show the corresponding process for the grounded-collector connection.

From Eqs. (10-5) and (10-9), the value of a for the grounded-emitter connection is

$$\frac{i_2}{i_1} = \alpha_{cb} = \frac{r_m - r_e}{R_L + r_e + r_c - r_m} \quad (10\text{-}22)$$

While this is true mathematically, from the physical standpoint this relation has limited use as a comparison number for transistors because the gain shown may differ over a very wide range depending on the value selected for R_L. It will be recalled that α for the grounded-base connection is measured with *the collector shorted*. Consider the equations of the grounded-base connection:

$$v_1 = (R_g + r_{11})i_1 + r_{12}i_2 \quad (10\text{-}23)$$
$$v_2 = r_{21}i_1 + i_2(R_L + r_{22}) \quad (10\text{-}24)$$

If we set v_2 equal to zero, $i.e.$, short-circuit the collector, and put R_L equal to zero

$$-\frac{i_2}{i_1} = \frac{r_{21}}{r_{22}} \tag{10-25}$$

which is α_{ce} by definition.

Hence, to get a comparable figure of merit and render the result independent of R_L, the current gain α_{cb} for the grounded-emitter connection is obtained by putting $R_L = 0$ in Eq. (10-22).

$$\alpha_{cb} = \frac{r_m - r_e}{r_e + r_c - r_m} = \frac{(r_m/r_c) - (r_e/r_c)}{(r_e/r_c + 1) - (r_m/r_c)} \tag{10-26}$$

Neglecting r_e/r_c compared to r_m/r_c and to unity and using the grounded-base α definition $\alpha_{ce} = r_{21}/r_{22} \approx r_m/r_c$, obtain

$$\alpha_{cb} = \frac{\alpha_{ce}}{1 - \alpha_{ce}} \tag{10-27}[6]$$

Note that Eq. (10-27) does not depend on the load resistance and shows how the current gain for the grounded-emitter connection varies with the grounded-base current gain α_{ce}. A significant aspect of the grounded-emitter connection is that current gains greater than unity are entirely possible, using junction transistors. Typical values are

$$\alpha_{cb} = -1.66 \text{ for point contact units} \tag{10-28}$$

[The minus sign indicates phase reversal. Compare Eq. (10-10) and value of VG.]

$$\alpha_{cb} = 24 \text{ for junction units} \tag{10-29}$$

134. FREQUENCY RESPONSE OF GE CONNECTION

Bearing in mind that the ordinate in Fig. 10-6 is α_{cb} of Eq. (10-27), we may now perceive the reason for the relatively poor frequency response of the grounded-emitter connection compared with the grounded-base arrangement.

Because of the capacitance, both stray and internal, and the transit-time dispersion effects, let us assume that, at some frequency below cutoff, α_{ce} falls off by 10 per cent. This would be point X of Fig. 10-5. When α'_{ce} is $0.9\alpha_{ce}$, what is the value of α_{cb}? Using Eq. (10-27),

$$\alpha'_{cb} = \frac{0.9\alpha_{ce}}{1 - 0.9\alpha_{ce}}$$

For the junction type,

$$\alpha'_{cb} = 6.34$$

Comparing this value with $\alpha_{cb} = 24$, [see Eq. (10-29)] when α_{ce} was 0.96, it is seen that, because of the nature of the $\alpha_{ce}/(1 - \alpha_{ce})$ function, when α_{ce} falls off by 10 per cent, the grounded-emitter α, α_{cb}, *falls off by almost 75 per cent.* Hence, the observed effect is that the frequency response of the grounded-emitter connection falls off much more rapidly than the inherent frequency response of the transistor as measured by α_{ce}.

These effects are illustrated by Figs. 10-5 and 10-6. Both curves are for the same transistors, but Fig. 10-5 was obtained using the grounded-base arrangement and Fig. 10-6 using the grounded-emitter arrangement. A rule of thumb sometimes useful is to consider that the frequency of α cutoff, using the grounded-emitter connection, may be a fifth or less of the response using the grounded-base arrangement. The frequency of α cutoff is that frequency at which α is 0.707 of its value at some lower reference frequency. Since most transistors show a flat frequency response over a range of frequencies up to very nearly 50 kc, the value of the reference frequency at which α is measured is some convenient frequency below 10 kc.[7]

135. PHASE INVERSION—VOLTAGE AND CURRENT

As the numerical example shows [see Eq. (10-28)] for point contact transistors the grounded-emitter current gain will usually be negative. It is clear from Eq. (10-27) that if α_{ce} is greater than unity, as in the case of point contact units, α_{cb} is negative, representing a 180° phase reversal in current.

It is desirable to bear in mind that:

1. When the signal is fed into the emitter, and the output taken from the collector, the transistor will usually introduce no significant phase change, regardless of the method of connection. Under special conditions of loading and frequency dependence of parameters, changes in phase may be observed. The significant point is that phase change is essentially associated with the method of feeding the signal into the transistor; the method of connection introduces a phase change only because it determines the method of feeding the signal. The grounded-base connection is an illustration of feeding the signal into the emitter and taking the output from the collector—no significant phase change is observed.

2. A phase change is usually observed in the grounded-emitter connection because the signal is fed into the base. A similar effect will be observed for the grounded-collector connection, where the signal is also fed into the base.

Unlike the vacuum tube, which is usually considered to be essentially a voltage amplifier, the transistor usually amplifies both voltage and current concomitantly. For the grounded-emitter connection both current gain and voltage gain are usually greater than unity for both point contact and junction units, and the transistor is a *power* amplifying device. As an illustration, in transistor equipments using several stages in cascade, or in a typical superheterodyne arrangement beginning with the very first rf stage, one computes power gain stage by stage, so that there is a successive power build-up. This method of computation should be compared with the vacuum-tube analog, where voltage gains only are normally computed up to the one or two last power-gain stages. It should be clear that, while admittedly this stage-by-stage power build-up does not decrease the power-handling requirements for the last stage, it reduces the power gain required of the last stage. An over-all result is that, if the last or output stage fails, a useful amount of power is still available in an emergency by taking the output from the preceding stage. Also, in the practical testing of cascaded stages using transistors, we will have to become accustomed to, and get equipment capable of, measuring power levels stage by stage.

136. GROUNDED-COLLECTOR CONNECTION

The third principal method of connection of transistors is in the grounded-collector or common-collector connection. An equivalent circuit diagram is given in Fig. 10-8.

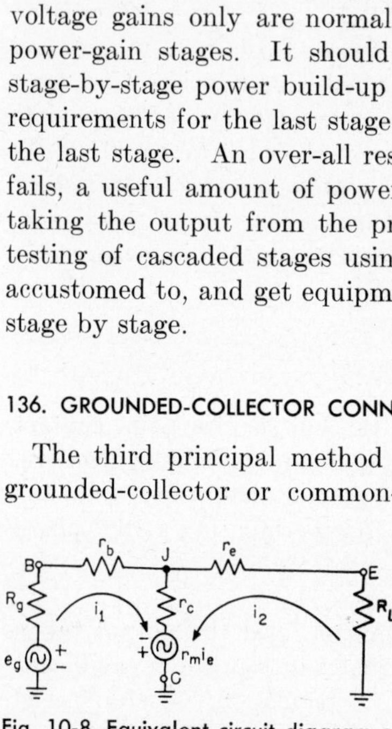

Fig. 10-8. Equivalent circuit diagram of the grounded-collector connection. Current directions indicated are arbitrary for analysis. Note that the signal is fed into the base and taken out at the emitter.

In writing the circuit equations, bearing in mind the rules previously laid down in Chap. 8, the following must be considered for the grounded-collector circuit:

1. $+i_e$ = current through r_e which flows toward junction J and is in this case given by i_2, that is, $i_2 = i_e$.

2. The polarity of $r_m i_e$, consistent with the usage for the grounded-emitter and grounded-base connections, is chosen minus toward junction J and plus toward the collector terminal.

3. For the grounded-collector connection, i_c = current through $r_c = i_1 + i_2$.

The current-determining equations are:

$$(R_g + r_b + r_c)i_1 + (r_c - r_m)i_2 = e_g \qquad (10\text{-}30)$$
$$r_c i_1 + (R_L + r_e + r_c - r_m)i_2 = 0 \qquad (10\text{-}31)$$

$$i_1 = \frac{e_g(R_L + r_e + r_c - r_m)}{(R_g + r_b + r_c)(R_L + r_e + r_c - r_m) - r_c(r_c - r_m)} \quad (10\text{-}32)$$

$$i_2 = \frac{-e_g r_c}{(R_g + r_b + r_c)(R_L + r_e + r_c - r_m) - r_c(r_c - r_m)} \quad (10\text{-}33)$$

$i_2' =$ the value of i_2 when e_g is considered to be in series with R_L:

$$i_2' = \frac{e_g(R_g + r_b + r_c)}{(R_g + r_b + r_c)(R_L + r_e + r_c - r_m) - r_c(r_c - r_m)} \quad (10\text{-}34)$$

137. INPUT RESISTANCE—GC

The input resistance of the grounded-collector circuit is

$$R_{i_c} = \frac{e_g}{i_1} - R_g$$

$$= r_b + r_c - \frac{r_c(r_c - r_m)}{R_L + r_e + r_c - r_m} \quad (10\text{-}35)$$

Using typical values:

$$R_{i_c} = \quad 2 \text{ megohms for point contact units}$$
$$R_{i_c} = 0.7 \text{ megohm for junction units}$$

The high input resistance obtainable from the common- or grounded-collector connection is in sharp contrast to the input resistance of a few hundred ohms for the grounded-base connection.

Thus it is seen that the grounded-base connection exhibits a low input resistance, while the grounded-emitter and grounded-collector connections show quite a high input resistance. An insight into the physical reason for this condition will be found profitable in many ways.

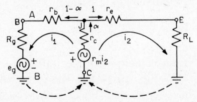

Fig. 10-9. Equivalent circuit diagram of the grounded-collector connection, using electron flow direction of current. Note the current division at junction J.

Let us redraw Fig. 10-8, using this time instantaneous electron current flow paths, instead of the arbitrarily selected current directions of Fig. 10-8. This is shown in Fig. 10-9.

138. INPUT CURRENT WHEN R_L EQUALS ZERO

If a unit change of current occurs through r_e, since the current gain is α_{ce}, a current change of $\alpha_{ce} \times 1$ will occur through r_c. At the junction point J, since the sum of the currents at a junction must be zero, a current of $1 - \alpha_{ce}$ units will flow through r_b. This is the condition for $R_L = 0$, i.e., output shorted, for the current through r_c is not exactly α_{ce} times the current in r_e unless $R_L = 0$, by definition. When α_{ce} is very near unity, $1 - \alpha_{ce}$ is very near zero, and therefore a very small current flows in loop 1, and the circuit to the right of points AB presents a high impedance to the generator e_g. Observe also from this analysis that the current gain for the grounded-collector connection is given by

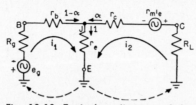

Fig. 10-10. Equivalent diagram of the grounded-emitter connection, using electron flow direction of current. Note that the generator e_g has been reversed to give correct polarity with current directions as shown. The current division at the imaginary junction point J is explained in the text.

$$\alpha_{eb} = \frac{i_2}{i_1} = \frac{-1}{1 - \alpha_{ce}} \quad (10\text{-}36)$$

Typical values are:

0.77 for point contact units
−25 for junction units[3]

In Fig. 10-10 for the grounded-emitter case, a unit change in current through r_e results in α_{ce} times that change in current through r_c, for $R_L = 0$. The net current change through r_b is $1 - \alpha_{ce}$ and tends to make i_1 very nearly equal to zero and the input impedance high, as α approaches unity. Note also how the current gain is now

$$\frac{i_2}{i_1} = \frac{\alpha_{ce}}{(1 - \alpha_{ce})}$$

in agreement with Eq. (10-27).

In Fig. 10-11 for the grounded-base connection, unit current change through r_e produces $\alpha_{ce} \times 1$ current change through r_c, and therefore $1 - \alpha_{ce}$ current change in r_b. Hence the input current through r_e does not approach zero as α_{ce} approaches 1. We would not expect that the input resistance for the grounded-base connection would ever become very high.

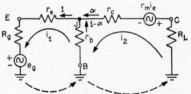

Fig. 10-11. Equivalent circuit diagram of the grounded-base connection using electron flow current directions. As explained in the text, current division at J indicates that very high input impedances are improbable.

139. INPUT CURRENT WHEN R_L IS NOT ZERO

When R_L is not zero, a slightly different approach will provide the physical interpretation for the high input resistance. In Fig. 10-9 for the grounded-collector connection when R_L and i_2 have values such that

$$e_g \cong i_2(r_e + R_L) \tag{10-37}$$

or when

$$e_g \cong i_2(r_m - r_c) \tag{10-38}$$

a very small drop in $r_b + R_g$ only is involved, *i.e.*, $i_1 \cong 0$, and the input impedance is high. If Eqs. (10-37) and (10-38) are valid, then we must have

$$r_e + R_L \cong r_m - r_c \tag{10-39}$$

The significance of Eq. (10-39) can be seen by considering Eq. (10-32). Since none of the terms in the denominator can ever be infinite for finite values of load resistance, the only way for i_1 to be close to zero is for the numerator to be nearly zero, *i.e.*, we must have

$$R_L + r_e + r_c - r_m \cong 0 \tag{10-40}$$

When a value of R_L is used which makes Eq. (10-40) true, R_i may become very high [see Eq. (10-35)] and the physical interpretation is that *an insignificant amount of current is drawn from the source generator e_g*. The condition expressed by Eq. (10-40) is identical to that in Eq. (10-39), verifying the conditions for high input resistance.

Similar remarks apply to the grounded-emitter connection (see Fig. 10-10). When

$$e_g \cong -(i_2 + i_1)r_e = (R_L + r_c - r_m)i_2 \tag{10-41}$$

i_1 is approximately zero and the drop across $R_g + r_b$ is negligible. When $i_1 \cong 0$, from Eq. (10-41)

$$-i_2 r_e \cong (R_L + r_c - r_m)i_2 \tag{10-42}$$

Transposing Eq. (10-42), R_L must be selected so that

$$R_L + r_e + r_c - r_m \cong 0 \tag{10-43}$$

exactly as in Eq. (10-40). This is confirmed by Eq. (10-5), where we see that, if Eq. (10-43) is true, loop 1 current is negligible. From Eq. (10-6) one can observe that if Eq. (10-43) is valid the input resistance may be quite high.[8]

The essence of the discussion is that using the grounded-collector or grounded-emitter connection it is possible to choose the load resistance so that the input resistance will be quite high.

But these remarks do not apply to the grounded-base connection. For the grounded-base case,

$$i_1 = \frac{e_g(R_L + r_b + r_c)}{(R_g + r_b + r_e)(R_L + r_b + r_c) - r_b(r_b + r_m)}$$

and by inspection this cannot be made to approach zero by any choice of R_g and R_L; therefore a high input resistance is impossible.

140. VOLTAGE GAIN—GC

Returning now to our analysis of the grounded-collector connection,

$$VG = \frac{-i_2 R_L}{e_g}$$

and, using Eq. (10-33),

$$VG_c = \frac{r_c R_L}{(R_g + r_b + r_c)(R_L + r_e + r_c - r_m) - r_c(r_c - r_m)} \quad (10\text{-}44)$$

Typical values for VG are slightly less than unity, but positive, for both point contact transistors and junction transistors.

141. OUTPUT RESISTANCE—GC

Since $R_{o_c} = (e_g/i_2') - R_L$, using Eq. (10-34), we find

$$R_{o_c} = r_e + r_c - r_m - \frac{r_c(r_c - r_m)}{R_g + r_b + r_c} \quad (10\text{-}45)$$

Typical values are:

$$R_{o_c} = -650 \text{ ohms for point contact units}$$
$$R_{o_c} = 65 \text{ ohms for junction units}$$

One observes immediately that the grounded-collector connection is a low-resistance output connection. While the negative sign of R_o for the point contact connection is generally undesirable, producing an unstable condition, nonetheless, proper operation is possible. If a stabilizing resistance greater than 650 ohms is added in series with the output, i.e., in series with r_e at the emitter, the net output resistance becomes positive.

142. CATHODE FOLLOWER ACTION OF GC CONNECTION

Considering the high input resistance and low output resistance levels of the grounded-collector connection, and bearing in mind the low-voltage-gain figures obtained, one can see the analogy between this method of connection and the cathode follower of vacuum-tube practice. We have already noted [Eq. (10-36)] how the current gain for the junction type is 25, further improving the analogy.

For the point contact type, the current gain is rather poor, 0.77, and combined with the negative output resistance indicates that, in general, the applications of point contact transistors connected in this way are rather limited. It is worthwhile to note that, for the junction transistors, both input and output resistances are positive, and the relative magnitudes suggest strongly the transformer step-down effect obtainable in the cathode follower.

A noteworthy disadvantage of the grounded-collector connection arises from the fact that the output is taken from the emitter terminal (see Fig. 10-8). Because of this, it should be evident that large output

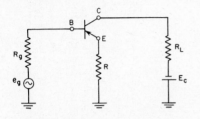

Fig. 10-12. A practical transistor amplifier stage using the grounded-emitter connection. Resistor R provides negative current feedback for stability. The circuit shown is for point contact and PNP transistors.

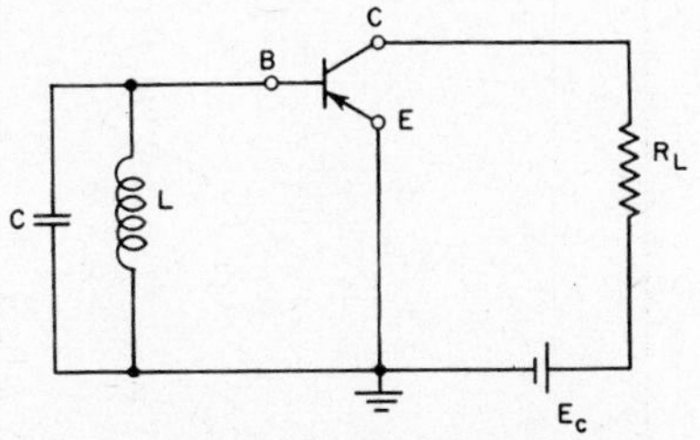

Fig. 10-13. A practical Colpitts oscillator using a transistor connected in the grounded-emitter arrangement. As oscillators, transistors may operate at frequencies often as high as five times the frequency of α cutoff. The connection shown is for NPN units.

voltage swings are not feasible. In general, emitter biases are of the order of 1 volt and collector biases up to 50 volts. Excessive voltage swings in the emitter will move it into regions where the transistor either is entirely inoperative as a transistor or has reached saturation as evidenced by clipping.

Regarding the power capabilities, using Eq. (10-33)

$$PG = \frac{4R_g R_L i_2{}^2}{e_g{}^2}$$

$$= \frac{4R_g R_L r_c{}^2}{[(R_g + r_b + r_c)(R_L + r_e + r_c - r_m) - r_c(r_c - r_m)]^2} \quad (10\text{-}46)$$

Typical values for power gain in the grounded-collector connection are:

$$PG = 0.1 \text{ for point contact units}$$
$$PG = 0.02 \text{ for junction units}$$

The power gain of the grounded-collector connection may be made somewhat higher by suitable choice of R_L and R_g, but in general tends to be unimpressive. In practice, the grounded-collector connection is used principally as a coupling device for impedance matching and,

TABLE 10-1

	Grounded base	Grounded emitter	Grounded collector
Input-resistance formula	$r_b + r_e - \dfrac{r_b(r_b + r_m)}{R_L + r_b + r_e}$	$r_b + r_e + \dfrac{r_e(r_m - r_e)}{R_L + r_c - r_m}$	$r_b + r_e - \dfrac{r_c(r_c - r_m)}{R_L + r_e + r_c - r_m}$
Typical values pc	≈ 150 ohms	≈ 35,000 ohms	≈ 2,000,000 ohms
Typical values j	≈ 90 ohms	≈ 700 ohms	≈ 700,000 ohms
Output-resistance formula	$r_c + r_e - r_m - \dfrac{r_b(r_b + r_m)}{R_g + r_b + r_e}$	$r_e + r_c - r_m + \dfrac{r_e(r_m - r_e)}{R_g + r_e + r_b}$	$r_e + r_e - r_m - \dfrac{r_e(r_c - r_m)}{(R_g + r_e + r_b)}$
Typical values pc	≈ 9,500 ohms	≈ −13,000 ohms	≈ −650 ohms
Typical values j	≈ 530,000 ohms	≈ 63,000 ohms	≈ 65 ohms
Voltage-gain formula	$\dfrac{(r_b + r_m)R_L}{(R_g + r_e + r_b)(R_L + r_b + r_c) - r_b(r_b + r_m)}$	$\dfrac{(r_e - r_m)R_L}{(R_g + r_b + r_e)(R_L + r_e + r_c - r_m) + r_e(r_m - r_e)}$	$\dfrac{r_c R_L}{(R_g + r_b + r_e)(R_L + r_e + r_c - r_m) + r_c(r_m - r_e)}$
Typical values pc	≈ 30	≈ −130	< 1
Typical values j	≈ 150	≈ −575	< 1
Power-gain formula	$\dfrac{4R_L R_g(r_b + r_m)^2}{[(R_g + r_e + r_b)(R_L + r_b + r_c) - r_b(r_b + r_m)]^2}$	$\dfrac{4R_L R_g(r_m - r_e)^2}{[(R_g + r_b + r_e)(R_L + r_e + r_c - r_m) + r_e(r_m - r_e)]^2}$	$\dfrac{4R_g R_L r_c^2}{[(R_g + r_b + r_e)(R_L + r_e + r_c - r_m) + r_c(r_m - r_e)]^2}$
Typical values pc	≈ 100 (20 db)	≈ 1,700 (32 db)	≈ 0.1
Typical values j	≈ 440 (26 db)	≈ 6,600 (38 db)	≈ 0.02
Current-gain formula	$\alpha_{cb} = -(i_c/i_e)$	$\alpha_{ce} = \dfrac{\alpha_{ce}}{1 - \alpha_{ce}}$	$\dfrac{-1}{1 - \alpha_{cb}}$
Typical values pc	≈ 2.3	≈ −1.66	≈ 0.77
Typical values j	≈ 0.96	≈ 24	≈ −25
Stability pc	Stable unless $R_L = 0$ (PC transistors are possible which are short-circuit stable)	Unstable	Unstable
Stability j	Stable	Stable	Stable
Phase pc	No phase reversal unless R_L is very low or α high	Voltage and current phase reversal	No phase reversal, usually
Phase j	No phase reversal	Voltage phase reversal	Current phase reversal
Advantages pc	Current gain	High input resistance, single battery supply	Good frequency response
Advantages j	High output resistance	High output resistance, single battery supply; high voltage and power gains	Cathode follower action; high current gain
Disadvantages pc	Low input resistance; low gain	Unstable	May be unstable, voltage and power gains poor
Disadvantages j	Low input resistance	Input resistance low unless α is high and R_L low	Low voltage and power gains

Abbreviations: pc point contact
j junction

using the junction transistor, for current gain.   It is clearly not suited for voltage or power amplification.   There is experimental evidence that the frequency response of this connection holds some promise.

Figures 10-12 and 10-13 show typical grounded-emitter amplifier and oscillator circuits.

143. SUMMARY

This chapter has pointed out the pertinent operating characteristics of transistors in grounded-emitter and grounded-collector connections as compared with the grounded-base connection explained in the previous chapter.

These characteristics are summarized in Table 10-1.

REFERENCES

1. Ryder, R. M., and R. J. Kircher: Some Circuit Aspects of the Transistor, *Bell System Tech. J.*, Vol. 28, No. 3, pp. 367–400, July, 1949.
2. Roddam, T.: Earthed-emitter and earthed-collector circuits as amplifiers and osciilators, *Wireless World*, Vol. 59, pp. 175–178, April, 1953.
3. Shea, R. F.: "Transistor Circuits," pp. 72ff., John Wiley & Sons, Inc., New York, 1953.
4. Roddam, T.: Transistors.   Introduction to Junction Transistors, *Wireless World*, Vol. 49, pp. 205–210, May, 1953.
5. Transistor Circuitry Research, Sixth Quarterly Progress Report, Contr. DA36-039 sc-15544, pp. 3–7, Purdue University, Engineering Experiment Station, Lafayette, Ind., Aug. 1, 1953, to Oct. 31, 1953.
6. Wallace, Jr., R. L., and W. J. Pietenpol: Some Circuit Properties and Applications of NPN Transistors, *Proc. IRE*, Vol. 39, pp. 753–767, July, 1951.
7. Coblenz, A., and H. L. Owens: Variation of Transistor Parameters with Temperature, *Proc. IRE*, Vol. 40, pp. 1472–1476, see Fig. 11, p. 1475, November, 1952.
8. Stansel, F. R.: The Common Collector Transistor Amplifier at Carrier Frequencies, *Proc. IRE*, Vol. 41, pp. 1096–1102, September, 1953.

11 THEORY OF TRANSISTOR

SWITCHING CIRCUITS

In previous chapters of this book, emphasis has been placed on the small-signal characteristics of transistors and their operation in circuits where stability was essential. In this chapter, attention will be focused on the so-called large-signal characteristics and the behavior of the transistor in portions of its V-I characteristics where it is unstable. Large-signal behavior is important in switching operations as well as in class C operation, particularly where the unit is used as an oscillator, or in clipping or pulse-forming circuits. In switching, the instability of the transistor is used to advantage, and circuit rearrangements are made to bring the device into and out of its unstable region.

144. LARGE-SIGNAL THEORY

Small-signal theory for vacuum tubes has been highly developed and is currently considered quite satisfactory for practical use. Large-signal theory, on the other hand, is not so well developed and is generally regarded as incomplete. While a great deal of literature exists on the subject, mathematical prediction of circuit performance for large-signal applications in vacuum-tube practice, *i.e.*, switching and grid current flow operation, is much more difficult than for small-signal performance. In practice, engineers usually work out the circuit breadboard fashion, supplementing the experimental work by a theoretical analysis to obtain particular desired results. The situation is analogous in transistors but, because of the youthfulness of the field, is even less satisfactory. No truly large-signal theory for transistors exists today that can be applied directly by the design engineer. The small-signal parameters may be used to describe large-signal operation at least in the case of switching circuits, and the region of operation is divided into three main parts where the small-signal parameters may be applied.

From Fig. 11-7 it is evident that the switching characteristic for transistors is extremely nonlinear, and the division of the over-all characteristic into three regions is intended to bring the curve, for each region, nearer to linearity.   In general, even in the three regions into which the operation is divided, small-signal theory cannot be said to apply, because in point of fact relatively large signals are involved in each of the three regions.   The use of the small-signal parameters implies that in each of the three regions (see Fig. 11-7) the characteristics being used depart to a negligible extent from true linearity. This assumption, except possibly for region I, is not valid, and it must be borne in mind that we are dealing with an approximation at best.

145. CLASS C OPERATION

In this chapter, only the switching application of large-signal parameters will be considered, class C operation representing a phase in which insufficient work has been done to date to warrant detailed attention here.   While a very large number of oscillator circuits utilizing transistors are known to be practical, detailed mathematical analyses of such instances of class C operation are not yet available to any important extent.

146. VOLTAGE-CURRENT CHARACTERISTIC

Several of the V-I characteristics considered in previous chapters are suitable for analysis of switching action.   The V_e-I_e characteristic modified according to the following ideas will be used for the analysis because of its simplicity.   It is also possible to use the V_e-I_b or V_c-I_c characteristic, but in any case the common factor that must be possessed by the curve is that it shall have a region where the slope is negative, or since the slope is $-V/I$, a resistance, it must display a negative resistance portion.

147. ON-OFF CONDITION

Switching, as used in electronics, implies a condition of on and off not in the absolute sense of the words, but as a significant change in the circuit conditions.   The on and off condition in the case of transistors is somewhat different from the corresponding condition for vacuum tubes.   In vacuum-tube practice, when the plate current is cut off, the resistance in the plate circuit may be of the order of

several megohms.   Leakage currents when the grid is biased to cut off
may, particularly for pentodes, be of the order of a few microamperes
or less.   When the tube is ON, a plate current for several milliamperes,
with a plate voltage about 150 volts, produces a circuit whose internal
resistance is of the order of tens of thousands of ohms in average cases.
We may say, then, that an external system, to sense whether the
switching tube is ON or OFF, must be able to distinguish between several
megohms and, say, 20,000 ohms or less.

The ON and OFF conditions are quite different for the transistor;
in the ON condition, the device acts as a true transistor but far in its
saturation region, and the circuit impedance is of the order of a few
thousand ohms or less.   But in the OFF condition, the biasing potentials raise the operating point to the no-transistor-action condition,
and the maximum possible resistance in the circuit is then the reverse
resistance of a diode.   For point contact transistors, this back resistance is of the order of 20,000 ohms, and in general the OFF condition
resistance of several megohms is not usually encountered.

The point is that for transistors the circuit must sense, unam-
biguously, a change from 20,000 ohms to perhaps a thousand ohms, so
that the problem of identification of the ON and OFF conditions is
somewhat more difficult for transistors than for vacuum tubes.   The
OFF condition focuses interest on I_{co}, the parameter which expresses
collector current for emitter open or biased into its reverse current
region.   Often the switching analysis is carried on in the emitter
circuit, with the sensing circuit connected as a load in the collector
circuit.   It is also useful to note that experience with switching circuits
indicates that the effect of a collector load resistance is very nearly
the same as that of an emitter load resistance.   In any case, since the
resistance presented by the circuit in the OFF condition is V_c/I_{co}, one
can see why it is desirable to make I_{co} small.

148. TRANSITION FROM OFF TO ON

Having established that the essence of a switching circuit involves
two unambiguous conditions, ON and OFF, we may next study the
transition from one operating point to the other.   There are two
principal desiderata here:

1. The transition from OFF to ON and back should be as fast as
possible.   Not only does rapid switching increase the maximum
possible repetition rate for switching, but it also decreases the duty
cycle so that larger transient pulses are permissible.

2. The system must be capable of setting and resetting itself, not
merely following an impressed signal.   Thus one can easily apply a

pulse to the emitter, which brings the transistor operating point from a region where transistor action occurs to one where there is no transistor action.   The rate of switch-over for a nonswitching system is a function of the pulse applied, and the system will not stay in the OFF position when the pulse is past.

149. NEGATIVE RESISTANCE

The circuit characteristic which enables an amplifying device such as a vacuum tube or a transistor to fulfill both the above conditions is negative resistance.   In the range of operating values where a circuit or a device exhibits negative resistance, it is said to be unstable. Whereas a system will, in general, stay at its operating point if the point is stable, it will not stay at its operating point if it is unstable, but will shift quickly from the unstable point to a stable one.   All one has to do is to bring the system into an unstable region, and the circuit itself will do the rest, *i.e.*, it will switch rapidly to the nearest stable operating point.   And, within the restraints set upon the circuit such as capacitance or inductances, it will make this shift virtually instantaneously.

The transistor, in certain regions of its operating range, exhibits a negative resistance characteristic.   For switching purposes, this instability is not only useful but indispensable.

150. STABLE EQUILIBRIUM

Having discussed the need for negative resistance, we may profitably now describe briefly what negative resistance is, and why it performs the circuit functions necessary for switching.   Consider an object falling on a table.   The reason it comes to rest is because the force of gravity is counterbalanced by the push of the table upward against it.   Stated somewhat differently, the only force that could make it move after hitting the table top, *i.e.*, gravity, sets into action a reaction, *i.e.*, the push of the table upward, and the object is then in stable equilibrium.   The general principle involved is that, if a certain action sets into effect other actions (or reactions) which offer resistance to it, the action will come to a stop and equilibrium conditions are attained.

151. UNSTABLE EQUILIBRIUM

But now suppose that there is a hole drilled into the table top and arrangements are made so that in falling the object activates a mechanism to give it a sharp blow downward as it passes the hole. Clearly the object would be accelerated in its downward motion. If we had a series of such holes one above the other each with the same arrangement, the object would soon attain a great velocity. Such an object is then in unstable equilibrium, and we may speak of the resistance of the table top as then being negative in so far as this object is concerned, because instead of opposing the original action, it aids or strengthens it.

In brief, then, any action such as setting an object in motion or starting a current flow, which sets into operation forces to resist or oppose it, encounters positive resistance; any action which sets into motion forces that aid or strengthen the original action encounters negative resistance. Note that such a reinforcing action implies addition of energy from some outside source. We shall observe presently the application of this interesting principle in transistor switching circuits.

152. REASON FOR USE OF BASE RESISTOR

We have established that negative resistance is essential for switching action, but we have not yet determined how to obtain such negative resistance in our circuit. In previous chapters we have encountered several cases where R_i or R_o was negative, but in such cases fortuitous combinations of parameters might give a positive resistance. For switching action, a controlled method is needed so that we may be sure of getting the desired negative resistance. For the grounded-base connection, the input resistance is given by

$$R_i = r_e + r_b - \frac{r_b(r_b + r_m)}{R_L + r_b + r_c} \qquad (11\text{-}1)^1$$

Assuming other parameters in Eq. (11-1) constant, R_i is plotted as a function of R_b in Fig. 11-1 for both point contact and junction transistors, using the typical values seen in Table 11-1. R_b represents the r_b of Table 11-1 plus added series resistance to bring the total to the value shown in the abscissas. Curves A through D are for point contact transistors, with $R_L = 30$, 20, 5, and 2 kilohms, respectively, and curve E for junction units, $R_L = 0.1$ megohm. For the point contact units, after R_b reaches approximately 200 ohms, R_i is negative; but for the junction units, R_i *never* goes negative. We may infer two significant facts from this information:

1. It is possible, by addition of series resistance into the base, to force the point contact transistor connected grounded base to exhibit

a negative resistance characteristic. It can be shown that this characteristic is associated with α's greater than unity.

2. It is not possible, by addition of series resistance, to bring a junction transfer into a negative resistance range, and we may say that it is unconditionally stable. By reference to Table 10-1, the reader will see that junction transistors are stable not only in the grounded-base connection but in the grounded-emitter and grounded-collector connections as well. This explains why a single junction transistor,

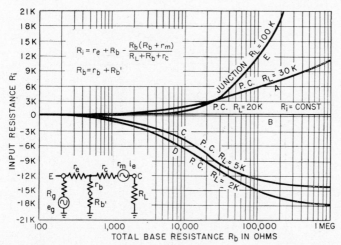

Fig. 11-1. Variation of input resistance of the grounded-base transistor with total base resistance. For junction units, R_i never goes negative. For point contact units, after the base resistance exceeds several hundred ohms, the input resistance becomes increasingly negative.

with typical values of parameter, is not ordinarily suitable for switching.[2] It is useful to observe in passing that combinations of PNP and NPN transistors can be made to exhibit negative resistance characteristics,[3] and considerable attention is now being given to this application for junction units.

153. SWITCHING ACTION—REGION I

In Fig. 11-2 is shown a basic transistor switching circuit using the grounded-base connection.

R'_e is the input load resistance, usually considered to include the internal pulse generator resistance R_g. In Fig. 11-1 there is a transition point between the regions of positive and negative resistance where $R_i = 0$. In the negative-resistance region beginning at $R_i = 0$, i_1 can easily become high enough to damage the unit—note that we are usually dealing with a recurrent phenomenon—and one of the principal functions of R_e is to limit this current to permissible values.

Note the addition of the external base resistance R'_b. As the curves of Fig. 11-1 show, for R_L greater than 20 kilohms, R_i never goes negative; for $R_L = 20$ kilohms, $R_i = r_b$ and is constant; for R_L less than 20 kilohms, values of R_b greater than a few hundred ohms bring the input characteristic to a negative resistance region. A typical value of R_b is 10,000 ohms.

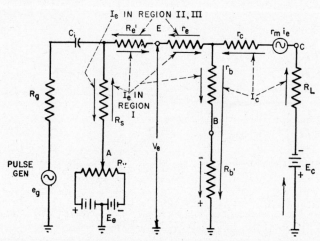

Fig. 11-2. Basic point contact switching circuit for bistable operation. A positive pulse triggers the circuit to a stable point in region III, a negative pulse to a stable point in region I. Note the reversal of the emitter current I_e from region I to regions II and III.

Note the variable emitter bias potentiometer R_v. In the OFF condition, as mentioned, the emitter is biased in its reverse or high-resistance direction; R_v is adjusted so that the amplitude of the pulse is just sufficient to shift the emitter-diode operating point from the reverse to the forward current region where transistor action can take place. For many purposes, it is convenient to consider the transistor as consisting of an emitter diode and a collector diode.[4]

154. SWITCHING CIRCUIT DETAILS

In so far as the triggering action is concerned, the transistor requires only that the leading edge bring the emitter-diode operating point into the forward current region. However, if freedom from jitter is desired, steep leading edges and well-formed pulses must be used for triggering. Regarding repetition rates, 100,000 pps is an average value attainable from point contact switching transistors. Rates of 1 mc and greater are obtainable from special high-speed switching transistors in various stages of production by several manufacturers. Fifty-volt pulse amplitudes are possible on the output, although much lower pulse voltages are frequently preferred in order to reduce power consumption and to prevent false triggering.

Input pulse amplitudes of tenths of a volt are adequate for triggering purposes.

R_s, in Fig. 11-2, provides dc bias. Replacing R_s with an inductance to provide a high ac shunt impedance may be impractical because inductance at critical frequencies may markedly affect the operation of the switching transistor.

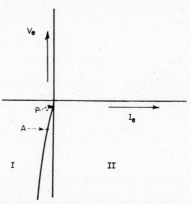

As shown in Fig. 11-3, in region I the emitter bias is such that the emitter diode is biased in the reverse direction and, at least for the region of primary interest, the current varies approximately linearly with the voltage.

It will be observed that the point of transition P is not in the V_e+ region nor even at $V_e = 0$. The criterion for determination of whether the emitter is biased forward or reverse is the polarity of emitter voltage with respect to the base.

Fig. 11-3. The V_e-I_e curve in region I, before any switching action takes place. The diode characteristic shown represents an approximation to linearity.

When the emitter is positive with respect to the base,[5] and a forward current of 50 μa or more flows, transistor action may be initiated. From Fig. 11-2 it will be observed that the collector current, flowing through the added base resistance R_b', biases the emitter positive with respect to the base. Thus the measured emitter voltage, which is the ordinate in Fig. 11-3, may be negative, and yet the emitter is *de facto* biased in the forward direction sufficiently to permit transistor action to take place.

Region I corresponds to the switching transistor OFF condition, when the emitter diode is biased in the reverse direction. It is desirable for the emitter-diode resistance to be as high as possible to reduce loading effects. When the transistor is in the OFF condition, the collector current is I_{co}. For switching applications, transistors with low I_{co} are desirable to limit the I^2R loss. A low value of I_{co} tends to make the ON and OFF conditions more readily distinguishable. A typical value of emitter-diode reverse resistance is 100 kilohms and for the collector diode, 20,000 ohms.

The reader acquainted with V–I curves for diodes will recognize that the straight-line relationship (see Fig. 11-3), particularly at low current values, is only an approximation. Germanium diodes exhibit a nonlinear decrease of resistance in the neighborhood of $V = 0$. This points up a further desideratum for the emitter diode: a high order of linearity for low current values in the reverse direction, at least near the turnover point P. The penalty for marked deviations from true linearity is unreliable or ambiguous switching, where the start of the next portion of the V-I characteristic, region II, cannot be predicted with certainty. This rounding off of the transition point, as well as a poorly shaped pulse, may lead to jitter.

155. TYPICAL VALUES IN REGION I

In Table 11-1 are shown the values of the parameters used to characterize point contact transistors when operating in region I:

TABLE 11-1*

r_e	100	For this region, r_e becomes the reverse resistance of the emitter diode
r_b	0.12	This parameter is very nearly independent of the point of operation
r_c	25	See Note 1 below
r_m	0	See Note 2 below
α'	0	See Note 2 below
R'_e	2	This is the added series load resistance of the emitter (see Fig. 11-2)
R'_b	10	Added base resistance to bring operating point into negative-resistance region
R_L	2	Compare the typical value of 20 kilohms for amplifier application, Table 8-1. Note from Fig. 11-1 how small values of R_L ensure positive switching action
R_g	0.5	

* All resistances in kilohms.

Note 1. When the transistor is first assembled, the collector diode may have a reverse resistance of the same order of magnitude as that of the emitter. To make a satisfactory transistor, however, experience has shown that the collector point must be formed, *i.e.*, pulsed with a relatively high current for a short interval, using a specified polarity (point $-$, base $+$). In this process, the collector diode resistance may drop by $\frac{1}{2}$ or more. When the device is operating as a transistor, holes injected at the emitter modify the collector resistance, and hence for $I_e = 0$, *i.e.*, no hole injection, the collector-diode resistance is somewhat higher than r_c of Table 8-1.

Note 2. Since there is no hole injection in region I, there is no transistor action and therefore no current gain. Since $\alpha = r_m/r_c$ has no significance in this region, r_m similarly has none.

If we now put

$$R_b = R_b' + r_b \tag{11-2}$$
$$R_e = R_e' + r_e \tag{11-3}$$

the expression for the input resistance R_i, Eq. (11-1), becomes

$$R_i = R_e + R_b - \frac{R_b(R_b + r_m)}{R_L + R_b + r_c} \tag{11-4}$$

and using the values of Table 11-1

$$R_i = 109 \text{ kilohms}$$

indicating that in the no-transistor-action region, region I, the input resistance is of the order of the emitter-diode reverse resistance.

It is of interest to observe the output resistance, as seen by R_L, under these conditions:

$$R_o = r_c + R_b - \frac{R_b(R_b + r_m)}{R_g + R_e + R_b}$$
$$= 34 \text{ kilohms} \tag{11-5}$$

156. SWITCHING ACTION—REGION II

Let it be assumed that the quiescent operating point is at A, Fig. 11-3. Since further switching action is to occur in the right-hand portion of Fig. 11-3, we infer that a positive pulse will be required to bring the circuit into region II.

When the initiating pulse brings the operating point far enough over to the right so that the emitter can inject holes into the bulk material, transistor action is instituted, and the operating values are those of Table 8-1, except that $R_L = 2$ kilohms, as noted in Table 11-1. Equations (11-2) and (11-3) also apply since we are still using the circuit of Fig. (11-2). Using the typical values of Table 8-1

$$R_i = -4,600 \text{ ohms}$$

The negative input resistance in region II is shown in Fig. 11-4. For subsequent applications we shall also need R_o, the output resistance:

$$R_o = -10,700 \text{ ohms}$$

In order to facilitate the analysis near the turnover point P, the encircled region of Fig. 11-4 is redrawn in Fig. 11-5 to a much larger scale.

In a typical transistor for which measurements were made, the turnover point was very nearly at $V_e = -8$ volts for the parameter values shown in Table 11-1. A pulse amplitude of 1.0 volt is used for illustrative purposes.

Consider the action in the input circuit after turnover point P, bearing in mind that R_i, the input circuit resistance, is negative in this region and the discussion regarding instability and negative resistance. Note that the load line intersects at point A in region I, $R'_e = 2$ kilohms and represents a stable operating point since R_i is positive in

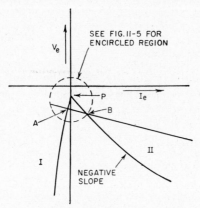

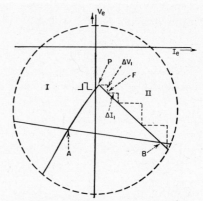

Fig. 11-4. The V_e-I_e curve in regions I and II. Note the negative slope of the curve in region II, indicating negative resistance: $-R_i = -V_e/I_e$. Line **AB** represents the load line corresponding to R'_e (see Fig. 11-2).

Fig. 11-5. Magnified portion of characteristic encircled in Fig. 11-4. Note how an increase in I_e causes V_c to increase (in magnitude) because of negative resistance, in spite of the increased drops in the circuit resistors (see Fig. 11-6). The input pulse will trigger the circuit to the second stable point shown at C in Fig. 11-7.

this region; in region II, the point of intersection is B, a nonstable point since R_i is negative.

The input pulse shifts the instantaneous operating point from A to B along APB. After point P has been reached, transistor action commences, and I_e goes positive. By observing the direction of I_e in region II as indicated in Fig. 11-2, it can be seen that, once transistor action has started, all current is supplied by the collector battery E_c. Note that the polarity of E_e makes the emitter negative with respect to ground. In Fig. 11-6A is shown the equivalent circuit seen by the battery E_c in region II, and note that R_o is negative, as shown above. R' represents the transistor internal resistance from emitter to collector. E'_e is the potential at point A in Fig. 11-2, and represents the net potential at the negative terminal of R_s, so that the internal resistance of E'_e is zero. Note that V_e, the ordinate in Fig. 11-5, is the measured potential from point E of Fig. 11-6A to ground and that I_e, the abscissa in Fig. 11-5, flows through R'_e, the series load in the emitter circuit. While the pulse lasts, some of the current through R'_e is needed to charge the condenser C_i, Fig. 11-2, but when the pulse is past, the dc paths are indicated in Fig. 11-2, and the circuit is then equivalent to that in Fig. 11-6A in so far as the collector battery is concerned. Note that $-R_o$ includes the transistor base resistance, plus the added series resistance R'_b.

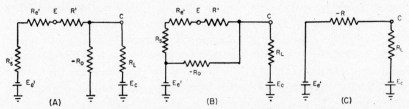

Fig. 11-6A. The equivalent circuit in region II as seen by the load and E_c.

Fig. 11-6B. Since E'_e as defined has zero internal resistance, $-R_o$ may be considered connected as shown, and the circuit is equivalent to Fig. 11-6A.

Fig. 11-6C. Combining the parallel resistances in Fig. 11-6B, the resultant as seen by R_L and E_c is given in Fig. 11-6C. Note $R' + R'_e + R_s > R_o$ to get equivalent negative resistance of parallel circuit in Fig. 11-6B.

Figure 11-6A is redrawn in Fig. 11-6B, and two principal effects must be observed:

1. E'_e has zero internal resistance by definition, and therefore the return of R_o may be made as shown without error.

2. The current through R_o is reversed with respect to the current in R'_e and R'. $I = V/-R$. Therefore, the current in R'_e is increased by the presence of R_o when it is negative. When R_o is paralleled with R'_e and R', the circuit which is equivalent to Fig. 11-6B is shown in Fig. 11-6C and the circuit as seen by the collector battery consists of R_L in series with an equivalent negative resistance R. The current in this loop is

$$I = \frac{E_c}{(R_L - R)} \tag{11-6}$$

V_e is the voltage from point E of Fig. 11-6B to ground. When I_1 has been made to increase by virtue of the pulse applied, the voltage at point E would normally drop, because of the drop in R'. But, because R_o is negative, the voltage at point C, Fig. 11-6C, will rise (in the negative direction), because

$$V_c = (-R)I \tag{11-7}$$

Clearly, if V_c increases, V_e will also increase. Hence, the effect of the negative resistance is to increase the loop current I and, at the same time, *decrease* the drops so that V_e increases.   This is represented by point F in Fig. 11-5.   When V_c (and V_e) increases, the potential acting in the loop of Fig. 11-6C increases, and I increases again, but this time without benefit of the outside pulse.   Thus the increase in current in the negative-resistance region causes an increase in voltage V_e, which in turn causes a further increase in current, and so on.

The initial action, *viz.*, the increase of current into the transistor-action region II, sets into motion a sequence: the increase in V_e, which in turn increases I_e, which further enhances the original action or current increase, and so on.   As discussed under the section on unstable equilibrium, Sec. 151, this fulfills the requirement for an unstable circuit condition, and the system rapidly traverses this region to land at the next suitable equilibrium point which is stable.   The action is sometimes compared to an avalanche, and the emitter current increases sharply and rapidly until forces come into play which oppose the avalanche.

The opposing effects are:

1. Decrease of α
2. Emitter current saturation (with no further increase in V_e)

157. SWITCHING ACTION—REGION III

When I_e becomes very large, the transistor operating point is such that the parameter values given in Tables 8-1 and 11-1 are no longer applicable.   The negative resistance of region II exists only if α is greater than 1, and this is why junction units, without special arrangements, will not switch (see Fig. 11-1).   When I_e becomes high, $r_m/r_c \cong 0.1$.   The effect on the remaining parameters may be seen by examination of Table 11-2.

TABLE 11-2

r_e	100	This is a function of the emitter-diode resistance, and in region III the emitter is biased forward
r_b	120	See Table 11-1
r_c	1,000	With I_e very large, the holes available to decrease the resistance of the CB path bring the effective collector-diode resistance to a low value. Note that V_c is constant
r_m	100	With I_e high, the control effect of small changes in I_e is negligible, α is small, and therefore r_{21}

Other parameters have the same values as those given in Table 11-1.

With the values of parameters as given in Table 11-2, the input resistance is no longer negative:

$$R_i = r_e + R_b - \frac{R_b(R_b + r_m)}{R_L + R_b + r_c}$$

$$R_i = 2 \text{ kilohms} \qquad (11\text{-}8)$$

The operating point goes briefly through a point G (see Fig. 11-7) of zero resistance and settles at the new equilibrium point C. The reason why the system settles down at point C is that, for the value of positive input (and output) resistance at C, current I_{e_c} flows when V_e is given by V_{e_c} as in any dc circuit. Note how R'_e is in series with the circuit where emitter current flows and therefore determines the operating point C. Here the emitter current is high, of the order of
several milliamperes, and the input
resistance relatively low, of the
order of 2 kilohms as compared
with 109 kilohms for region I.

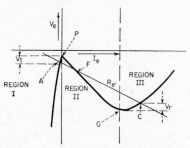

158. REVERSE PROCESS—ON TO OFF

When at point C, a negative trigger such as V_r in Fig. 11-7 brings
the operating point once more to a
negative-resistance region. When
I_e decreases, V_e decreases, Eqs.
(11-6) and (11-7), and the decrease
in V_e still further lowers I_e so that
the action is cumulative and ava-
lanches to the nearest equilibrium

Fig. 11-7. The V_e-I_e characteristic in regions I, II, and III. The emitter current and voltage vary along the N-shaped curve, with stable points at A and C. Point F is unstable. V_t is the positive trigger voltage amplitude needed to trigger from A to C; V_r is the negative trigger voltage needed to trigger from point C back to A.

point, point A, and a switching cycle is complete. In general, the angle at point P is much more acute than that at point G. The effect is that triggering from point C is not so well controllable as from point A.

159. ONE-SHOT SWITCHING

Where one-shot, or monostable, switching is desired, as opposed to "counter"-type switching, the circuit may be made to return to the starting point by the use of a condenser across the emitter. As is well known, a condenser will not change its state of charge instantaneously. When the sudden change of V_e occurs in the negative-
resistance region, the condenser presents a short-circuit load line, *i.e.*, load line of zero slope in Fig. 11-8. The condenser therefore holds the terminal voltage constant, while a large value of I_e flows to charge the condenser. At point H, I_e is so large that transistor action is poor,

and we are in region III. It is significant that point H, Fig. 11-8, is reached along the straight line PH. While the transistor is internally changing to operating point H, values of V_e corresponding to points $PGCH$ are not observed, of course, because of the capacitor C, so that

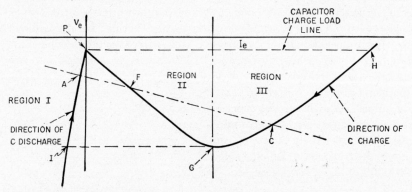

Fig. 11-8. Emitter characteristic for the monostable operation of the circuit in Fig. 11-9. The condenser C charges from P to H and to G, then discharges from point I back to the starting point A.   Point C has limited significance now because V_e is measured right across condenser C. I_e may become quite high—compare Fig. 11-7—because C acts as a short circuit until it begins to charge at point H.

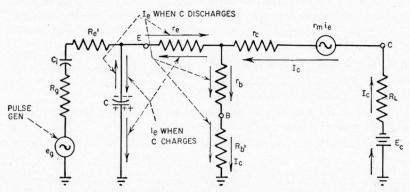

Fig. 11-9. Basic circuit for one-shot transistor action, where a trigger pulse causes the operating point to shift from point A of Fig. 11-8 to point H and back to region I, point A, without a second triggering pulse.   Note the charge and discharge paths.

this curve must be considered merely auxiliary to the discussion, and not a realizable path for the circuit of Fig. 11-9. The current I_e is supplied by the collector battery, as before, and at point H it is as high as the transistor parameters will permit it to rise. This action is extremely rapid, and no appreciable charging of the condenser occurs until region HG, where the voltage across C, which is V_e, rises as the condenser charges through r_e and r_c.   When the point G is reached, we are again in a negative-resistance region. The transistor moves rapidly through this region, but V_e cannot follow, and again voltage inertia causes the V_e-I_e curve to go along a horizontal line GI until the current is negative and small, and determined by the series resistance of the emitter diode.

The reader should note the charge and discharge paths indicated in Fig. 11-9, because these determine the time constants and therefore the pulse width. The flat top of the pulse begins when C begins charging, at H, and it can be seen that the width of the pulse is a function of r_c and R_L.

Note that the circuit started at point A, went through a complete cycle, and went back to A, with the application of a single pulse.   This is typical of the monostable type of switching-circuit operation.

160. REFINEMENTS ON BASIC SWITCHING CIRCUITS

One of the difficulties presently encountered in transistor switching circuits is the interchangeability of units. Because present manufacturing techniques yield transistors whose parameter values may differ by as much as 20 per cent, it can be seen that operating points will differ, and with them the magnitude of the triggering pulse required. This means that an undesirably large pulse must be used; otherwise, when units are interchanged, the reliability of switching is endangered. In switching, reliability is paramount. To improve reliability in switching, stabilization of operating points is achievable by suitable circuit techniques. Added series resistance, separate bias supplies, and a biased diode in the base lead have been successfully used to effect a marked stabilization of operating points and to obtain a high order of interchangeability in switching transistors.[6,7]

While such circuit information as switching points, magnitudes of V_e and I_e involved, required amplitude of trigger pulse, etc., may be obtained from V_e-I_e characteristic, to predict waveform it is necessary to use the I_c-I_e curve[8] in addition.

It is clear that since the discharge path of the condenser is through r_e and this resistance is high in region I (see Fig. 11-9) the time constant is high, and the repetition rate is reduced.   To circumvent the high emitter path resistance during the interval when the operating point moves from point I to A of Fig. 11-8, a diode may be used across the emitter circuit, so placed that when V_e is greater than a preassigned (negative) value the diode presents a low impedance path.   In this way the repetition rate can be noticeably increased.

The width of the pulse obtained at the output has already been shown to depend on the time involved in going from point H to G. It turns out that it is almost equally sensitive to changes in α and temperature (r_c decreases with T).[9] Closest control of this width is obtained if a transmission line is used.[8]

If multivibrator (astable) action is desired, inductance or capacity may be used to get a free running action. The inductance or capacity charge or discharge sets up the initiating trigger pulse.[10]

Using the grounded-base connection, either a positive trigger may be used in the emitter, or to achieve the equivalent result, a negative trigger pulse may be used in the base.

Where the triggering source is seriously disturbed by the negative-resistance input of the transistor, an isolating diode may be placed in series. The diode is so biased that, after passing the triggering pulse in the low-resistance direction, the added current, as the input resistance turns negative, reverses the diode and it exhibits a high resistance.

161. HOLE-STORAGE EFFECTS

An interesting and important phenomenon connected with transistors for switching applications is that of hole storage. In region II (see Fig. 11-8) holes are injected and sent on their way to the collector. After point H, the unit should switch back rapidly and return to the OFF condition, either because of an applied trigger or because of the condenser action described. Unfortunately the desired effect is not always observed. It seems that holes are trapped[11] or stored during regions II and III and keep moving to the collector after point H has been passed in time, keeping the circuit ON for a few microseconds.[12] Such an effect can seriously disturb normal circuit operation and acts to decrease the maximum possible switching rate.

Also, if accurately controlled switching times are essential, the triggering pulse must extend into the turnoff time, since the storage effects are at present neither too well understood nor predictable. Since turnoff time for different types may vary between 1 and 20 μsec, this phenomenon is important and is receiving considerable study. For low-frequency applications, however, it does not introduce any special problems.

162. ADVANTAGES OF TRANSISTORS FOR SWITCHING

For switching application where noise, variations of characteristics with temperature or environment, and power-handling capacity are relatively unimportant, transistors seem to find their natural golden opportunity. To provide "yes" or "no" information and pulse shapes carrying intelligence rather than power, in a small, compact package requiring a very minimum of power, weight, and size, it is difficult at this time to conceive of a device more admirably suited to its purpose than the transistor. There are indications that many switching applications may ultimately be transistorized—the entire fields of counters, computers, relaxation oscillators of all kinds, and data transmission. The WE type 1698 (2N21) and its counterparts as presently produced by many manufacturers have already been demonstrated in a wide variety of switching applications.

In addition to low-power ON-OFF applications, switching transistors have been used as delay lines and to produce pulses up to 1 amp, using standard units at a low-duty cycle.[8] Using such high current pulses, however, the top of the pulse will usually not be flat-topped, because of the low value of r_c at the high current levels. Present indications are that the possible uses of transistors in switching applications are almost limitless.

163. SUMMARY

1. Point contact transistors may be made to exhibit a negative resistance characteristic and perform switching operations by addition of resistance in series with the base.

2. Large-signal theory for transistors has not yet been developed to a completely satisfactory stage. Nevertheless, results in good agreement with theory are obtained by use of small-signal theory and the three-region analysis.

3. Transistors may be used as one-shot or free-running multivibrators by use of L or C, or both, in the circuit. For more precise control, a transmission line may be used.

4. Switching represents an ideal application of transistors because the requirements of low power, ON OFF, small size, and light weight are ideally met by these semiconductor devices. Transistors may be used in circuits which are stabilized to minimize sensitivity to circuit and parameter variations.

REFERENCES

1. The Transistor, Selected Reference Material on Characteristics and Applications, Contr. DA36-039 sc-5589 (Task 3), p. 287, prepared by Bell Telephone Laboratories for Western Electric Co., Inc., New York, 1951.

2. Linvill, J. G.: Transistor Negative-Impedance Converters, *Proc. IRE*, Vol. 41, pp. 725–729, June, 1953.

3. Moll, J. L., and J. J. Ebers: Theory of Junction Transistors for Switching, presented before IRE-AIEE Transistor Research Conference, Pennsylvania State College, 1953.   To be published.

4. Adler, R. B.: A Large Signal Equivalent Circuit for Transistor Static Characteristics, MIT, RLE Transistor Group Report T-8, Nov. 12, 1952.

5. Bardeen, J., and W. H. Brattain: The Transistor, A Semiconductor Triode, *Phys. Rev.*, Vol. 74, pp. 230–231, July 15, 1948.

6. Shea, R. F.: Transistor Operation, Stabilization of Operating Points, *Proc. IRE*, Vol. 40, pp. 1435–1437, November, 1952.

7. Trent, R. L.: Idealized Negative Resistance Characteristics of the Transistor, The Transistor, Selected Reference Material on Characteristics and Applications, Contr. DA36-039 sc-5589 (Task 3), p. 249ff., prepared by Bell Telephone Laboratories for Western Electric Co., Inc., New York, 1951.

8. Lo, A. W.: Transistor Trigger Circuits, *Proc. IRE*, Vol. 40, pp. 1531–1541, November, 1952.

9. Coblenz, A., and H. L. Owens: Variation of Transistor Parameters with with Temperature, *Proc. IRE*, Vol. 40, pp. 1472–1476, (see Fig. 11, p. 1475) November, 1952.

10. Anderson, A. E.: Transistors in Switching Circuits, *Proc. IRE*, Vol. 40, pp. 1541–1558, November, 1952; and The Transistor, Selected Reference Material on Characteristics and Applications, Contr. DA36-039 sc-5589 (Task 3), p. 429ff., prepared by Bell Telephone Laboratories for Western Electric Co., Inc., New York, 1951.

11. Michaels, S. E., and L. A. Meacham: Observations of the Rapid Withdrawals of Stored Holes from Germanium Transistors and Varistors, *Phys. Rev.*, Vol. 78, pp. 175–176, Apr. 15, 1950.

12. Waltz, M. C.: On Some Transients in the Pulse Response of Point Contact Germanium Diodes, *Proc. IRE*, Vol. 40, pp. 1483–1487, November, 1952.

12 CASCADING OF TRANSISTORS

While transistors are capable of high voltage, current, and power gains, particularly in selected methods of connection, in many applications the over-all gain requirements cannot be met by a single stage. The transistor is adaptable to cascade applications where its resistive character permits economies in size, weight, power, and additional component requirements. In this chapter, small-signal theory will be applied to the cascading of transistors with direct and resistance coupling.

164. POSSIBLE CASCADED ARRANGEMENTS

Using the three basic circuit connections, grounded base (GB), grounded emitter (GE), and grounded collector (GC), the theoretically possible cascading arrangements are as shown in Table 12-1.

TABLE 12-1

GB↑ to ↓GB*	GE↑ to ↓GB**	GC↓ to ↓GB*
GB↑ to ↑GE*	GE↑ to ↑GE*	GC↓ to ↑GE*
GB↑ to ↑GC*	GE↑ to ↑GC	GC↓ to ↑GC**

Of these possible arrangements, not all are practicable circuit-wise. The arrangements marked with an asterisk may cause difficulty because of the inherent instability of one or both of the connections involved for point contact units. While these can at times be made stable by suitable resistance elements,[1] usually in series with r_e, the complexity of the circuit work necessary to stabilize the arrangement plus the loss in gain due to the series element added usually outweigh other advantages.

The circuit arrangements indicated by the double asterisk represent combinations where a serious impedance mismatch occurs. An arrow pointing upward following a connection, viz., GB↑ indicates that

165

the output impedance is high, usually greater than 1,000 ohms. An arrow pointing downward preceding, *viz.*, ↓GB, means that the input resistance is usually low, below 1,000 ohms. With this convention, arrows pointing in the same direction indicate the existence of an impedance match, while oppositely pointed arrows show a mismatch. On the basis of an impedance mismatch, four arrangements may be considered to have, potentially, limited application.

165. GB TO GB CONNECTION

Even though the GB to GB arrangement involves a mismatch and was apparently excluded from those with important potential applications by the preceding analysis, it is convenient for presentation of the

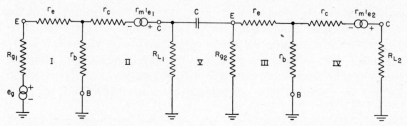

Fig. 12-1. Equivalent circuit diagram of the cascaded GB to GB transistor connection. Only basic ac paths are shown.

basic principles involved. A schematic diagram is shown in Fig. 12-1.

By a careful analysis of the details of loop V, one can replace the effect of this loop by a single resistance. Using typical values, collector current is of the order of 1 ma for junction units and 2.5 ma for point contact units. We shall use 1.75 ma for computational purposes. The emitter current is very nearly 1 ma for both types. In the transistor field a "typical" voltage supply, analogous to the well-recognized 250- or 300-volt supply in the vacuum-tube industry, has not yet been established. But it seems reasonable that a direct rectification of line voltage will be simplest, and for analytical purposes a 100-volt dc supply will be assumed. With these assumptions, a typical voltage-dropping resistor for collector circuits may be 60 kilohms and for the emitter circuit, 100 kilohms. A coupling condenser as high as 1 mf may be used since present-day miniature condensers with 100-volt ratings have satisfactorily low stray capacitances. The reactance of a 1-mf condenser at the test frequency, 270 cps, is approximately 600 ohms. The ac voltage division in the input circuit is very satisfactory, and loop V can be replaced by a single resistor of 40 kilohms. The resultant circuit is shown in Fig. 12-2.

Note that all dc supplies are omitted as only the ac circuits are under consideration. The current directions assumed are arbitrary. Identical stages are assumed because formulas become unduly cumbersome if nonidentical transistors are used. The rules for writing the Kirchhoff equations[2] outlined in Chap. 8 will be followed, and expressions will be obtained for the loop currents i_1 through i_4, and i_4', the loop IV current when the generator e_g is in series with R_{L_2}. As we shall show

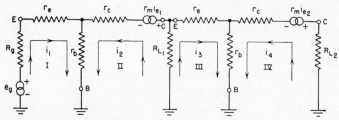

Fig. 12-2. The effect of loop V, Fig. 12-1, is replaced in this equivalent circuit by R_{L_1}. As proved in the text, this approximation introduces little error.

by this illustrative analysis, to find the four important circuit characteristics, i.e., R_i, R_o, VG, and PG, we need not solve for all these currents. However, to illustrate the theorems below, it will be necessary to solve for all four currents and perform a stage-by-stage analysis. It will also be necessary to test the circuit for stability since gain computations have limited meaning if the circuit breaks into oscillation.

166. INPUT RESISTANCE FOR GB TO GB CONNECTION

The loop equations are:

$$(R_g + r_e + r_b)i_1 + r_b i_2 \quad + 0 \qquad\qquad + 0 \quad = e_g \qquad (12\text{-}1)$$
$$(r_b + r_m)i_1 + (R_{L_1} + r_b + r_c)i_2 + R_{L_1}i_3 + 0 \quad = 0 \qquad (12\text{-}2)$$
$$0 + R_{L_1}i_2 + (R_{L_1} + r_e + r_b)i_3 \quad + r_b i_4 = 0 \qquad (12\text{-}3)$$
$$0 + 0 \quad + (r_b + r_m)i_3 \quad + (R_{L_2}$$
$$+ r_b + r_c)i_4 = 0 \qquad (12\text{-}4)$$

To find i_4', the equations are:

$$(R_g + r_e + r_b)i_1 + r_b i_2 \qquad\qquad + 0 \quad + 0 \quad = 0 \qquad (12\text{-}5)$$
$$(r_b + r_m)i_1 + (R_{L_1} + r_b + r_c)i_2 + R_{L_1}i_3 + 0 \quad = 0 \qquad (12\text{-}6)$$
$$0 + R_{L_1}i_2 \qquad\qquad + (R_{L_1} + r_e$$
$$+ r_b)i_3 + r_b i_4 = 0 \qquad (12\text{-}7)$$
$$0 + 0 \qquad\qquad + (r_b + r_m)i_3 + (R_{L_2}$$
$$+ r_b + r_c)i_4 = e_g \qquad (12\text{-}8)$$

$$R_i = r_e + r_b$$
$$- \frac{r_b(r_b + r_m)(R_{L_1} + r_e + r_b)(R_{L_2} + r_b + r_c) - (r_b + r_m)^2 r_b^2}{\{[R_{L_1}(r_e + r_b) + (r_b + r_c)(R_{L_1} + r_e + r_b)](R_{L_2} + r_b + r_c) - (R_{L_1} + r_b + r_c)(r_b + r_m)r_b\}} \quad (12\text{-}9)$$

167. SIMPLER FORMULA FOR R_i—GB TO GB

While Eq. (12-9) seems very cumbersome, it turns out fortunately that it is closely approximated by a familiar and very brief form. Using the values in Table 8-1, it will be found that the term $(r_b + r_m)^2 r_b^2$ is small compared to the other term in the numerator. It will also be found that the term $R_{L_1}(r_e + r_b)(R_{L_2} + r_b + r_c)$ very nearly cancels the term $(R_{L_1} + r_b + r_c)(r_b + r_m)r_b$ for a very large range of load-resistance values, and in all cases this difference is negligible compared with the major term of the denominator: $(R_{L_2} + r_b + r_c)(r_b + r_c)(R_{L_1} + r_e + r_b)$. With these simplifications, one observes that $(R_{L_1} + r_e + r_b)(R_{L_2} + r_b + r_c)$ very conveniently cancels in the numerator and denominator so that, using the definition for α_{ce}, we obtain:

$$R_i = r_e + r_b(1 - \alpha_{ce}) \quad (12\text{-}10)$$

Some interesting and useful information may be obtained by studying this result:

1. Equation (12-10) will be recognized[3] as the expression for the input resistance of the grounded-base transistor using a single stage, when $R_L = 0$. One observes that in essence the second stage, with its input resistance of the order of 100 ohms, acts like a virtual short circuit across the output resistance (10 kilohms for point contact and 0.5 megohms for junction)[4] of the first stage.

2. Typical values obtained directly from Eq. (12-10) are: point contact, -6 ohms; junction units, 45 ohms. The negative input resistance for point contact units indicates that in general, with this particular cascaded arrangement, parasitic oscillations may be expected.

3. Equation (12-10) should be regarded as a close approximation. Using the full expression in Eq. (12-9), we obtain: point contact, -5.2 ohms, junction, 44.6 ohms, using $R_{L_1} = 40$ kilohms. This is due to the effectiveness of the input impedance of the second stage in acting as a virtual short on the output of the first stage, particularly in the case of junction units.

4. Note that the input impedance, Eq. (12-10), is independent of R_{L_1}. We shall have an important application to make of this fact in what follows.

5. The negative resistance in the case of point contact units and the very low input impedance of the cascaded stages show why the GB to GB cascaded arrangement is not a particularly satisfactory one. Clearly, a pair of such cascaded transistors will present a load impedance to another stage even less than the input impedance of a single stage.

6. From Eq. (12-10) and item 4 above, however, we may infer theorem I:

Theorem I. The load impedance for the first stage is the input impedance of the second stage. Symbolically,

$$R_{L_1} = R_{i_{II}} \qquad (12\text{-}11)$$

To prove this theorem, we may reason that stage I, in Fig. 12-2, has for its load impedance R_{L_1} in parallel with the input impedance of the second stage.

R_{L_1} in parallel with the input impedance of second stage is:

$$\frac{R_{L_1} \left\{ r_e + r_b - \left[\dfrac{r_b(r_b + r_m)}{R_{L_2} + r_b + r_c} \right] \right\}}{R_{L_1} + r_e + r_b - \left[\dfrac{r_b(r_b + r_m)}{R_{L_2} + r_b + r_c} \right]} \qquad (12\text{-}12)$$

Using this expression to replace R_L in the equation for the input resistance of the first stage, it is easily verified by a direct substitution that Eq. (12-9) is obtained, thus proving the theorem. Because R_{L_1} can usually be made much higher than the input impedance of the second stage, however, the paralleling effect of R_{L_1} is unimportant and the effective load resistance is the input impedance of the second stage.

168. FURTHER SIMPLIFICATIONS

Equation (12-10) is independent of R_{L_1}, and in consequence Fig. 12-2 may be further simplified, in so far as the input resistance is concerned, into Fig. 12-3 where R_{L_1} is omitted entirely, *i.e.*, assumed high compared to the input impedance of stage II.

Here, $i_{e_1} = i_1$, $i_{e_2} = -i_2$, and the equations are:

$$(R_g + r_e + r_b)i_1 + r_b i_2 \qquad\qquad + 0 \qquad\qquad\quad = e_g \qquad (12\text{-}13)$$
$$(r_b + r_m)i_1 \qquad + (2r_b + r_e + r_c)i_2 - r_b i_3 \qquad\qquad = 0 \qquad (12\text{-}14)$$
$$0 - (r_b + r_m)i_2 \qquad\quad + (R_L + r_c + r_b)i_3 = 0 \qquad (12\text{-}15)$$

Solving for R_i, we now find:

$$R_i = r_e + r_b - \frac{r_b(r_b + r_m)(R_L + r_c + r_b)}{(2r_b + r_e + r_c)(R_L + r_c + r_b) - r_b(r_b + r_m)} \qquad (12\text{-}16)$$

If we divide numerator and denominator in Eq. (12-9) by R_{L_1}, and then allow R_{L_1} to become very large, Eq. (12-6) is obtained.

Using numerical values, $r_b(r_b + r_m)$ is negligible compared to the other term in the denominator of Eq. (12-16), and $2r_b + r_e$ can be neglected compared to r_c, leading again to Eq. (12-10). Finally, to illustrate the fact that Eq. (12-16) is capable of giving values of input

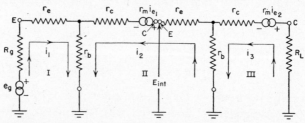

Fig. 12-3. Where R_{L_1} is large compared to R_o or R_{i_1} its effect can be neglected to produce the simplified equivalent diagram shown. No important errors are introduced by these approximations. This is the GB to GB arrangement.

resistance negligibly different from Eq. (12-9), note the following tabulation:

	Eq. (12-10)	Eq. (12-16)	Eq. (12-9)
Point contact............	-6	-6	-5.2
Junction................	45	45	44.6

Figure 12-3, at least in so far as the input resistance is concerned, adequately describes the GB to GB cascade, and the input resistance is given by Eq. (12-10) or, if desired, Eq. (12-16). The only important assumption involved in both Figs. 12-2 and 12-3 is that C, the coupling capacitor, at the lowest operating frequency, has an impedance negligible compared to the input resistance of the grounded-base stage. Admittedly this is not always true. With modern small-size high-capacity condensers, the approximation can usually be made close enough without the very cumbersome analysis associated with Fig. 12-1, where five lengthy simultaneous equations must be solved. Certainly for the input resistance, we have already shown that Eq. (12-10) is valid unless the reactance of the coupling condenser is quite large at the operating frequency.

169. OUTPUT RESISTANCE—GB TO GB

The approximation which led from Fig. 12-1 to Fig. 12-2 is still valid for the output resistance, but it remains to be established that the further simplification which led to Fig. 12-3 is valid for the output resistance also. From Eqs. (12-5) to (12-8), it is found that

$$R_o = r_b + r_c - \frac{r_b(r_b+r_m)[(R_g+r_e+r_b)(R_{L_1}+r_b+r_c)-r_b(r_b+r_m)]}{\{(R_g+r_e+r_b)[R_{L_1}(r_e+r_b)+(r_b+r_c)(R_{L_1}+r_e+r_b)]-r_b(r_b+r_m)(R_{L_1}+r_e+r_b)\}} \quad (12\text{-}17)$$

When numbers from Table 8-1 are substituted in Eq. (12-17) to obtain typical values, it becomes apparent that certain approximations can be made to simplify the formula. It will be found that $R_{L_1}(r_e + r_b)$ is negligible compared to $(r_b + r_c)(R_{L_1} + r_e + r_b)$; also, as has been noted previously, $r_m \gg r_b$, $r_c \gg r_b$ and R_{L_1} is normally much higher than $r_e + r_b$ unless very low-voltage supplies are used. Equation (12-17) then becomes:

$$R_o \cong r_c - \frac{r_b r_m[(R_g + r_e + r_b)(R_{L_1} + r_c) - r_b r_m]}{[(R_g + r_e + r_b)r_c - r_b r_m]R_{L_1}}$$

$$\cong r_c - \frac{r_b r_m}{R_{L_1}} - \frac{(R_g + r_e + r_b)r_b r_m}{(R_g + r_e + r_b)r_c - r_b r_m} \quad (12\text{-}18)$$

R_o obtained from:

	Eq. (12-17)	Eq. (12-18) for $R_{L_1} = 40$ kilohms
Point contact	14.6 kilohms	14.5 kilohms
Junction	0.987 megohms	0.987 megohms

As the table shows, Eq. (12-18) is an excellent approximation to Eq. (12-17) for the determination of the output resistance of the GB to GB cascaded arrangement. But study of Eq. (12-18) reveals further that R_o is not critically dependent on R_{L_1}, a conclusion reached also in connection with the input resistance.

170. $R_{g_{II}} = R_{o_I}$

Resistance-wise, what does stage II "see" when fed by stage I, according to Fig. 12-2? Stage II "sees" the resistance of the generator feeding it to be R_{L_1} in parallel with the output resistance of stage I. To check this statement, if the output-resistance formula given in Chap. 10 for the grounded-base connection is put in parallel with R_{L_1}, and the resulting expression used instead of R_g in the equation for R_o of the output stage, the result is Eq. (12-17) identically. This suggests that rather than go through the derivation of Eq. (12-17), by application of Kirchhoff's law, one may, if desired, use the expression for the output resistance of the first stage, parallel this with R_{L_1}, and then use the resulting resistance as R_g in obtaining the output resistance of stage II. The numerical values obtained are not given in the table because they are identical with the Eq. (12-17) column.

When typical values are substituted in Eq. (12-18), it will be found that, for the point contact transistor, the term involving R_{L_1} is negligible compared to the third term. Hence, if we made R_{L_1} infinite, the

accuracy of the result would not be appreciably affected.   For the
junction unit since r_c is 1 megohm, the effect of the entire expression to
the right of r_c is very small.   In electronics parlance, except for precision metering, 1 megohm and 0.987 megohm are considered inter-
changeable.   Hence, again, if R_{L_1} were made infinite when computing
the output resistance, the accuracy would not be affected appreciably.
One would not normally make R_{L_1} very small, say 500 ohms, because
this would imply that the output of the first stage is virtually shorted.
Accordingly, we infer that if R_{L_1} is reasonably high, over 20 kilohms,
its effect on the input and output resistance is negligible.   This fact
allows the important simplification afforded by Fig. 12-3 and Eqs.
(12-13) to (12-15) compared to Fig. 12-2 with Eqs. (12-5) to (12-8).

171. APPROXIMATION AND TYPICAL VALUES OF R_o

The output resistance of the grounded-base connection for junction
transistors is the highest of all the output resistances obtained (see
Table 10-1).   If the shunting effect of R_{L_1} for this case can be ignored,
it can be ignored for all the other cases.   We infer that the circuit of
Fig. 12-3 is adequate for all but the most precise computations in the
determination of input and output resistances.   Since it can be shown
that voltage and power gains are dependent on the input and output
resistances of transistors, we infer further that voltage and power gains
computed using Fig. 12-3 and Eqs. (12-13) to (12-15) will similarly
be sufficiently accurate for all normal electronics computations.
Parenthetically, it is felt that the present reproducibility and stability
of transistors does not warrant computations more precise than those
obtainable by these relatively excellent approximations.

Solving for R_o from Eqs. (12-13) to (12-15), we obtain

$$R_o = r_b + r_c - \frac{r_b(r_b + r_m)(R_g + r_b + r_e)}{(R_g + r_e + r_b)(2r_b + r_e + r_c) - r_b(r_b + r_m)} \qquad (12\text{-}19)$$

Making R_{L_1} large in Fig. 12-2 leads directly to Fig. 12-3, and the
same assumption in Eq. (12-17) must lead to Eq. (12-19).   If we divide
numerator and denominator in Eq. (12-17) by R_{L_1} and then let R_{L_1}
become very large, Eq. (12-19) is obtained.

By neglecting r_b compared to r_m or r_c

$$R_o \cong r_c - \frac{r_b r_m(R_g + r_b + r_e)}{(R_g + r_e + r_b)r_c - r_b r_m} \qquad (12\text{-}20)$$

Values obtained using Eq. (12-20) are:

        Point contact units............. 14,560 ohms
        Junction units................. 1 megohm

Note, finally, that Eq. (12-20) is obtainable directly from Eq. (12-18) if we let R_{L_1} become infinite.

Theorem II. We may now phrase theorem II. *The second-stage output resistance is obtained by using the output resistance of the first stage as the generator resistance of the second.*

172. VOLTAGE GAIN—FIRST STAGE

In order to establish the voltage-gain theorem to be proposed, the gain will be computed stage by stage.   In Fig. 12-3

$$E_{int} = -[r_b(i_2 - i_3) + r_e i_2]$$
$$= r_b i_3 - (r_b + r_e)i_2 \tag{12-21}$$

Using the values of i_2 and i_3 obtained by solving Eqs. (12-13) to (12-15) and noting that

$$VG_I = \frac{E_{int}}{e_g} \tag{12-22}$$

there is obtained

$$VG_I = \frac{(r_b + r_m)(r_e + r_b)(R_L + r_c + r_b) - r_b(r_b + r_m)^2}{[(R_L + r_b + r_c)(R_g + r_e + r_b)(2r_b + r_e + r_c)}$$
$$\qquad\qquad - (r_b + r_m)(R_L + R_g + 2r_b + r_e + r_c)r_b] \tag{12-23}$$

By applying theorem I, Eq. (12-23) is obtainable using the input resistance of stage II as R_L in the expression for the voltage gain of stage I, Eq. (12-24).   In general, for a grounded-base stage

$$VG = \frac{(r_b + r_m)R_L}{(R_g + r_b + r_e)(R_L + r_b + r_c) - r_b(r_b + r_m)} \tag{12-24}$$

and in this expression replace R_L by R_i, given by

$$R_i = r_b + r_e - \frac{r_b(r_b + r_m)}{R_L + r_b + r_c} \tag{12-25}$$

If R_L in Eq. (12-24) is replaced by Eq. (12-25), it will be found that Eq. (12-23) is obtained.   Typical values are:

$$
\begin{aligned}
\text{Point contact} &\ldots\ldots\ldots\ldots\ldots\ 0.7 \\
\text{Junction} &\ldots\ldots\ldots\ldots\ldots\ldots\ 0.156
\end{aligned}
$$

Comparing these values with 30 and 150, respectively, for the single-stage grounded-base transistor, it is seen that the gain of the first stage is necessarily small because of the low input impedance of the grounded-base stage.   This fact suggests once more why the grounded-base to grounded-base cascaded arrangement is not normally recommended.

173. VOLTAGE GAIN—SECOND STAGE

The gain of the second stage is given by

$$VG_{II} = \frac{-i_3 R_L}{E_{int}} \tag{12-26}$$

Using i_3 as obtained from Eqs. (12-13) to (12-15),

$$VG_{II} = \frac{-(r_b + r_m)R_L}{(0 + r_e + r_b)(R_L + r_b + r_c) - r_b(r_b + r_m)} \tag{12-27}$$

Typical values are:

$$
\begin{array}{ll}
\text{Point contact} \ldots \ldots \ldots \ldots & 133 \\
\text{Junction} \ldots \ldots \ldots \ldots \ldots & 990
\end{array}
$$

The significance of the zero in the denominator can be determined by comparing Eq. (12-27) with the standard expression for VG of a grounded-base stage, as given by Eq. (12-24). Note that if we set $R_g = 0$ in Eq. (12-24) the result is Eq. (12-27). This fact leads to the following theorem:

Theorem III. In computing the voltage gain of stage II in a cascaded arrangement, stage II may be considered to operate from a source of zero internal impedance, if when computing the gain of stage I it is assumed that its load resistance is the input resistance of stage II.

This theorem is an adaptation of the standard impedance-matching theorems of vacuum-tube cascading practice and illustrates that by using theorem I, we have already taken into account impedance-matching problems.[5] Thereafter, in computing the gain of the second stage, it may be considered to work from a generator of zero internal impedance. This theorem will be found to simplify and shorten materially the burden of computations in subsequent analyses of cascaded arrangements.

174. OVER-ALL VOLTAGE GAIN—GB TO GB

It is first necessary to verify that the product of the voltage gain in stage I, given by Eq. (12-23), and the voltage gain in stage II, given by Eq. (12-27), is the over-all gain. The over-all gain is given by

$$VG_o = \frac{-i_3 R_L}{e_g}$$

Using the value of i_3 from Eqs. (12-13) to (12-15), obtain

$$VG_o = \frac{(r_b + r_m)^2 R_L}{\begin{array}{l}[(R_g + r_e + r_b)(R_L + r_b + r_c)(2r_b + r_e + r_c) \\ \quad - r_b(r_b + r_m)(R_L + R_g + 2r_b + r_e + r_c)]\end{array}}$$

(12-28)

When Eq. (12-23) is multiplied by Eq. (12-27), the over-all voltage-gain expression in Eq. (12-28) is obtained.

By making the assumptions that $r_b \ll r_m$ or r_c, $r_e \ll r_c$ and $R_g \ll r_c$

$$VG_o \cong \frac{r_m^2 R_L}{(R_L + r_c)(R_g + r_e + r_b) - r_b r_m}$$

(12-29)

Typical values:

	Stage I	Stage II	Over-all	Remarks
Point contact	0.7	133	93	Unstable
Junction	0.156	990	155	Stable; low gain

Note that for the typical values, $VG_{\mathrm{I}} \times VG_{\mathrm{II}} = VG_o$.

175. CURRENT GAIN—GB TO GB

Using current values obtainable by solution of Eqs. (12-13) to (12-15), we find for the current gain

$$CG_o = \frac{-(r_b + r_m)^2}{(2r_b + r_e + r_c)(R_L + r_b + r_c) - r_b(r_b + r_m)}$$

(12-30)

$$CG_o \cong \frac{-r_m^2}{(R_L + r_c)r_c - r_b r_m}$$

(12-31)

Typical values:

	Stage I	Stage II	Over-all	Remarks
Point contact	−2.35	1	−2.35	Phase reversal
Junction	−0.96	0.872	−0.835	Phase reversal

Since the input resistance is negative for point contact units, unstable operation is indicated and the gain figure is not realizable without oscillation. If added resistance is used in series with r_e to make the input resistance positive, the gain falls sharply.

176. STAGE-BY-STAGE COMPUTATION OF POWER GAIN

The power gain may also be computed stage by stage. In addition to serving as a useful check on the computations, the stage-by-stage gain is useful for checking operating cascaded stages. Using theorem I, the power output of the first stage appears across the input resistance of the second. The analysis may be formulated as follows:

$$PG_o = \text{total power output of the two stages}$$
$$= \frac{i_3{}^2 R_L}{e_g{}^2/4R_g} \tag{12-32}$$

by definition.

$$PG_{\mathrm{I}} = \text{power gain of the first stage, by theorem I}$$
$$= \frac{i_2{}^2 R_{i_{\mathrm{II}}}}{e_g{}^2/4R_g} \tag{12-33}$$

and note how the load resistance of the standard power-gain formula has been replaced by the input resistance of stage II.

$$P_{i_{\mathrm{II}}} = \text{power input to stage II}$$
$$= \frac{e_g{}^2}{4R_g} \times PG_{\mathrm{I}} = \frac{e_g{}^2}{4R_g} \times \frac{i_2{}^2 R_{i_{\mathrm{II}}}}{e_g{}^2/4R_g} = i_2{}^2 R_{i_{\mathrm{II}}} \tag{12-34}$$
$$PG_{\mathrm{II}} = \text{power gain of stage II}$$
$$= \frac{i_3{}^2 R_L}{i_2{}^2 R_{i_{\mathrm{II}}}} \tag{12-35}$$

It is at once evident that

$$PG_{\mathrm{I}} \times PG_{\mathrm{II}} = PG_o \tag{12-36}$$

It can also be verified that if, in the expression for power gain of the grounded-base stage given below, R_L is replaced by the input impedance, Eq. (12-50), page 178, is obtained.

$$PG_{ce} = \frac{4R_L R_g (r_b + r_m)^2}{[(R_g + r_e + r_b)(R_L + r_b + r_c) - r_b(r_b + r_m)]^2} \tag{12-37}$$

177. GENERAL FORMS FOR POWER GAIN

It will be convenient to put Eqs. (12-33) and (12-35) into a slightly different form, both to render these equations more amenable to computation and to demonstrate theorem IV. Let us first put Eqs. (12-13) to (12-15) into a more general and briefer form as follows:

$$A_1 i_1 + B_1 i_2 + C_1 i_3 = e_g \tag{12-38}$$
$$A_2 i_1 + B_2 i_2 + C_2 i_3 = 0 \tag{12-39}$$
$$A_3 i_1 + B_3 i_2 + C_3 i_3 = 0 \tag{12-40}$$

where, by comparison with Eqs. (12-13), (12-14), and (12-15), respectively,

$$A_1 = R_g + r_b + r_e \qquad B_1 = r_b \qquad\qquad C_1 = 0$$
$$A_2 = r_b + r_{n.} \qquad\qquad B_2 = 2r_b + r_e + r_c \qquad C_2 = -r_b$$
$$A_3 = 0 \qquad\qquad\qquad B_3 = -(r_b + r_m) \qquad C_3 = R_L + r_b + r_c$$

If D denotes the denominator determinant obtained in the solution of Eqs. (12-38) to (12-40) for the currents, it is found that

$$i_2 = \frac{-e_g A_2 C_3}{D} \tag{12-41}$$

$$i_3 = \frac{e_g A_2 B_3}{D} \tag{12-42}$$

It follows directly that substituting in Eq. (12-35) for the power gain of stage II

$$PG_{II} = \frac{B_3{}^2}{C_3{}^2} \times \frac{R_L}{R_{i_{II}}} \tag{12-43}$$

From Eq. (12-32):

$$PG_o = 4R_g \frac{(A_2 B_3)^2 R_L}{D^2} \tag{12-44}$$

And from Eq. (12-33):

$$PG_I = 4R_g \frac{(A_2 C_3)^2}{D^2} R_{i_{II}} \tag{12-45}$$

By inspection it is seen that Eq. (12-36) is satisfied. In view of Eq. (12-43) we may state theorem IV.

Theorem IV. In computing the power gain of two cascaded transistor stages when the power gain of stage I is computed using the input resistance of stage II as the load resistance of stage I, the power gain of stage II is obtained as follows: Multiply the ratio of the load resistance to the input resistance of stage II, by the ratio of the squares of the coefficients of the loop II and loop III currents, respectively, in the Kirchhoff equation for loop III.

178. CHECK ON THEOREM IV

To illustrate the application of this theorem and of Eqs. (12-43), (12-45), and (12-36), we apply those formulas to the GB to GB circuit, using the typical values in Table 8-1. The D of Eqs. (12-41), (12-42), (12-44), and (12-45) is the denominator of Eq. (12-28) and appears again, squared, in Eq. (12-50). From Eq. (12-44) using the values of A_2 and B_2 and D, Eq. (12-50) is obtained directly. Using

Eq. (12-45)

$PG_1 =$

$$\frac{4R_g(r_b + r_m)^2[(R_L + r_b + r_c)(r_b + r_e) - r_b(r_m + r_b)]}{\{(R_g + r_e + r_b)[(R_L + r_b + r_c)(r_c + r_e + 2r_b) - r_b(r_b + r_m)]\}^2 \atop - r_b(r_b + r_m)(R_L + r_b + r_c)\}^2} \quad (12\text{-}46)$$

A good approximation is:

$$PG_I \cong \frac{4R_g r_m^2[(R_L + r_c)(r_e + r_b) - r_b r_m]}{(R_L + r_c)[r_c(R_g + r_e + r_b) - r_b r_m]^2} \quad (12\text{-}47)$$

From Eq. (12-43):

$$PG_{II} = \frac{(r_b + r_m)^2 R_L}{(R_L + r_b + r_c)[(R_L + r_b + r_e)(r_b + r_e) - r_b(r_b + r_m)]} \quad (12\text{-}48)$$

A good approximation is:

$$PG_{II} = \frac{r_m^2 R_L}{(R_L + r_c)[(R_L + r_c)(r_b + r_e) - r_b r_m]} \quad (12\text{-}49)$$

$$PG_o = \frac{4R_g R_L i_3^2}{e_g^2}$$

$$= \frac{4R_g R_L(r_m + r_b)^4}{\{(R_g + r_e + r_b)(R_L + r_b + r_c)(r_c + r_e + 2r_b) \atop - r_b(r_b + r_m)(R_L + r_b + r_c)\}^2} \quad (12\text{-}50)$$

More suitable for computation, however, is the approximation:

$$PG_o \cong \frac{4R_g R_L r_m^4}{\{(R_L + r_c)[(R_g + r_e + r_b)r_c - r_b r_m]\}^2} \quad (12\text{-}51)$$

Typical values are:

	PG_I	PG_{II}	PG_o	Remarks
Point contact...	6.8	133	900	Unstable; not realizable
Junction........	0.55	860	472	Stable

It will be found by substitution in Eq. (12-51) that, if resistance is added to r_e to make the input resistance of the point contact units positive, the power gain drops very rapidly. Of course, one might add just enough resistance to bring the input resistance only slightly positive, but this is not considered good design in view of the problem of interchangeability and stability of transistors.

179. SUMMARY OF GB TO GB ANALYSIS

The GB to GB arrangement has been analyzed in detail in order to establish the theorems for cascaded arrangements. The fact that

$R_{L_1} = R_{i_{II}}$ *in all cases;* that $R_{g_{II}} = R_{o_I}$ in computing the over-all output resistance; and that $R_{g_{II}} = 0$ when computing the over-all gain from the formula $VG_o = VG_I \times VG_{II}$; and the fact that

$$PG_{II} = \left(\frac{B_3{}^2}{C_3{}^2}\right) \times \left(\frac{R_L}{R_{i_{II}}}\right)$$

will be used in all future analyses of the permissible arrangements. An excellent check on the accuracy of all formulas is achieved through comparison of the results, using theorems I to IV, with those obtained using the solution of the Kirchhoff equations.

Each of the combinations will be treated using the Kirchhoff equations, but it will be understood that all forms are checked against formulas and values obtained using theorems I to IV. Typical values will be given for both point contact and junction units in order to make the treatment complete, and the associated commentary will show which are useful and which require further circuit modification.

It becomes evident, as one substitutes numbers, that comparatively large differences in the parameter values of the transistors in the two loops have an unimportant effect on the final resistances and gains computed.

180. GB TO GE

Equations:

$$(R_g + r_b + r_e)i_1 + r_b i_2 + 0 = e_g \tag{12-52}$$
$$(r_b + r_m)i_1 + (2r_b + r_e + r_c)i_2 - r_e i_3 = 0 \tag{12-53}$$
$$0 + (r_m - r_e)i_2 + (R_L + r_e + r_c - r_m)i_3 = 0 \tag{12-54}$$

$$R_i = r_e + r_b$$
$$- \frac{r_b(r_b + r_m)(R_L + r_e + r_c - r_m)}{(R_L + r_e + r_c - r_m)(r_c + 2r_b + r_e) + r_e(r_m - r_e)} \tag{12-55}$$

Good approximation to R_i:

$$R_i \cong r_e + r_b - \frac{r_b r_m (R_L + r_e + r_c - r_m)}{(R_L + r_e + r_c - r_m)r_c + r_e r_m} \tag{12-56}$$

Typical values:

$$\begin{array}{ll} \text{Point contact} \ldots\ldots\ldots & 165 \text{ ohms} \\ \text{Junction} \ldots\ldots\ldots\ldots \ldots & 1{,}000 \text{ ohms} \end{array}$$

$$R_o = r_e + r_c - r_m$$
$$+ \frac{(R_g + r_b + r_e)(r_m - r_e)r_e}{(R_g + r_e + r_b)(r_c + 2r_b + r_e) - r_b(r_b + r_m)} \tag{12-57}$$

Good approximation to R_o:

$$R_o \cong r_c - r_m + \frac{(R_g + r_b + r_e)r_m r_e}{(R_g + r_e + r_b)r_c - r_m r_b} \tag{12-58}$$

Typical values:

$$
\begin{array}{ll}
\text{Point contact} \ldots \ldots & -19{,}400 \text{ ohms} \\
\text{Junction} \ldots \ldots \ldots & 40{,}000 \text{ ohms}
\end{array}
$$

$$VG = \frac{-(r_b + r_m)(r_m - r_e)R_L}{\{(R_g + r_e + r_b)[(R_L + r_e + r_c - r_m)(r_c + 2r_b + r_e) + r_e(r_m - r_e)] - r_b(r_b + r_m)(R_L + r_e + r_c - r_m)\}} \tag{12-59}$$

Good approximation to VG:

$$VG \cong \frac{-r_m{}^2 R_L}{\{(R_g + r_e + r_b)[(R_L + r_e + r_c - r_m)r_c + r_e r_m] - r_b r_m(R_L + r_e + r_c - r_m)\}} \tag{12-60}$$

Typical values:

	Stage I	Stage II	Over-all	Remarks
Point contact	35	-133	$-4{,}650$	Unstable
Junction	1.23	1,015	1,240	Stable

$$CG_o = \frac{(r_b + r_m)(R_L + r_e + r_c - r_m)}{(2r_b + r_e + r_c)(R_L + r_e + r_c - r_m) + r_e(r_m - r_e)} \tag{12-61}$$

Good approximation:

$$CG_o \cong \frac{r_m(R_L + r_e + r_c - r_m)}{r_c(R_L + r_e + r_c - r_m) + r_e r_m} \tag{12-62}$$

Typical values:

	Stage I	Stage II	Over-all	Remarks
Point contact	-0.696	-230	162	No phase change
Junction	-0.96	-6.85	6.56	No phase change

$$PG = \frac{4R_L R_g(r_b + r_m)^2(r_m - r_e)^2}{\{(R_g + r_e + r_b)[(R_L + r_e + r_c - r_m)(r_c + 2r_b + r_e) + r_e(r_m - r_e)] - r_b(r_b + r_m)(R_L + r_e + r_c - r_m)\}^2} \tag{12-63}$$

Good approximation to PG:

$$PG \cong \frac{4R_L R_g r_m{}^2}{\{(R_g + r_e + r_b)[(R_L + r_e + r_c - r_m)r_c + r_e r_m] - r_b r_m(R_L + r_e + r_c - r_m)\}^2} \tag{12-64}$$

Typical values:

	Stage I	Stage II	Over-all	Remarks
Point contact	73.3	31,100	2,280,000	Unstable
Junction	4.36	6,720	29,600	Stable

Commentary on GB to GE Cascade. For the point contact unit the input resistance is somewhat higher than that of the single-stage grounded-base connection, but the negative output resistance indicates that the arrangement is unstable and will oscillate. For the junction unit, the cascade arrangement yields an input resistance of about 1,000 ohms and the over-all voltage gain is fair. For junction transistors, however, the power gain is approximately five times the

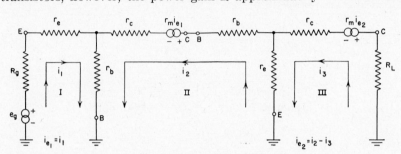

Fig. 12-4. Equivalent diagram of the GB to GE cascade arrangement, using the same assumptions as were used to obtain Fig. 12-3.

gain of a single grounded-emitter stage. The voltage, power, and current gains of the point contact units are given even though the unstable operation renders it impossible to realize these values. This is done in order to indicate that, if compensation is made to make the cascading stable, there is sufficient latent gain to make the effort worthwhile. Usually stabilization may be achieved by addition of resistance in series with r_e or by negative voltage or current feedback.[6,7] In general, this cascading arrangement, particularly for junction transistors, does not introduce any serious mismatch, and may be considered to represent a practical multistage connection for transistors.

181. GB TO GC

Equations:

$$(R_g + r_e + r_b)i_1 + r_b i_2 + 0 = e_g \qquad (12\text{-}65)$$

$$(r_b + r_m)i_1 + 2(r_b + r_c)i_2 - (r_c - r_m)i_3 = 0 \qquad (12\text{-}66)$$

$$0 - r_c i_2 + (R_L + r_e + r_c - r_m) = 0 \qquad (12\text{-}67)$$

$$R_i = r_e + r_b - \frac{r_b(r_b + r_m)(R_L + r_e + r_c - r_m)}{2(r_c + r_b)(R_L + r_e + r_c - r_m) - r_c(r_c - r_m)} \qquad (12\text{-}68)$$

Good approximation to R_i:

$$R_i \cong r_e + r_b - \frac{r_b r_m(R_L + r_e + r_c - r_m)}{r_c(2R_L + r_c - r_m)} \qquad (12\text{-}69)$$

Typical values:

$$
\begin{array}{ll}
\text{Point contact}\ldots\ldots\ldots\ldots & \text{268 ohms} \\
\text{Junction}\ldots\ldots\ldots\ldots\ldots & \text{245 ohms}
\end{array}
$$

$$
R_o = r_e + r_c - r_m - \frac{(R_g + r_e + r_b)(r_c - r_m)r_c}{(R_g + r_e + r_b)(2r_c + 2r_b) - r_b(r_b + r_m)} \tag{12-70}
$$

Good approximation to R_o:

$$
R_o \cong r_c - r_m - \frac{(R_g + r_e + r_b)(r_c - r_m)r_c}{(R_g + r_e + r_b)2r_c - r_b r_m} \tag{12-71}
$$

Typical values:

$$
\begin{array}{ll}
\text{Point contact}\ldots\ldots\ldots & -7{,}800 \text{ ohms} \\
\text{Junction}\ldots\ldots\ldots\ldots & 14{,}000 \text{ ohms}
\end{array}
$$

$$
VG = \frac{r_c(r_b + r_m)R_L}{\{(R_g + r_e + r_b)[(2r_c + 2r_b)(R_L + r_e + r_c - r_m) - r_c(r_c - r_m)] - r_b(r_b + r_m)(R_L + r_e + r_c - r_m)\}} \tag{12-72}
$$

Good approximation to VG:

$$
VG \cong \frac{r_c r_m R_L}{(R_g + r_e + r_b)(2R_L + r_c - r_m)r_c - r_b r_m(R_L + r_e + r_e - r_m)} \tag{12-73}
$$

Typical values:

	Stage I	Stage II	Over-all	Remarks
Point contact...	45.6	0.998	45.5	Unstable; not realizable
Junction........	535	1	535	Stable

$$
CG_o = \frac{-r_c(r_b + r_m)}{2(r_c + r_b)(R_L + r_e + r_c - r_m) - r_c(r_c - r_m)} \tag{12-74}
$$

Good approximation:

$$
CG_o \cong \frac{-r_m}{2R_L + r_c - r_m} \tag{12-75}
$$

Typical values:

	Stage I	Stage II	Over-all	Remarks
Point contact....	−0.0175	100	−1.75	Phase reversal
Junction........	−0.56	7.14	−4	Phase reversal

$$
PG_o = \frac{4R_g(r_b + r_m)^2 r_c^2 R_L}{\{(R_g + r_e + r_b)[(2r_c + 2r_b)(R_L + r_e + r_c - r_m) - r_c(r_c - r_m)] - r_b(r_b + r_m)(R_L + r_e + r_c - r_m)\}^2} \tag{12-76}
$$

Good approximation to PG_o:

$$PG_o \cong \frac{4R_g R_L r_m{}^2 r_c{}^2}{[(R_g + r_e + r_b)(2R_L + r_c - r_m)r_c \\ - r_b r_m (R_L + r_e + r_c - r_m)]^2} \tag{12-77}$$

Typical values:

	Stage I	Stage II	Over-all	Remarks
Point Contact..............	2.07	100	207	Unstable
Junction...................	788	7.3	5,760	Stable

Commentary on GB to GC Cascade. There does not appear to be any advantage in using this particular cascaded arrangement. Gains are poor, the stages are unstable for point contact units, and the impedance levels are low. There are, however, two points of interest in the

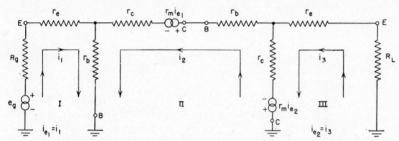

Fig. 12-5. Equivalent diagram of the GB to GC cascade arrangement.

results: (1) For the point contact type, the input resistance is very nearly the maximum possible for a grounded-base stage and results from the very high (2-megohm) load upon the first stage (see theorem I). (2) The low power gain of stage I indicates that the output impedance of the grounded-base stage is very poorly matched by the input impedance of the common-collector stage (see Table 10-1) particularly for the point contact unit. Nevertheless, the over-all gain for point contact units is still about twice the typical gain per stage of the grounded-base connection, but is, of course, unrealizable due to the negative R_o. The power gain for the junction units is good, but does not compare with the GB to GE connection, *q.v.*

182. GE TO GB

$$(R_g + r_b + r_e)i_1 + r_e i_2 + 0 = e_g \tag{12-78}$$
$$(r_e - r_m)i_1 + (2r_e + r_b + r_c - r_m)i_2 - r_b i_3 = 0 \tag{12-79}$$
$$0 - (r_b + r_m)i_2 + (R_L + r_c + r_b)i_3 = 0 \tag{12-80}$$

$$R_i = r_b + r_e$$

$$- \frac{r_e(r_e - r_m)(R_L + r_c + r_b)}{(2r_e + r_b + r_c - r_m)(R_L + r_c + r_b) - (r_b + r_m)r_b} \quad (12\text{-}81)$$

A good approximation for R_i:

$$R_i \cong r_b + r_e + \frac{r_e r_m(R_L + r_c + r_b)}{(r_c - r_m)(R_L + r_c) - r_b r_m} \quad (12\text{-}82)$$

Typical values:

Point contact........... 5 ohms
Junction............... 1,125 ohms

$$R_o = r_b + r_c$$

$$- \frac{(R_g + r_e + r_b)(r_b + r_m)r_b}{(R_g + r_e + r_b)(2r_e + r_b + r_c - r_m) - r_e(r_e - r_m)} \quad (12\text{-}83)$$

A good approximation to R_o:

$$R_o \cong r_c - \frac{(R_g + r_e + r_b)r_m r_b}{(R_g + r_e + r_b)(r_c - r_m) + r_e r_m} \quad (12\text{-}84)$$

Typical values:

Point contact........... 15.3 ohms
Junction............... 1 megohm

$$VG_o = \frac{(r_e - r_m)(r_b + r_m)R_L}{\{(R_g + r_b + r_e)[(2r_e + r_b + r_c - r_m)(R_L + r_c + r_b) - r_b(r_b + r_m)] - r_e(r_e - r_m)(R_L + r_b + r_c)\}} \quad (12\text{-}85)$$

A good approximation to VG_o:

$$VG_o \cong \frac{-r_m^2 R_L}{(R_L + r_c)[(R_g + r_b + r_e)(r_c - r_m) - r_e r_m]} \quad (12\text{-}86)$$

Typical values:

	Stage I	Stage II	Over-all	Remarks
Point contact......	0.52	133	69	Stable (see commentary)
Junction..........	−1.31	980	−1,290	Stable

$$CG_o = \frac{-(r_e - r_m)(r_b + r_m)}{(2r_e + r_c - r_m)(R_L + r_c + r_b) - r_b(r_b + r_m)} \quad (12\text{-}87)$$

Good approximation:

$$CG_o \cong \frac{r_m^2}{(r_c - r_m)(R_L + r_c) - r_b r_m} \quad (12\text{-}88)$$

Typical values:

	Stage I	Stage II	Over-all	Remarks
Point contact.....	−1.74	1	−1.74	Phase reversal
Junction.........	24.3	0.872	21.2	No phase reversal

$$PG_o = \frac{4R_gR_L(r_e - r_m)^2(r_b + r_m)^2}{\{(R_g + r_b + r_e)[(2r_e + r_b + r_c - r_m)(R_L + r_c + r_b) - r_b(r_b + r_m)] - r_e(r_e - r_m)(R_L + r_b + r_c)\}^2} \quad (12\text{-}89)$$

A good approximation:

$$PG_o \cong \frac{4R_gR_Lr_m^4}{\{(R_L + r_c)[(R_g + r_e + r_b)(r_c - r_m) - r_er_m]\}^2} \quad (12\text{-}90)$$

Typical values:

	Stage I	Stage II	Over-all	Remarks
Point contact.......	3.54	133	470	See commentary
Junction...........	39.2	845	33,200	Stable

Commentary on GE to GB Cascade. One of the interesting aspects of this connection is that the input and output resistances for the point

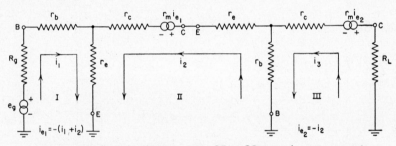

Fig. 12-6. Equivalent diagram of the GE to GB cascade arrangement.

contact unit are both positive. It will be recalled (see Table 10-1) that the grounded-emitter connection exhibits a very definite negative resistance in the output; when connected with the grounded-base stage as the load, the output resistance becomes positive. The reason is found by examination of the formula for the output resistance of the grounded-emitter stage, which is reproduced below:

$$R_{o_e} = r_c + r_e - r_m + \frac{r_e(r_m - r_e)}{R_g + r_e + r_b} \quad (12\text{-}91)$$

When R_g is 500 ohms, a typical source impedance, the ratio term in Eq. (12-91) is too small to overcome the approximately −20 kilohms of the other terms and R_o is negative.

With the *GE* to *GB* arrangement, the output stage is a grounded-base stage which has for its R_g the output resistance of the grounded-emitter stage (see theorem II). As this output resistance is negative, the sign of the ratio term in the expression for R_{o_e} of the grounded-base stage is reversed because R_{o_b} is a large negative number (see Eq. (12-92). The result is that the output resistance is positive and higher than it would be for the grounded-base stage alone.

$$R_{o_b} = r_b + r_c - \frac{r_b(r_b + r_m)}{R_g + r_b + r_e} \tag{12-92}$$

The input resistance is only slightly positive and may even become negative with transistor parameter variations. Resistance in series with r_e of the first stage should be added to ensure R_i being positive. This arrangement has much to offer, particularly in the junction units: high input and output resistance and excellent voltage and power gains, compared to a single grounded-emitter stage. Note that the junction units provide phase reversal in voltage, and the point contact units do not. The over-all point contact power and voltage gains are not impressive.

183. GE TO GE

Equations:

$$(R_g + r_b + r_e)i_1 + r_e i_2 + 0 = e_g \tag{12-93}$$
$$(r_e - r_m)i_1 + (2r_e + r_b + r_c - r_m)i_2 - r_e i_3 = 0 \tag{12-94}$$
$$0 + (r_m - r_e)i_2 + (R_L + r_e + r_c - r_m)i_3 = 0 \tag{12-95}$$
$$R_i = r_b + r_e$$
$$- \frac{r_e(r_e - r_m)(R_L + r_e + r_c - r_m)}{(2r_e + r_b + r_c - r_m)(R_L + r_e + r_c - r_m) + r_e(r_m - r_e)} \tag{12-96}$$

Good approximation:

$$R_i \cong r_b + r_e + \frac{r_e r_m(R_L + r_e + r_c - r_m)}{(r_c - r_m)(R_L + r_e + r_c - r_m) + r_e r_m} \tag{12-97}$$

Typical values:

$$\text{Point contact} \ldots \ldots \quad 620 \text{ ohms}$$
$$\text{Junction} \ldots \ldots \ldots \quad 1{,}125 \text{ ohms}$$

$$R_o = r_e + r_c - r_m$$
$$+ \frac{r_e(r_m - r_e)(R_g + r_b + r_e)}{(R_g + r_b + r_e)(2r_e + r_b + r_c - r_m) - r_e(r_e - r_m)} \tag{12-98}$$

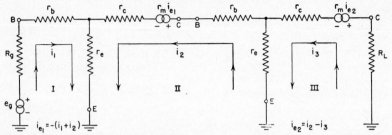

Fig. 12-7. Equivalent diagram of the GE to GE cascade arrangement. This is the most commonly used connection, see Table 12-1.

Good approximation:

$$R_o \cong r_c - r_m + \frac{r_e r_m (R_g + r_b + r_e)}{(R_g + r_b + r_e)(r_c - r_m) + r_e r_m} \quad (12\text{-}99)$$

Typical values:

$$\begin{aligned}
&\text{Point contact} \ldots \ldots \ldots \quad -20{,}400 \text{ ohms} \\
&\text{Junction} \ldots \ldots \ldots \ldots \quad 44{,}000 \text{ ohms}
\end{aligned}$$

VG_o

$$= \frac{(r_m - r_e)^2 R_L}{\{(R_g + r_b + r_e)[(2r_e + r_b + r_c - r_m)(R_L + r_e + r_c - r_m) - r_e(r_m - r_e)] - r_e(r_e - r_m)(R_L + r_e + r_c - r_m)\}} \quad (12\text{-}100)$$

Good approximation:

$$VG_o \cong \frac{r_m^2 R_L}{\{(R_g + r_b + r_e)[(r_c - r_m)(R_L + r_e + r_c - r_m) - r_e r_m] + r_e r_m (R_L + r_e + r_c - r_m)\}} \quad (12\text{-}101)$$

Typical values:

	Stage I	Stage II	Over-all	Remarks
Point contact	-73.5	-133	9,720	Unstable
Junction	-10.22	-985	10,100	Stable; no phase reversal

CG_o

$$= \frac{-(r_m - r_e)^2}{(2r_e + r_b + r_c - r_m)(R_L + r_e + r_c - r_m) + r_e(r_m - r_e)} \quad (12\text{-}102)$$

Good approximation:

$$CG_o \cong \frac{-r_m^2}{(r_c - r_m)(R_L + r_e + r_c - r_m) + r_e r_m} \quad (12\text{-}103)$$

Typical values:

	Stage I	Stage II	Over-all	Remarks
Point contact	2.33	-233	-545	Unstable
Junction	23.9	-6.85	-164	Stable

PG_o

$$= \frac{4R_g R_L (r_m - r_e)^4}{\{(R_g + r_b + r_e)[(2r_e + r_b + r_c - r_m)(R_L + r_e + r_c - r_m) - r_e(r_m - r_e)] - r_e(r_e - r_m)(R_L + r_e + r_c - r_m)\}^2} \quad (12\text{-}104)$$

Good approximation:

PG_o

$$\cong \frac{4R_g R_L r_m{}^4}{\{(R_g + r_b + r_e)[(r_c - r_m)(R_L + r_e + r_c - r_m) - r_e r_m] + (R_L + r_e + r_c - r_m)r_e r_m\}^2} \quad (12\text{-}105)$$

Typical values:

	Stage I	Stage II	Over-all	Remarks
Point contact......	304	31,160	9,450,000	Unstable; not realizable
Junction..........	302	6,700	2,040,000	Stable; realizable

Commentary on GE to GE Cascade. This particular cascaded arrangement appears to hold most promise for practical application.[6] For junction units, the current, voltage, and power gains are quite substantial, and a most desirable improvement over a single stage. The two voltage phase reversals in the grounded-emitter stages cancel, and the output shows no phase reversal in voltage. Input and output resistances are above 1 kilohm, and can be made even higher by suitable choice of units and associated parameters. The connection is finding favor in the field and promises to supplant most of the others except for special applications.

The extremely high voltage and power gain shown for point contact units indicate, as in the case of the GB to GE connection, that reserve gain is available to permit adding series resistance to bring the operation into the positive-resistance region. As an exercise, the student of transistor theory should increase r_e until R_o becomes positive and then compute the resultant input resistance, current, voltage, and power gains.

184. GE TO GC

Equations:

$$(R_g + r_b + r_e)i_1 + r_e i_2 + 0 = e_g \quad (12\text{-}106)$$
$$(r_e - r_m)i_1 + (2r_c + r_b + r_e - r_m)i_2 - (r_c - r_m)i_3 = 0 \quad (12\text{-}107)$$
$$0 - r_c i_2 + (R_L + r_e + r_c - r_m)i_3 = 0 \quad (12\text{-}108)$$

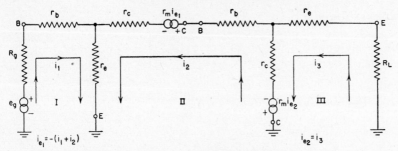

Fig. 12-8. Equivalent diagram of the GE to GC cascade arrangement.

$R_i = r_e + r_b$

$$- \frac{r_e(r_e - r_m)(R_L + r_e + r_c - r_m)}{(2r_c + r_e + r_b - r_m)(R_L + r_e + r_c - r_m) - r_c(r_c - r_m)} \quad (12\text{-}109)$$

Good approximation:

$$R_i \cong r_e + r_b + \frac{r_e r_m(R_L + r_e + r_c - r_m)}{(2r_c - r_m)(R_L + r_e + r_c - r_m) - r_c(r_c - r_m)} \quad (12\text{-}110)$$

Typical values:

Point contact.............. 273 ohms

Junction.................. 557 ohms

$R_o = r_e + r_c - r_m$

$$- \frac{(R_g + r_b + r_e)(r_c - r_m)r_c}{(R_g + r_b + r_e)(2r_c + r_e + r_b - r_m) - r_e(r_e - r_m)} \quad (12\text{-}111)$$

Good approximation:

$$R_o \cong r_c - r_m - \frac{(R_g + r_b + r_e)(r_c - r_m)r_c}{(R_g + r_b + r_e)(2r_c - r_m) + r_e r_m} \quad (12\text{-}112)$$

Typical values:

Point contact......... 122,000 ohms

Junction............. 2,300 ohms

$$VG_o = \frac{r_c(r_e - r_m)R_L}{\{(R_g + r_e + r_b)[(2r_c + r_b + r_e - r_m)(R_L + r_e + r_c - r_m) \atop - r_c(r_c - r_m)] - r_c(r_e - r_m)(R_L + r_e + r_c - r_m)\}} \quad (12\text{-}113)$$

Good approximation:

$$VG_o \cong \frac{-r_c r_m R_L}{\{(R_g + r_e + r_b)[(2r_c - r_m)(R_L + r_e + r_c - r_m) \atop - r_c(r_c - r_m)] + r_c r_m(R_L + r_e + r_c - r_m)\}} \quad (12\text{-}114)$$

Typical values:

	Stage I	Stage II	Over-all	Remarks
Point contact.............	−45.5	1	−45.5	Stable
Junction.................	−86	1	−86	Stable

$$CG_o = \frac{-r_c(r_e - r_m)}{(2r_c + r_e + r_b - r_m)(R_L + r_e + r_c - r_m) - r_c(r_c - r_m)} \quad (12\text{-}115)$$

Good approximation:

$$CG_o \cong \frac{r_c r_m}{(2r_c - r_m)(R_L + r_e + r_c - r_m) - r_c(r_c - r_m)} \quad (12\text{-}116)$$

Typical values:

	Stage I	Stage II	Over-all	Remarks
Point contact.....	0.0174	100	1.74	Stable; no reversal
Junction........	1.27	7.14	9.1	Stable; no reversal

PG_o

$$= \frac{4R_g R_L(r_e - r_m)^2 r_c^2}{\{(R_g + r_e + r_b)[(2r_c + r_b + r_e - r_m)(R_L + r_e + r_c - r_m) - r_c(r_c - r_m)] - r_c(r_e - r_m)(R_L + r_e + r_c - r_m)\}^2} \quad (12\text{-}117)$$

Good approximation:

$$PG_o \cong \frac{4R_g R_L r_m^2 r_c^2}{\{(R_g + r_e + r_b)[(2r_c - r_m)(R_L + r_e + r_c - r_m) - r_c(r_c - r_m)] + r_c r_m(R_L + r_e + r_c - r_m)\}^2} \quad (12\text{-}118)$$

Typical values:

	Stage I	Stage II	Over-all	Remarks
Point contact.............	2.07	100	207	Stable
Junction.................	2,000	7.3	14,600	Stable

Commentary on GE to GC. The unusual aspect of this combination is the positive output resistance for point contact units. In analyzing the mathematics to determine how this arrangement produces a positive output resistance even though the grounded-emitter or grounded-collector connections, per se, produce a negative R_o, it is observed that the negative R_o of the first stage is counteracted by the very high input resistance (2 megohms) of the grounded-collector stage. A high positive output resistance is thus obtainable using the point contact transistor, which is not obtainable using a single grounded-emitter or grounded-collector stage.

The voltage and power gains are small, and the current gain is unimpressive. The high input resistance of the grounded-collector stage makes i_2 low, and the current gain of the first stage is poor. The power gain, using junction transistors, is good but does not compare favorably with the GE to GE case.

The worthwhile feature of this connection is that it is uniformly stable for both point contact and junction transistors.

185. GC TO GB

Equations:

$$(R_g + r_b + r_c)i_1 + (r_c - r_m)i_2 + 0 = e_g \tag{12-119}$$
$$r_c i_1 + (2r_e + r_b + r_c - r_m)i_2 - r_b i_3 = 0 \tag{12-120}$$
$$0 - (r_b + r_m)i_2 + (R_L + r_b + r_c)i_3 = 0 \tag{12-121}$$
$$R_i = r_b + r_c$$
$$- \frac{r_c(r_c - r_m)(R_L + r_b + r_c)}{(2r_e + r_b + r_c - r_m)(R_L + r_b + r_c) - r_b(r_b + r_m)} \tag{12-122}$$

Good approximation:

$$R_i \cong r_b + r_c - \frac{r_c(r_c - r_m)(R_L + r_c)}{(2r_e + r_b + r_c - r_m)(R_L + r_c) - r_b r_m} \tag{12-123}$$

Typical values:

$$\begin{aligned}
&\text{Point contact} \ldots \ldots \quad -10 \text{ ohms} \\
&\text{Junction} \ldots \ldots \ldots \quad 2{,}400 \text{ ohms}
\end{aligned}$$

$$R_o = r_b + r_c$$
$$- \frac{(R_g + r_b + r_c)(r_b + r_m)r_b}{(R_g + r_b + r_c)(2r_e + r_b + r_c - r_m) - r_c(r_c - r_m)} \tag{12-124}$$

Good approximation:

$$R_o \cong r_b + r_c$$
$$- \frac{(R_g + r_b + r_c)r_m r_b}{(R_g + r_b + r_c)(2r_e + r_b + r_c - r_m) - r_c(r_c - r_m)} \tag{12-125}$$

See note in commentary.

Typical values:

$$\begin{aligned}
&\text{Point contact} \ldots \ldots \quad 26{,}000 \text{ ohms} \\
&\text{Junction} \ldots \ldots \ldots \quad 26{,}000 \text{ ohms}
\end{aligned}$$

$$VG_o = \frac{r_c(r_b + r_m)R_L}{\{(R_g + r_b + r_c)[(2r_e + r_b + r_c - r_m)(R_L + r_b + r_c)}{} \tag{12-126}$$
$$- r_b(r_b + r_m)] - r_c(r_c - r_m)(R_L + r_b + r_c)\}$$

Good approximation:

$$VG_o \cong \frac{r_c r_m R_L}{\{(R_g + r_b + r_c)[(2r_e + r_b + r_c - r_m)(R_L + r_c) - r_b r_m] - r_c(r_c - r_m)(R_L + r_c)\}} \quad (12\text{-}127)$$

Typical values:

	Stage I	Stage II	Over-all	Remarks
Point contact...............	-0.292	133	-40	Unstable
Junction..................	0.75	985	740	Stable

$$CG_o = \frac{-r_c(r_b + r_m)}{(2r_e + r_b + r_c - r_m)(R_L + r_b + r_c) - r_b(r_b + r_m)} \quad (12\text{-}128)$$

Good approximation:

$$CG_o \cong \frac{-r_c r_m}{(2r_e + r_b + r_c - r_m)(R_L + r_c) - r_b r_m} \quad (12\text{-}129)$$

Typical values:

	Stage I	Stage II	Over-all	Remarks
Point contact.......	0.76	1	0.76	No phase reversal
Junction...........	-25	0.872	-21.8	Phase reversal

$$PG_o = \frac{4R_g R_L r_c^2(r_b + r_m)^2}{\{(R_g + r_b + r_c)[(2r_e + r_b + r_c - r_m)(R_L + r_b + r_c) - r_b(r_b + r_m)] - r_c(r_c - r_m)(R_L + r_b + r_c)\}^2} \quad (12\text{-}130)$$

Good approximation:

$$PG_o \cong \frac{4R_g R_L r_c^2 r_m^2}{\{(R_g + r_b + r_c)[(2r_e + r_b + r_c - r_m)(R_L + r_c) - r_b r_m] - r_c(r_c - r_m)(R_L + r_c)\}^2} \quad (12\text{-}131)$$

Typical values:

	Stage I	Stage II	Over-all	Remarks
Point contact............	1.135	133	151	Unstable
Junction................	12.8	845	10,900	Stable

Commentary on GC to CB. This circuit arrangement appears to have good power gain, using junction transistors, and usable input and output resistance levels. For the point contact transistors, the circuit is unstable, and does not appear to have enough gain to indicate any useful potentialities. Of interest, however, is the input resistance of -10 ohms for the point contact unit. When this is compared with the input resistance of 2 megohms when the unit is used in the grounded-collector connection, and bearing in mind theorem I, it is noticeable how rapidly the input resistance of the grounded-collector stage varies with R_L, the load resistance.   Note also how the grounded-collector stage, acting as R_g for the grounded-base stage (see theorem II) brings R_o down, for the junction unit, from 0.5 megohm when the grounded-base stage is used alone to barely 26 kilohms in this cascaded arrangement.   Voltage and current gains are unimpressive for both types.

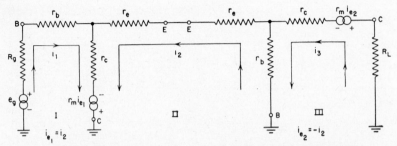

Fig. 12-9. Equivalent diagram of the GC to GB cascade arrangement.

NOTE: In the arrangements involving the grounded-collector connection it will be found that, for typical values of parameters, differences between large numbers, each of which is quite large compared to the value of the difference, are involved.   To maintain accuracy, care must be taken in the approximations.   Neglecting certain of the parameters can lead to erroneous results.

186. GC TO GE

Equations:

$$(R_g + r_b + r_c)i_1 + (r_c - r_m)i_2 + 0 = e_g \tag{12-132}$$
$$r_c i_1 + (2r_e + r_b + r_c - r_m)i_2 - r_e i_3 = 0 \tag{12-133}$$
$$0 + (r_m - r_e)i_2 + (R_L + r_e + r_c - r_m)i_3 = 0 \tag{12-134}$$
$$R_i = r_b + r_c$$
$$- \frac{r_c(r_c - r_m)(R_L + r_e + r_c - r_m)}{(R_L + r_e + r_c - r_m)(2r_e + r_b + r_c - r_m) + r_e(r_m - r_e)} \tag{12-135}$$

Good approximation:

$$R_i \cong r_c - \frac{r_c(r_c - r_m)(R_L + r_e + r_c - r_m)}{(R_L + r_e + r_c - r_m)(2r_e + r_b + r_c - r_m) - r_e r_m} \tag{12-136}$$

Typical values:

$$
\begin{array}{ll}
\text{Point contact} \ldots \ldots \ldots & 34{,}500 \text{ ohms} \\
\text{Junction} \ldots \ldots \ldots \ldots \ldots & 40{,}000 \text{ ohms}
\end{array}
$$

$$R_o = r_e + r_c$$

$$- r_m + \frac{(R_g + r_b + r_c)(r_m - r_e)r_e}{(R_g + r_b + r_c)(2r_e + r_b + r_c - r_m) - r_c(r_c - r_m)} \quad (12\text{-}137)$$

Good approximation:

$$R_o \cong r_c - r_m$$

$$+ \frac{(R_g + r_b + r_c)r_m r_e}{(R_g + r_b + r_c)(2r_e + r_b + r_c - r_m) - r_c(r_c - r_m)} \quad (12\text{-}138)$$

Typical values:

$$\begin{aligned}
&\text{Point contact}\ldots\ldots\quad -24{,}000 \text{ ohms}\\
&\text{Junction}\ldots\ldots\ldots\quad 82{,}500 \text{ ohms}
\end{aligned}$$

VG_o

$$= \frac{-r_c(r_m - r_e)R_L}{\{(R_g + r_b + r_c)[(2r_e + r_b + r_c - r_m)(R_L + r_e + r_c - r_m) + r_e(r_m - r_e)] - r_c(r_c - r_m)(R_L + r_e + r_c - r_m)\}} \quad (12\text{-}139)$$

Good approximation:

VG_o

$$\cong \frac{-r_c r_m R_L}{\{(R_g + r_b + r_c)[(2r_e + r_b + r_c - r_m)(R_L + r_e + r_c - r_m) + r_e r_m] - r_c(r_c - r_m)(R_L + r_e + r_c - r_m)\}} \quad (12\text{-}140)$$

Typical values:

	Stage I	Stage II	Over-all	Remarks
Point contact	0.98	−133	−130	Unstable
Junction	0.975	−985	−958	Stable

CG_o

$$= \frac{r_c(r_m - r_e)}{(2r_e + r_b + r_c - r_m)(R_L + r_e + r_c - r_m) + r_e(r_m - r_e)} \quad (12\text{-}141)$$

Good approximation:

$$CG_o \cong \frac{r_c r_m}{(2r_e + r_b + r_c - r_m)(R_L + r_e + r_c - r_m) + r_e r_m} \quad (12\text{-}142)$$

Typical values:

	Stage I	Stage II	Over-all	Remarks
Point contact	−0.975	−230	224	Unstable
Junction	−24.5	−6.86	168	Stable

PG_o

$$= \frac{4R_g R_L r_c^2(r_m - r_c)^2}{\{(R_g + r_b + r_c)[(2r_e + r_b + r_c - r_m)(R_L + r_e + r_c - r_m) + r_e(r_m - r_e)] - r_c(r_c - r_m)(R_L + r_e + r_c - r_m)\}^2} \quad (12\text{-}143)$$

Good approximation:

PG_o

$$\cong \frac{4R_gR_Lr_c{}^2(r_m - r_c)^2}{\{(R_g + r_c)[(2r_e + r_b + r_c - r_m)(R_L + r_e + r_c - r_m) + r_er_m] - r_c(r_c - r_m)(R_L + r_e + r_c - r_m)\}^2} \quad (12\text{-}144)$$

Typical values:

	Stage I	Stage II	Over-all	Remarks
Point contact............	0.054	31,000	1,720	Unstable
Junction................	2.69	6,740	18,100	Stable

Commentary on GC to GE. This connection has some very worthwhile features, particularly for the junction transistors. The point contact units tend to be unstable, and the over-all gains possible are not very great—it is not considered that this connection has much to offer, therefore, when using typical point contact units.

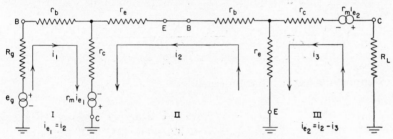

Fig. 12-10. Equivalent diagram of the GC to GE cascade arrangement.

While the over-all gains possible with this connection, particularly the power gain, are not so great as with the GE to GE connection, it will be observed that the input resistance is 40,000 compared to 1,125 for the GE to GE arrangement. The output resistance is nearly 80,000, so that this arrangement presents an ideal and nearly constant impedance level device, capable of giving good voltage gains and power gains. Certainly the very high input impedance of this arrangement offers impedance-matching possibilities which are clearly absent with the GE to GE arrangement. See also the general summary comments.

187. GC TO GC

Equations:

$$(R_g + r_b + r_c)i_1 + (r_c - r_m)i_2 + 0 = e_g \quad (12\text{-}145)$$
$$r_ci_1 + (2r_c + r_b + r_e - r_m)i_2 - (r_c - r_m)i_3 = 0 \quad (12\text{-}146)$$
$$0 - r_ci_2 + (R_L + r_e + r_c - r_m)i_3 = 0 \quad (12\text{-}147)$$

$$R_i = r_b + r_c$$
$$+ \frac{r_c(r_c - r_m)(R_L + r_e + r_c - r_m)}{(R_L + r_e + r_c - r_m)(2r_c + r_e + r_b - r_m) - r_c(r_c - r_m)} \quad (12\text{-}148)$$

No approximation feasible.
Typical values:

$$\text{Point contact} \ldots \ldots \ldots \quad 15{,}270 \text{ ohms}$$
$$\text{Junction} \ldots \ldots \ldots \ldots \quad 947{,}000 \text{ ohms}$$

$$R_o = r_e + r_c - r_m$$
$$- \frac{(R_g + r_b + r_c)(r_c - r_m)r_c}{(R_g + r_b + r_c)(2r_c + r_b + r_e - r_m) - r_c(r_c - r_m)} \quad (12\text{-}149)$$

No approximation feasible.
Typical values:

$$\text{Point contact} \ldots \ldots \ldots \quad 700 \text{ ohms}$$
$$\text{Junction} \ldots \ldots \ldots \ldots \quad 50 \text{ ohms}$$

VG_o

$$= \frac{r_c{}^2 R_L}{\{(R_g + r_b + r_c)[(2r_c + r_b + r_e - r_m)(R_L + r_e + r_c - r_m) - r_c(r_c - r_m)] - r_c(r_c - r_m)(R_L + r_e + r_c - r_m)\}} \quad (12\text{-}150)$$

No important approximation feasible.
Typical values:

	Stage I	Stage II	Over-all	Remarks
Point contact	0.99	0.994	0.98	Stable
Junction	1	1	1	Stable

PG_o

$$= \frac{4R_g R_L r_c{}^4}{\{(R_g + r_b + r_c)[(2r_c + r_b + r_e - r_m)(R_L + r_e + r_c - r_m) - r_c(r_c - r_m)] - r_c(r_c - r_m)(R_L + r_e + r_c - r_m)\}^2} \quad (12\text{-}151)$$

No important approximation possible.
Typical values:

	Stage I	Stage II	Over-all	Remarks
Point contact	0.001	100	0.1	Stable
Junction	0.00274	7.26	0.02	Stable

$$CG_o = \frac{-r_c{}^2}{(2r_c + r_e + r_b - r_m)(R_L + r_e + r_c - r_m) - r_c(r_c - r_m)} \quad (12\text{-}152)$$

No approximation feasible.
Typical values:

	Stage I	Stage II	Over-all	Remarks
Point contact	0.0075	−100	−0.75	Stable
Junction	1.33	−7.14	−9.52	Stable

Commentary on GC to GC.   While this method of connection is stable for point contact units as well as junction units, the gains are extremely poor.   For point contact units, two such cascaded stages provide a more suitable approximation to the cathode follower than a single grounded-collector stage, since for the latter the output resistance is negative.   For junction transistors, cascading two stages provides a small improvement in the input impedance, at a loss in gain.   Except

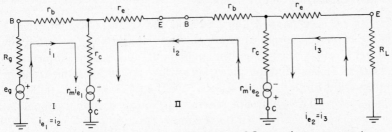

Fig. 12-11. Equivalent diagram of the GC to GC cascade arrangement.

for impedance matching, this arrangement does not seem to offer any advantages.

188. GENERAL REMARKS REGARDING CASCADING FORMULAS

In general, the results obtained must be considered to represent approximations, but approximations sufficiently close to be suitable for general design decisions.   For example, while the actual voltage gain for the GE to GE connection in a particular application may well be considerably different from the figures given, approximately 10,000, one would not expect the gain to be under 500, nor over 20,000.   By the same token, to obtain a stable arrangement, one would not try to use point contact transistors in the GB to GE connection, in spite of the theoretically attractive power gain, because of the instability indicated.   The figures given, therefore, are more indicative of anticipated trends and general probabilities than of specific numbers. It must be stated, however, that the stable configurations have been investigated in the laboratory and results sufficiently close to predicted values obtained to warrant publication of the formulas.

Results obtainable in practice will differ from the values given for two principal reasons:

1. Variation for r_c with temperature[7]
2. Use of low values of dc biasing resistors

The errors introduced by dc biasing resistors, as discussed in the text, are unimportant for values above 1,000 or 2,000 ohms, since the parameters given are not particularly sensitive to these shunt paths. However, variation of r_c with temperature will markedly affect results, because examination of the gain equations, particularly voltage and power gains, will show a dependence on r_c. As r_c falls quite rapidly with temperature, operation at high ambient temperatures will assuredly give results at variance with those given.

189. BEST CASCADING ARRANGEMENTS

It can be seen from Table 12-2 that the GE to GE connection is capable of the highest orders of power, voltage, and current gains, with very satisfactory magnitudes of input and output impedances. This refers to the junction units, since this connection is unstable for point contact units. The GE to GB, GB to GE, and GC to GE are runners-up, also for junction units. The only cascading connection which appears to be stable for point contact transistors is GE to GC, but the gains are unimpressive and no particular improvement over a single unit. The GE to GB connection cannot be considered unconditionally stable since the input resistance is 5, too close to negative values for comfort. For the junction units, however, cascading appears to offer some formidable advantages by proper selection of the cascading arrangement.

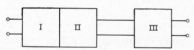

Fig. 12-12. Block diagram to indicate extension of theorems I through IV to more than two stages in cascade. Stages I and II may be considered as the two stages discussed in the text and treated as a single equivalent stage; stage III is then treated as a pre- or postamplifier stage to which theorems I through IV may be applied.

190. CASCADING OF MORE THAN TWO STAGES

Theorems I, II, III, and IV are applicable to cascading of more than two stages. The block diagram of Fig. 12-12 is used to illustrate the technique. Let

R_{i_I} = input resistance of system
R_{i_III} = input resistance of stage III (or system of stages)
R_{o_I} = output resistance of stages I and II in cascade
R_{o_III} = output resistance of stage III

R_i. By theorem I, the input resistance of the system is found by using the formula for the input resistance of stages I and II, such as may be given by Eqs. (12-16), (12-55), (12-68), (12-81), etc., and by replacing the value of R_L by R_{i_III}. In this way either the formulas or numerical values without use of the formulas are obtainable.

R_o. By theorem II, the output resistance is obtained by using the

TABLE 12-2. TYPICAL VALUES OF R_i, R_o, VG, AND PG FOR TRANSISTORS IN CASCADE

Connection	R_i, K	R_o, K	VG_I	VG_{II}	VG_o	CG_I	CG_{II}	CG_o	PG_I	PG_{II}	PG_o	Stability	Phase reversal	Remarks
GB-GB: pc	-0.006	14.560	0.7	133	93	-2.35	1	-2.35	6.78	133	900	U	C	
j	0.045	1,000	0.156	990	155	-0.96	0.87	-0.84	0.55	860	472	S	C	
GB-GE: pc	0.165	-19.4	35	-133	-4,650	-6.96	-230	162	73.5	31,100	2,280,000	U	V	Next best after GE-GB
j	1	40	1.23	1,015	1,240	-0.96	-6.85	6.56	4.36	6,720	29,600	S		
GB-GC: pc	0.268	-7.8	45.6	0.998	45.5	-0.0175	100	-1.75	2.07	100	207	U	C	
j	0.245	14	535	1	535	-0.56	7.14	-4	788	7.3	5,760	S	C	
GE-GB: pc	0.005	15.3	0.52	133	69	-1.74	1	-1.74	3.54	133	470	S*	C	Next best after GE-GE
j	1.125	1,000	-1.31	980	-1,290	24.3	0.872	21.2	39.2	845	33,200	S	V	
GE-GE: pc	0.620	-20.4	-73.5	-133	9,720	2.33	-233	-545	304	31,160	9,450,000	U	C	Best arrangement
j	1.125	44	-10.22	-985	10,100	23.9	-6.85	-164	302	6,700	2,040,000	S	C	
GE-GC: pc	0.273	122	-45.5	1	-45.5	0.0174	100	1.74	2.07	100	207	S	V	Stable point contact arrangement
j	0.557	2.3	-86	1	-86	1.27	7.14	9.1	2,000	7.3	14,600	S	V	
GC-GB: pc	-0.010	26	-0.292	133	-40	-0.76	1	-0.76	1.135	133	151	U	V	
j	2.4	26	0.75	985	740	-25	0.872	-21.8	12.8	845	10,900	S	C	
GC-GE: pc	34.5	-24	0.98	-133	-130	-0.975	-230	224	0.054	31,000	1,720	U	V	Fourth best
j	40	82.5	0.975	-985	-958	-24.5	-6.86	168	2.69	6,740	18,100	S	V	
GC-GC: pc	15.27	0.7	0.99	0.994	0.98	0.0075	-100	-0.75	0.001	100	0.1	S	C	Gains too low to be practical
j	947	0.05	1	1	1	1.33	-7.14	-9.52	0.00274	7.26	0.02	S	C	

* May easily be unstable. See text.

Abbreviations: pc point contact
j junction
U unstable
S stable
C current (phase reversal)
V voltage (phase reversal)
K kilohms

formula for the output of stage III, such as given in Table 10-1, and replacing R_g by the output resistance of stages I and II, as given by Eqs. (12-19), (12-57), (12-70), (12-83), etc. Both the formulas and numerical values are obtainable in this way.

VG_o. By theorem III, the voltage gain of stages I and II is found by using the formula for the voltage gain of stages I and II, as in Eqs. (12-28), (12-72), (12-85), (12-100), etc., and replacing R_L by $R_{i_{III}}$. When this has been done, the voltage gain of stage III is obtained by replacing R_g, in the formula for the voltage gain of the third stage, by zero. The over-all voltage gain is then the product of the voltage gains computed in the two preceding steps.

P_o. By theorem IV, the power gain of the first two stages, I and II, is found by using the power gain of stages I and II, as computed by Eqs. (12-50), (12-76), (12-89), etc., and replacing R_L by $R_{i_{III}}$. To find the power gain of the third stage, write the Kirchhoff equation for stage III. *It is not necessary to solve for the currents or to use any equivalent resistor across the input to stage III.* Take the square of the ratio of the coefficients of the loop IV current to the loop III current (note that with three stages there will be four loops; with n stages, $n + 1$ loops), and multiply by the ratio of R_L to $R_{i_{III}}$. The product of the power gains obtained in these two steps will be the over-all power gain.

191. SUMMARY

1. Point contact transistors tend to be unstable in cascaded arrangements. Where they are stable, gains are low.

2. Significant improvements in single-stage gains are entirely possible with cascaded transistor stages using junction transistors.

3. For junction transistors, the GE to GE connection gives best all-around gains. The GE to GB, GB to GE, and GE to GC connections are capable of less gain.

4. Theorems I through IV are useful to check computations and to give a rapid method of calculation of input and output resistance and voltage and power gains.

5. Theorems I through IV may be used to compute quickly R_i, R_o, VG, and PG for more than two stages in cascade.

REFERENCES

1. Roddam, T.: Stabilizing the Working Point, *Wireless World*, Vol. 59, pp. 311–313, July, 1953.
2. Terman, F. E.: "Radio Engineering," McGraw-Hill Book Company, Inc., New York, 1947.

3. Ryder, R. M., and R. J. Kircher: Some Circuit Aspects of the Transistor, *Bell System Tech. J.*, Vol. 28, No. 3, pp. 367–400, July, 1949.

4. Shea, R. F.: "Transistor Circuits," pp. 120ff., John Wiley & Sons, Inc., New York, 1953.

5. Research Study of Transistor Preamplifier for Dynamic Microphones, Third Quarterly Progress Report, Contr. DA 36-039–sc-42501, Altec Lansing Corporation, Jan. 1, 1953 to Apr. 1, 1953.

6. Transistor Circuits for Telegraph Terminal TH-5/TG, and Telegraph-Telephone Signal Converter TA-182/U, Fourth Quarterly Progress Report, Contr. DA 36-039-sc-42529, Kellogg Switchboard and Supply Co., Apr. 1, 1953, to June 30, 1953.

7. Shea, R. F.: "Transistor Circuits," pp. 169ff., John Wiley & Sons, Inc., New York, 1953.

13 MANUFACTURING PROCESSES

The preparation of germanium will be discussed briefly in this chapter, and some details of manufacturing processes will be presented to give the reader an insight into the manufacturing problems. By close study of manufacturing techniques, the observant student will obtain a better understanding of the performance to be anticipated from transistors under various conditions. In this field, possibly as much as in any, the operation is markedly influenced by the method of manufacture.

192. GERMANIUM PREPARATION

In the United States, germanium is obtained primarily as a by-product of zinc-mining operations. It is obtainable also from coal ash, and in England where germanium-rich coal deposits have been found this is the source of all germanium produced commercially. Because there is considerable waste in transistor manufacturing processes, the weight of germanium which must be produced is far greater than the weight of germanium in the finished transistor pellets. At present the preparation of the germanium is one of the most important and expensive steps in transistor manufacture.

193. REDUCTION

Commercially, germanium is available in the form of germanium dioxide (GeO_2), a white powder. The dioxide is heated at approximately 650°C in a reducing atmosphere, usually hydrogen, for several hours, and is thereby reduced to the germanium element itself in the form of a gray-green powder. The latter is heated, usually in a high-purity graphite or quartz boat, to a temperature of about 1000°C to produce molten germanium, resembling molten lead in appearance. The melting process is carried out with a gas, such as hydrogen, helium, or argon, surrounding the melt to prevent oxidation. Alternately, the melting may be done in a vacuum, but this is usually regarded as less convenient than a gas atmosphere. The molten mass is cooled, and solid germanium is obtained in the form of bars several inches to a foot long and about a square inch in cross-sectional area. In this state, the purity is usually not satisfactory for transistor manufacture; also, the germanium is usually polycrystalline and has a low lifetime, whereas for transistor work, single-crystal material with good lifetime is desirable.

194. PURIFICATION

Next, the germanium is purified by any one of a number of processes,[1] but the most efficient and most commonly used is that of zone purification, or zone melting.[2] The impurities present in the greatest concentration are usually nickel, calcium, copper, manganese, arsenic, iron, and silicon, although not necessarily in the order given with regard to per cent concentration. It must always be borne in mind that, when dealing with transistors, germanium must be used with extremely high orders of purity because concentrations of impurities which would not cause difficulty in the highest purity copper, for example, would render germanium virtually useless for transistor applications. It is for this reason that purification processes in transistor preparation are much more difficult and extensive than in comparative purification processes for other materials. As an illustration, purification may be accomplished by fractional distillation of the germanium dioxide, but the material obtained is usually not sufficiently free of impurities to be suitable for transistor manufacture.

In preparing germanium the most successful approach has been to purify the material to the maximum extent possible, as will be discussed subsequently. This produces germanium of higher resistivity than is desired for transistor fabrication. It is then possible to deliberately add impurities of the type and quantity desired to yield germanium of the type (N or P) and specific resistivity required.

195. ZONE MELTING

In the zone-melting process the ingot is usually placed in a carbon container or boat and the entire assembly surrounded by a quartz tube in which a suitable inert gas, such as argon, is continuously circulated. A short section of the germanium ingot is melted and the molten

Fig. 13-1. Zone-purification furnace, using six rf heating coils. Note the mechanism for moving the germanium-filled boat from left to right, and hose for the gas, usually argon. Coils are in series, and approximately 2 kw of rf power is usually required. (*Courtesy of the Western Electric Co.*)

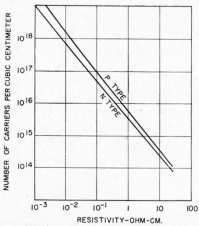

Fig. 13-2. A graph showing the empirical relationships between carrier concentration per cubic centimeter versus resistivity, in ohm-cm at room temperature, for N- and P-type germanium. Extrapolated, it is seen that highest purity germanium, of 50 ohm-cm and higher, will contain less than 10^{14} carriers per cubic centimeter.

region moved slowly along the bar. The gas serves to maintain a small internal pressure so as to keep out undesirable impurities and air. One or more rf coils, of two or three turns each, are wound around the quartz container to provide the induction heating necessary to melt the germanium (see Fig. 13-1). The use of as many as six coils is common to permit purification, in one pass, equal to that possible

Fig. 13-3. A single-crystal pulling furnace, using the Czochralski technique of dipping a seed into the melt to start the crystal-growing process. In addition to provisions for pulling the crystal holder upward (at rates of fractions of an inch per hour), some furnaces have mechanisms to rotate the seed slowly. Close temperature control in this process is imperative. (*Courtesy of the General Electric Co.*)

with six passes using a single coil. The boat is pulled through at a rate of a few inches per hour.

Most impurities in germanium prefer the liquid phase rather than freeze into the solid state,[3] and will be swept along with the molten zone. The impurities will thus be concentrated toward one end, of which a length of about one inch is usually cropped off. Except for this end region, germanium with a resistivity as high as 60 ohm-cm may be obtained. There is theoretical and experimental evidence that the maximum resistivity of germanium may be as high as 65 ohm-cm. Some elements when present as impurities add to the available carriers of electric current, and hence the observed resistivity increases with purity and may be used as a measure of purity. The relationship between carrier concentration and resistivity for N- and P-type germanium is shown in Fig. 13-2 (see also Ref. 14).

Fig. 13-4. A close-up of the furnace showing the crystal in the pulling process. Note the coils about the furnace for rf heating. Uniformity of crystal cross section is desirable. (*Courtesy of the General Electric Co.*)

196. CRYSTAL PULLING

The single-crystal germanium necessary for transistor manufacture is obtained by a process called "crystal pulling." Sometimes referred to as the Czochralski technique,[4] this is the preferred method although other techniques for preparation of single-crystal germanium have been used successfully.[1] A typical crystal-pulling apparatus is shown in Fig. 13-3; in Fig. 13-4 a close-up of the ingot as it is pulled upward is shown. In the pulling process, purified germanium is melted in a crucible, and into this melt, maintained in a non-reacting atmosphere, a germanium seed is lowered. The seed is a small piece of single-crystal germanium. The crystallographic orientation of the seed with respect to the surface of the molten germanium determines the orientation of the resulting crystal obtained. For reference purposes, the most common directions of orientation of the seed, and the resultant crystal, are shown in the diagram in Fig. 13-5. It must be remembered that when speaking of cubic crystals, such as characterize germanium or silicon, the Miller indices identifying the faces are also used to identify the direction normal to that face. The indices and the method of identification of crystal planes are explained in the figure. The figures apply only for the cubic crystal. More general information is available in the literature.[5]

As the seed is slowly withdrawn from the melt, the molten ger-

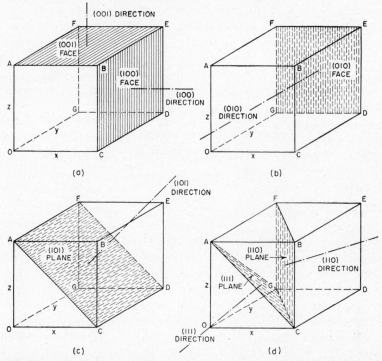

Fig. 13-5. Identification of principal planes of cubic crystals. Miller indices are small integers to locate quickly the principal planes and axes of crystals. Because of the high order of symmetry of the cubic crystal, the scheme using Miller indices may be particularized for cubic crystals into the following:

(a) Select a corner as origin of axes, such as 0 in (a), (b), (c), (d), and consider the xyz axes as shown. The first number of the index then relates to x, the second to y, and the third to z.

(b) To find the (111) plane, locate a point unit distance from 0 along x, another along y (starting from 0), and a third along z. The plane through the three points so located is the (111) plane, [see (d)].

(c) To locate (001) face, move 0 units along x, 0 units along y, and 1 unit along z. The only face possible is ABEF as in (a).

(d) The indices denote a single plane, or a set of parallel planes. Thus (001) in effect represents all the infinite set of planes in (a) parallel to ABEF, since unit distance is not specifically defined, except for plane ABEF itself, where the "1" in (001) means the lattice constant.

(e) The axis, for cubic crystals, corresponding to a given Miller index face, is given the same indices and is understood to be perpendicular to the face stated. Note face (010) and (010) axis in (b).

(f) It is not necessary to select the origin as shown. To locate a plane different from the ones shown, select a different origin. But, because of the symmetry, *the planes indicated are the principal planes.* If the origin is chosen at B, say, the (111) plane will pass through points A, C, E, but it is evident that this is the same plane as AGC in (d) and is obtainable by suitable rotation of the symmetrical crystal.

manium adheres to it and grows over the seed to form a single crystal upon solidification. Ingots of germanium of a kilogram or more in weight may be obtained in this manner. Close temperature control is essential during the pulling process, and controllers accurate to the order of 0.1°C have been developed for this purpose. To promote uniform crystal growth and mixing of added impurities, the melt is often agitated by superimposing on the withdrawing, vertical motion a small-amplitude vibratory motion. In addition, the seed is usually spun at a speed of about 100 rpm. With good control of the melt temperature and rate of seed withdrawal, very uniform crystals may be grown.

197. IMPURITY CONTROL

As previously described, the zone-purification process yields germanium of greater purity than is optimum for transistor manufacture. During the crystal-pulling process, impurities in controlled amounts may be added to decrease the resistivity to desired values. When the impurities are added, they are usually small pellets of elements such as arsenic or indium. Since a pellet of the impurities alone would be quite small, a common practice is to prepare a germanium-impurity element alloy which can be tested and handled more conveniently. The agitation of the bath serves to promote uniform distribution of the impurity added throughout the melt. This is necessary in order to accurately determine the number of impurity atoms which must be added to obtain the desired resistivity germanium and to obtain a crystal of uniform characteristics.

198. FOUR-PROBE RESISTIVITY MEASUREMENT

At the end of the reduction process, but more commonly after the zone-purification and crystal-pulling processes, it is desirable and often necessary to test the resistivity of the ingot for process-control purposes. In the early days, a specimen had to be cut, carefully finished to size, and its resistivity measured by a potentiometer method. Not only was the preparation of the specimen time-consuming, but in addition, cutting up of the ingot was necessary. If the resistivity was not acceptable, the ingot had to be broken up into smaller pieces and the entire operation from melting to purification repeated. With the development of the four-probe method,[6,7] it is no longer necessary to cut out a specimen since the resistivity is obtainable directly from the ingot. Figure 13-6 shows a four-probe measurement apparatus.

Four equally spaced probes located along a straight line are placed on the ingot, and a voltage is applied between the two outer contacts. It can be shown (see Ref. 6) that, if the current is adjusted to a critical value, the voltage between the inner probes is exactly the resistivity of the material, in suitable units.[8] This mathematicophysical contribution to material processing has substantially shortened measurement time.

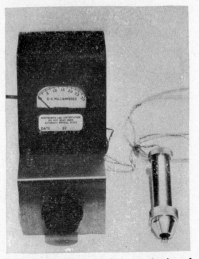

Fig. 13-6. Four-probe method of resistivity measurement. A minimum of associated apparatus is required, the readings are sufficiently accurate for most purposes and, with suitable calibration, indicate resistivity directly. (*Courtesy of the General Electric Co.*)

199. SINGLE CRYSTAL

When the crystal is obtained from the pulling process, with a little experience, one can determine by visual inspection whether the crystal is mono- or polycrystalline. The absence of grain boundaries at the bottom and sides is usually a sufficient indication that a single crystal is at hand; where doubt exists, the crystal is etched, *i.e.*, treated in an acid bath in the manner to be described below. Differential etching, if properly done, will bring out grain boundaries in an unmistakable manner clearly visible to the unaided eye.

200. SLICING AND DICING

If the crystal is a single crystal, and if the resistivity measurement indicates that the purity is correct for the application desired, the ingot, now in the form of an irregular cylinder perhaps 8 in. long and 1 in. in diameter, is ready for the slicing operation. It is necessary to distinguish between the slicing operation—in which the cylindrical ingot is cut into slices perhaps 0.020 in. thick by cutting at right angles to the longitudinal axis—and dicing, where the resulting slices, or wafers, are cut into small squares of about 0.1 in. on a side, the size depending on the application. Slicing is done by diamond saws, approximately 0.020 in. thick, which are usually single, see Fig. 13-7, but may be ganged. Dicing is similarly done by means of somewhat

Fig. 13-7. A cutting tool and machine for slicing wafers from the single-crystal ingot. A coolant is usually desirable. The ingot may be fastened to the adjustable table shown by means of a hot plastic compound. If the crystal has been pulled properly, it is desirable to cut exactly perpendicular to the long axis. (*Courtesy of the Raytheon Manufacturing Co.*)

Fig. 13-8. Ganged diamond-edge cutting wheels used for the dicing operation. A coolant, usually water, is necessary. The table has provisions for turning the wafer through 90° after cutting through in one direction. Usually sealing wax is used to hold the wafer in place. (*Courtesy of the General Electric Co.*)

thinner diamond saws, but usually ganged, as in Fig. 13-8.   Recently, there has appeared another method of dicing wherein the wafers or slices are scratched, just as one scratches glass for cutting, and then the slice is broken up into component dice.   Dicing is also done by cutting blades vibrating in a vertical plane at supersonic rates.   The amplitude of vibration is quite small.   It is useful to observe in passing that germanium is quite brittle, with a hardness approximately equal to that of glass.   The die of single-crystal germanium of correct resistivity is the starting point for the construction and assembly of the transistor.

201. ETCHING

One of the most important steps in the procedure outlined above, from the reduction to the preparation of the dice, is that of etching. The ingot obtained from the reduction process may be etched to remove surface oxides or other impurities and occasionally to reveal the grain structure.   A common etch for this purpose consists of one-half hydrofluoric acid (HF) and one-half nitric acid (HNO_3).   After the zone-purification process it may be desirable to clean again to remove surface oxides and reveal grain boundaries.   The same etch may be used.   After the crystal is pulled, the ingot may again be etched to assist in locating grain boundaries if a perfect single-crystal structure has not been attained.   Here an etch called superoxol, which is the strongest concentration of peroxide obtainable, may be used.[1] Or, ferric chloride ($FeCl_2$) may be used and the sample heated for about 15 min until the liquid boils.   After slicing, the wafer is usually etched to remove saw marks and to reduce the wafer size to the thickness desired.   Sometimes, when deep saw marks are present which cannot be removed by etching, the wafers may be ground with a fine carborundum powder paste to obtain a very smooth surface.   Carborundum lapping may also be used to get a smooth surface for the four-probe test.   All surface cracks and irregularities must be removed from the germanium die or chip before construction of the transistor if a high reject rate is to be avoided.   For this reason and to get a uniform thickness for the diffusion process to be described, lapping and etching are essential steps in transistor fabrication.   When the dice have been cut to size, they are etched again to remove surface films and oxides before final transistor assembly operations are undertaken.   In general, the etches mentioned are representative, but by no means all inclusive.   Many variations and combinations of the very active acids are in use, particularly mixtures of hydrofluoric acid, nitric acid, and hydrogen peroxide (H_2O_2).   Each laboratory through practical experience has established mixtures suitable for its own requirements (see also note 7 in Ref. 16).

202. CAT WHISKERS

Superficially, cat whiskers appear to serve an elementary role: that of providing a convenient electrode connection to the semiconductor material. It is not an ohmic contact such as this would imply, however, but a nonlinear or rectifying contact. In the case of germanium crystal diodes, because of the presence of surface states, the theoretical differences of rectification by metal-semiconductor contacts due to metals of different work functions are not usually observed. To a large extent in the manufacture of crystal diodes, cat whisker materials have been selected on the basis of mechanical considerations. As cat whiskers are placed in pressure contact with the semiconductor, materials which can be formed into good springs are preferred.

In the case of point contact transistors, the mechanical considerations outlined are equally important; however, it is found experimentally that the choice of cat whisker material has a profound influence on the electrical properties of the transistor. In the case of N-type point contact transistors, it is customary to "form" or electrically pulse the collector during manufacture in order to improve and stabilize transistor action.[25] Phosphor bronze wire has been found to possess excellent spring properties and to "form" better than most materials investigated. "Forming" is not well understood, and it is not clear why phosphor bronze cat whiskers form more readily than cat whiskers of other materials. One hypothesis is that a small region of P-type germanium is created under the collector during forming and that the phosphor in the phosphor bronze diffuses into the germanium during forming. Phosphorus is pentavalent.

Phosphor bronze wires are sometimes also used for the emitter cat whisker. Forming of the emitter, however, is unnecessary and may even render the transistor's characteristics less useful by reduction of the emitter reverse resistance. The material for the emitter cat whisker may therefore be selected on the basis that it will not form readily and that it possesses suitable mechanical properties. Beryllium copper satisfies the first requirement and can be shaped into wires and pointed with the same tools and fixtures necessary for phosphor bronze. It is therefore widely used as the emitter cat whisker material in point contact transistors.

Cat whisker wire is usually 0.005 in. in diameter and of the specified material and hardness. The wires are bent into the desired shape,

welded or soldered to the supporting members (see Fig. 13-9), and cut
to length.   The wires are pointed either by cutting or grinding at an
angle to reduce the area of contact with the surface of the germanium
and to permit close spacing of the points.

In the preparation of the germanium pellet, one face may be plated
for convenience in soldering to the base plug or mounting tab.   After
the cat whiskers are mounted and correctly spaced and the germanium

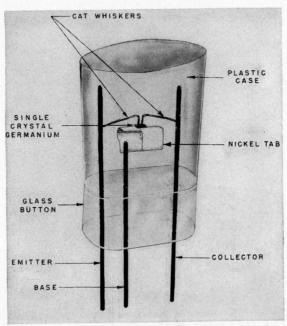

Fig. 13-9. Point contact transistor assembly.   In one form of assembly, the uprights are
not cut to size until the plastic sealing is complete to ensure a minimum of motion of the
parts after the original alignment of the cat whiskers.   (Courtesy of RCA.)

wafer is soldered in place, the assembly operation may proceed.   The
subassemblies are introduced into a case (if applicable) or mounted on a
suitable stem.   The germanium pellet is then brought up to the
whiskers by an operator who views the operation through a microscope
or with the aid of a shadowgraph, and adjustments are made for the
correct spacing and pressure of contacts.   The collector is formed[9] by
means of a suitable high voltage and current pulse, usually obtained
from a condenser discharge circuit.   Electrical tests are performed as
the transistor is pulsed to obtain the desired characteristics (see Appendix III, par. 4.57).   A typical flow chart for transistor assembly
operations is indicated in Fig. 13-10.

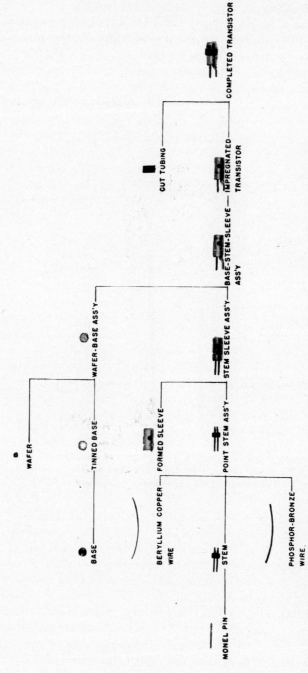

Fig. 13-10. Components and steps in the assembly of the WE type A transistor, 2N22 (1698). Note that different metals are used for the emitter and collector wires. This type has now been replaced for many applications by the structure using a button as in type 1858 shown in Fig. 2-2.

203. PRECAUTIONS

Throughout the entire assembly process a high order of cleanliness is maintained to avoid films of oil, dirt, or oxides on the germanium pellet or adjacent surfaces. Many manufacturers apparently feel that air conditioning is an asset during assembly, although it does not provide the full degree of dryness and cleanliness actually required. In some cases, the germanium pellets are deliberately coated with an inert wax until ready for use to avoid contamination. It has been found that a monomolecular layer of moisture on the surface of germanium is sufficient to produce deleterious effects. In the assembly process, the units may be either hermetically sealed or encased in a suitable plastic to protect the germanium surface and, incidentally, to make the unit opaque to light (see Appendix III, par. 4.64). The base-lead arrangement in Fig. 13-11 is an industry and military-service standard used by many manufacturers.

204. EFFECTS OF MANUFACTURING CONTROL

With regard to the point contact transistor, the details of manufacturing have a noticeable and profound influence on the characterizing parameters. For instance, low-resistivity germanium will produce low values of base resistance r_b and r_{11} and conversely. The resistance of the emitter diode increases with increased-resistivity germanium and conversely. Decreased point spacing will increase base resistance and frequency cutoff for germanium of a given resistivity (see Ref. 6, before Appendix I of reference). Forming the collector decreases r_{21} and r_{22}, but their ratio, α, increases somewhat at the expense of increased I_{co}. The temperature dependence of a transistor's electrical characteristics tends to increase with the resistivity of the germanium. It can be seen from this general outline how one characteristic may be improved at the expense of another, but in general manufacturing processes can aim at particular characteristics to obtain special desiderata. The control of transistor parameters in manufacture cannot be said to be very precise at present, and the field of quality control will undoubtedly experience many significant changes and improvements in the next few years. The foregoing is not intended to disparage in any way the rapid progress which has been made in transistor technology, but rather to point out that further progress must be made before all variables will be under adequate control.

205. HALL EFFECT AND MOBILITY

Consider the motion of the injected carriers, holes or electrons, from emitter to collector. We have observed in previous discussions that,

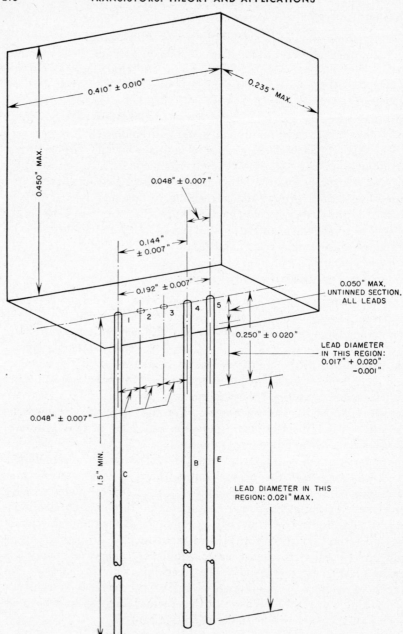

Fig. 13-11. A proposed base arrangement rapidly gaining favor among all transistor manufacturers and the services, which is now in the final stages of acceptance by industry standardization committees. The shape of the transistor is not specified, but must preferably fit within the volume indicated.

if the material is too impure, transistor action is impeded, and one may explain this in a general way by saying that the impurities prevent the normal motion of holes or electrons by providing many excess electrons (or holes). These excess particles either produce too many collisions or else render the material so highly conducting that control of collector current by emitter current is ineffective. We thus observe the need for control of the impurities, and, as Fig. 13-2 shows, if the resistivity is measured, one obtains a good index of the number of impurity atoms per cubic centimeter. (It can be shown that each impurity atom contributes, on the average, a single excess hole or electron.)

But for good transistor action this is not the whole story. The velocity with which the electrons, or holes, move in the germanium determines their transit time and, therefore, the frequency response and pulse response. The force on an electron due to an electric field is given by

$$F = Ee \qquad (13\text{-}1)$$

$$\text{Force} = \frac{\text{force}}{\text{charge}} \times \text{charge on the electron}$$

The factor E in Eq. (13-1), variously called electric field intensity or force per unit charge, is computed by taking the potential difference across two points, say, the emitter and collector, and dividing by the distance between. Thus

$$E = \frac{V}{d} \qquad (13\text{-}2)$$

where V is the potential difference. When an electron is moving in a region where the electric field intensity has some value E, the force on it is Ee or Ve/d:

$$F = \frac{Ve}{d} \qquad (13\text{-}3)$$

Of course, the greater the force on it, the faster it will move, so that if V is large, or d very small for a given V, the force is large and the electron will move rapidly. A measure of the velocity of the electron is the mobility, which is defined as the velocity, in centimeters per second, for each volt per centimeter, or for each unit of electric intensity, as in Eq. (13-2). That is, the mobility given by the Greek letter mu (μ) is defined as

$$\mu = \frac{\text{velocity in cm per sec}}{\text{electric field intensity}}$$

$$= \frac{v}{E} \qquad \text{or by Eq. (13-2)}$$

$$= \frac{vd}{V} \qquad (13\text{-}4)$$

where v is the velocity in centimeters per second. From Eq. (13-4), it is seen that the units or dimensions of mobility are

$$\frac{\text{cm}}{\text{sec}} \times \frac{\text{cm}}{\text{volts}} = \text{cm}^2 \text{ per volt-sec} \qquad (13\text{-}5)$$

Since the mobility is so important a parameter of the material and because it determines pulse and frequency response, it is necessary to determine the value of this parameter of the bulk germanium if transistors are to be manufactured in accordance with design requirements.

The mobility can be measured directly by a technique to be described later in this chapter. Another method of measuring mobility, which is, however, not without its disadvantages, makes use of the Hall coefficient. As will be explained, the Hall coefficient provides data regarding the carrier or impurity concentration or density for each sample as well as the conductivity type. In addition, the Hall value in conjunction with resistivity enables one to determine mobility. When carrier concentration and mobility are known or measurable, and their temperature dependence is studied, valuable data regarding the temperature range of useful transistor action are provided. Accordingly, the Hall coefficient is an important parameter for the evaluation of properties of bulk material to be used in the manufacture of transistors.

206. HALL EFFECT

We have noted above, Eq. (13-1), that an electron, or hole, in an electric field of V volts per centimeter, experiences a force on it equal to Ve/d or Ee. Similarly, an electron or hole in a magnetic field experiences a force on it which varies with the magnitude of the charge, the velocity of the particle, and the number of magnetic lines per unit area, as well as the angle which these lines of magnetic flux make with the direction of motion. There is an important difference, however, between these two forces: by agreement or convention, the direction of the electric field is taken as that in which a positive charge, or hole, would move if placed in the field. For example, we would say that if the electric field were from left to right on this page, parallel to the lines of type, a positive charge or hole would move to the right and a negative charge or electron would be urged to the left. In the case of the magnetic field, the force is always so directed that the particle, hole or electron, is urged in a direction which is perpendicular both to its original direction and to the direction of the magnetic field. Thus the magnetic field continually urges the particle sidewise and in a circular orbit.

Let us take a sample of germanium of known resistivity, as in Fig. 13-12, and subject it to both electric and magnetic fields simultaneously. The electric field is obtained by connecting the right side of the germanium sample to the positive terminal of a battery, and the left-hand end to the negative terminal. The electric field, which we will assume uniform for the illustration, is V, the potential of the battery, divided by the length of the sample, d, in centimeters. A magnetic field of B lines per square centimeter is assumed (practical values range upward of 2,000 lines per square centimeter) in the z direction, corresponding to a magnetic field intensity H.

The electrons are urged to the right (see Eq. (13-1)), as shown by the arrow OA, by the force of the electric field; they are simultaneously urged along OB by the action of the magnetic field. Their net displacement is along OC; observe that the combined electric and magnetic fields displace the particles to one side of the specimen. If the electric alone were used, the electrons would go from left to right only; if a magnetic field alone were used, they would move in circular paths. The displacement of these electrons to the side creates a concentration of electrons at one side and, of course, a deficiency on the other. A deficiency of electrons, as the reader knows, constitutes a positive net charge. Hence across the sample, between points P and Q, say, there will be developed a potential difference, plus at Q, minus at P. But such a potential will tend to pull the electrons which provide the negative charge at P back toward Q. Hence the potential developed across PQ in time balances out the effect of the electric and magnetic fields, and no more charges will accumulate at P (on the P side, understood). It is actually possible to place a voltmeter across points P and Q and measure a voltage. This displacement voltage, due to the motion of charges under crossed electric and magnetic fields and which comes to equilibrium as explained above, is called the Hall voltage and the phenomenon which produces it is called the Hall effect after its discoverer.

207. APPLICATION OF HALL EFFECT

For a complete analysis of the Hall effect and its ramifications, the reader is referred to Refs. 10 to 12, but the derivation will be presented in sufficient detail to provide an understanding of the method and possible complications that are involved in the measurement of the Hall voltage.

In Fig. 13-12, the force Ee, due to the electric field, is proportional to the length of the vector OA, and the force due to the magnetic field, which is given by evH/c, is proportional to the length of the vector OB.

Hence

$$\tan \theta = \frac{evH}{Eec}$$

and for small angles, since the effect is usually quite small,

$$\theta = \frac{evH}{Eec} = \frac{vH}{Ec} \tag{13-6}$$

By Eq. (13-4), v/E is the mobility μ; so we may write Eq. (13-6)

$$\theta = \mu \frac{H}{c} \tag{13-7}$$

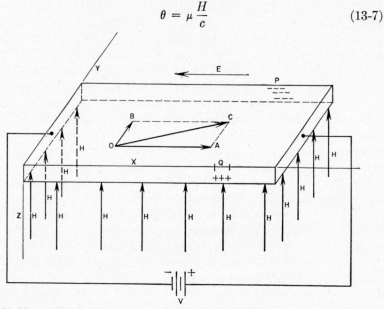

Fig. 13-12. A sketch to indicate the essentials of the Hall effect. The potential from point P to Q is the Hall voltage. A rather thin slice is usually necessary. Note X, Y, Z directions.

The electric intensity from P to Q which is developed because of the Hall effect will be denoted by E_y while the longitudinal electric intensity will be denoted by E_x. From the same figure,

$$E_y = E_x \tan \theta \qquad \text{and if } \theta \text{ is small}$$
$$= E_x \theta \tag{13-8}$$

E_x is the IR drop along the length of the specimen, per unit length.

$$E_x = \frac{IR}{L}$$

and if we want to express E_x in terms of current density, I per square centimeter (to be denoted by i), and ρ the resistivity, we may write as follows:

$$E_x = \frac{I}{cm^2} \times cm^2 \times \frac{ohms}{cm}$$

$$= i \times ohm\text{-}cm = i\rho \qquad (13\text{-}9)$$

since ρ, the resistivity, is specified in ohm-centimeters.

Equation (13-9) states that the electric field intensity in the specimen along the x direction is the product of the current density (total current along X divided by the cross-sectional area) times the resistivity of the material ρ. Using this value in Eq. (13-8)

$$E_y = i\rho\theta \qquad (13\text{-}10)$$

or by Eq. (13-7)

$$E_y = \mu \frac{\rho H i}{c} \qquad (13\text{-}11)$$

By definition, the Hall coefficient is the coefficient of Hi in Eq. (13-11) and is denoted by R_H:

$$R_H = \frac{\mu\rho}{c} \qquad (13\text{-}12)$$

In general

$$\sigma = \text{conductivity} = \frac{1}{\rho}$$

$$= Ne\mu$$

$$= \frac{particles}{cm^3} \times \frac{charge}{particles} \times \frac{cm^2}{volt\text{-}sec}$$

$$= \text{charge per } \frac{cm}{volt\text{-}sec} = \text{reciprocal ohm-cm} \qquad (13\text{-}13)$$

We must henceforth distinguish between the particles of $+$ and $-$ sign. For electrons, the particles per cubic centimeter will be denoted by n; for holes it will be denoted by p. Mobility of holes, which is usually less than for electrons, will be denoted by μ_h, and for electrons, by μ_e; and the charge is $+e$ on the holes and $-e$ on the electrons. Where the majority carriers are holes, we would attribute the conductivity to holes and write

$$\sigma_h = pe\mu_h = \frac{1}{\rho_n} \qquad (13\text{-}14)$$

and for electrons,

$$\sigma_e = -ne\mu_e = \frac{1}{\rho_p} \qquad (13\text{-}15)$$

Using Eqs. (13-14) and (13-15), in Eq. (13-12) we have for the Hall coefficient

$$R_H = \frac{1}{pec} \text{ for holes} \quad \text{and} \quad R_H = \frac{-1}{nec} \text{ for electrons} \quad (13\text{-}16)$$

The negative sign of the Hall coefficient for electrons is important when compared to the positive sign for holes, since the sign of the Hall coefficient and, in practice, of the Hall voltage is a direct indication of whether the sample is N or P type. This is one of the most positive methods of determining the conductivity type of semiconductor materials known.

In practice, the Hall coefficient is obtained from the formula

$$R_H = \frac{V_H t \times 10^8}{HI} \quad (13\text{-}17)$$

where V_H is the Hall voltage, H is the magnetic field intensity, and is obtained by multiplying the applied magnetic field density B by the permeability of Ge,[13] t is the thickness in centimeters, and I is the total longitudinal current. R_H is obtained in the so-called practical units from Eq. (13-17), in cubic centimeters per coulomb, if V is in volts, t in centimeters, H in amperes per centimeter using the proper units for the permeability, and I in amperes.

208. FINDING n, p, AND μ

Once R_H is known, from Eq. (13-17), and note that the sign of V_H is different for holes and electrons, we can use Eq. (13-16) to find the hole or electron concentration and therefore the impurity concentration:

$$n = -\frac{1}{R_{H_e}ec} \quad \text{and} \quad p = \frac{1}{R_{H_h}ec} \quad (13\text{-}18)$$

c is the velocity of light in centimeters per second, usually taken as 3×10^{10}.

When n and p are known, we can use Eqs. (13-13) to (13-15) to get the mobility. Or, preferably, we can use Eq. (13-12) directly if the resistivity of the material is known.

$$\mu_h = \frac{cR_{H_h}}{\rho} \quad \text{and} \quad \mu_e = \frac{cR_{H_e}}{\rho} \quad (13\text{-}19)$$

Looking at Eq. (13-12), we may properly infer that, other parameters constant, high-resistivity material will yield high values of Hall coefficient and conversely. For germanium at room temperature with a resistivity of a few ohm-centimeters such as commonly used for transistor manufacture, the Hall coefficient is of the order of 10,000 for P-type and 20,000 for N-type material. Very pure germanium, 60 ohm-cm, will have a Hall coefficient of approximately 150,000 cm³ per coulomb.[14] It is important to note that the Hall coefficient is not a function of the magnetic or electric field strength used—it is a function only of the mobility and resistivity of the material [see Eq. (13-12)]. However, the advantage of using large field strengths is that larger Hall voltages are obtained, facilitating accurate measurements.

Electron mobilities are found up to approximately 3,700 cm² per volt-sec, and hole mobilities to 1,800 cm² per volt-sec, for germanium.

In general, as the temperature is increased, resistivity decreases because additional valence bonds are broken and provide additional carriers.[14] The mobility also decreases with increase in temperature[13] because the average speed of the particles increases, increasing the number of collisions and hence decreasing the average distance traversed in a given time. By Eq. (13-12) one can predict that the Hall coefficient also decreases with increase in temperature, and this is borne out experimentally.

209. DETAILS OF PROCEDURE

The general theory derived for the Hall effect and the determination of mobilities and impurity densities is accurate for many purposes, but certain corrections and precautions are used to obtain theoretical results more nearly equal to those obtained experimentally. For instance, Eq. (13-18) is usually regarded as insufficiently accurate for general application. At room temperature, where Hall measurements are normally made, the crystal lattice in the case of germanium is in a relatively violent state of vibration—note that germanium becomes intrinsic, for low-resistivity samples, at slightly over 100°C—and the usual assumptions made to obtain Eq. (13-18) are not entirely accurate (see Ref. 10, p. 277). A correction factor is introduced, and each of the equations is modified:

$$n = \frac{1.178}{R_{H_e}ec} \qquad p = \frac{1.178}{R_{H_h}ec} \qquad (13\text{-}20)$$

In any given sample, at any time, there will be both holes and electrons. Equations given thus far assumed that either one or the other is present. If both are present, usually a still different formula must be used (see Ref. 10, pp. 217 and 280). For samples which are predominantly N or P type, the relations in Eq. (13-20) give satisfactory results. Because of the corrections and difficulties of using the more correct formula, direct measurement of mobility is preferred in many cases.

In performing the Hall coefficient measurements, certain difficulties must be overcome. From Fig. 13-12 one can see that it is important to have points P and Q "diametrically" opposite. For this reasons the specimen must be carefully ground to size and shape, and the measurement points accurately and carefully located. As noted above, the Hall coefficient varies with temperature; therefore, currents must be small to prevent heating, but cannot be too small if readable Hall voltages are to be obtained. Finally, other voltages appear when using dc because of thermal and galvanic effects,[12] and these may introduce important errors. For this reason, ac is generally used, and by proper techniques extraneous voltages are kept to a minimum. Amplifiers are usually needed to obtain readable voltages. Currents of a few milliamperes are usually employed.

210. DIRECT MEASUREMENT OF MOBILITY

The mobility obtained using the Hall coefficient in an equation like (13-19) is sometimes called the Hall mobility, and may not be the true mobility. True mobility is defined as the measured velocity, per volt per centimeter, as opposed to a mobility obtained indirectly by measurement of some other constant such as R_H. Since, for computation or prediction of frequency response and pulse response and for determination of extremes of temperature range, true mobility is needed, many manufacturers prefer to measure mobility directly.

Direct measurement of mobility is effected by measuring the actual transit time between emitter and collector[15] and dividing this time into the accurately measured spacing between emitter and collector contacts. Oscilloscopic indications are used to measure the arrival of injected carriers, and suitable means are provided in the electronics of the circuit to indicate time of departure and time of arrival. To prevent spreading effects and measure only the in-direction velocity, electric fields as large as possible are used. Also, the presence of holes (or injected electrons) tends to alter or modulate the resistivity of the germanium sample used, giving incorrect indications of the potential difference and hence of the electric field intensity. To minimize this so-called conductivity modulation, very small emitter currents are used, and amplification of the ouput signal is necessary. Another reason for the use of small currents is to prevent a temperature rise of the sample, since mobility varies quite rapidly with temperature ($T^{-3/2}$ law). For highest accuracy a pulse method is used, employing relatively low repetition rates and pulse duration times. Details of the experimental technique are to be found in Ref. 15, q.v. (see also Ref. 13).

211. LIFETIME

Even when the mobility, resistivity, Hall coefficient, and carrier concentrations of the germanium are known, there is still at least one important parameter for which the germanium must be measured. When the minority carriers are injected into a material, they tend to disturb the electrical neutrality of the bulk of the substance. Since the equilibrium tendency of all materials is to remain electrically neutral, and since injected carriers always find carriers of opposite sign in the material, recombinations take place to restore the electrical neutrality. Thus hole-electron recombinations are continually taking place during transistor action. However, it is clear that, if all injected holes recombined before reaching the collector, the current amplification observed in point contact transistors could not exist; in junction units, injected carriers moving through regions of opposite carrier type would die out, and the input signal would not be amplified. To keep the injected carriers from dying out, one might either reduce the spacing or increase the lifetime. Reducing the spacing has obvious mechanical contraindications, and may produce transistors with electrical characteristics less desirable than those obtainable by a specific spacing. Control of lifetime is a much more general solution, but is unfortunately one of the most difficult problems to be solved in the preparation of suitable germanium for transistors.

No complete theoretical explanation for the manner in which lifetime varies with resistivity, mobility, or carrier concentration is available, and this parameter, usually denoted by the Greek letter tau (τ), does not appear explicitly in mathematical expressions describing transistor behavior to any desirable extent. Yet, its effect on transistor performance is direct and immediate, and it is sufficiently important to exclude new materials from consideration as the basic substance for transistor work, when the lifetime is too low. It is also a parameter sometimes difficult to measure; many research workers in the field perform carefully arranged experiments to measure lifetime, only to discover that they are measuring a related parameter. For instance, the lifetime parameter is distinguished in the bulk and on the surface; it is sometimes very difficult to determine whether a surface, bulk, or combined lifetime is being measured.

212. MEASURING LIFETIME

There are several methods of direct measurement of lifetime, of which two are most commonly used. The pulse method[16] uses low repetition rates and low currents to prevent heating and results in an oscilloscopic presentation of the variation of sample resistance with time. From the curves, the lifetime is computed. It is extremely important to maintain a small dc voltage across the sample all the time, in order that injected carriers be swept out after the end of the injected pulse. Due to the hole-storage phenomenon discussed in Chap. 11, holes would accumulate if this were not done, particularly if the repetition rate were high, so that incorrect lifetimes would be indicated. The formulas used to obtain lifetime take into account the effect of the sweeping-out field on the resistance of the specimen.

As mentioned, recombinations are continually taking place on the surface, and within the bulk material; lifetimes τ_s and τ_v are obtainable for the surface and bulk, respectively. Lifetimes can be shown to add like resistances in parallel, *i.e.*, their reciprocals are additive arithmetically.

$$\frac{1}{\tau} = \frac{1}{\tau_s} + \frac{1}{\tau_v} \tag{13-21}$$

One way of looking at Eq. (13-21) is to say that the reciprocal of a lifetime is the rate of recombination, and of course rates of recombination add arithmetically. Actually measured is $1/\tau$, and the problem is to separate the recombination rates. The lifetime which is independent of sample dimensions is considered to be the volume lifetime; for small samples, the lifetime measured varies appreciably with sample size and with surface treatment, and may be identified in this way as the surface lifetime.

The other commonly used method of measuring lifetime[17] utilizes a beam of light as the means of injecting minority carriers. The light photons in essence produce new carriers by disruption of valence bonds or raising energy levels into the conduction band. As these carriers drift to the collector under the influence of the applied electric field, a lifetime is measurable associated with these light-formed carriers. It has been shown experimentally,[18] and mathematically,[19] that the current at the collector is linearly related to the carrier concentration, or hole density in the case of point contact operation. A plot is obtained in this method showing signal voltage versus distance from illuminated area, and the slope is used in a suitable formula (see Ref. 17) to obtain the diffusion length for the carriers, L. Knowing the diffusion length, the lifetime is computed from

$$\tau = \frac{L}{D} \tag{13-22}$$

At room temperatures, the diffusion constant D is known, see Ref. 13.

While this method is simple and relatively easy to perform, it requires certain assumptions which render the results not too accurate;

also, surface treatment of the sample appears to introduce complications. Typical lifetimes vary from a few microseconds to over 1,000 μsec.

213. CHARACTERISTICS OF LIFETIME

Lifetime is known to vary considerably with method of preparation, surface treatment, and heat-treatment history. Such treatments are selected with great care lest the treatment actually result in a serious reduction of lifetime. Bombardment by energetic particles, strains in the ingot during preparation, presence of certain types of impurities, imperfections of all types in the crystal, presence of strong electric and magnetic fields, improper grinding of the surface, certain chemical etches, etc., all unfortunately lower the lifetime. It can be seen, therefore, that attainment of good lifetime is a formidable problem, since values of at least 100 μsec are desirable for transistors of good grade. For special applications, lifetimes as low as several microseconds may be suitable, but usually several-hundred-microsecond-lifetime material is preferred. The subject is not well understood at present, and apparently represents a phase of material preparation which is open to considerable further research. Usually, the lower the resistivity, the lower the lifetime, but even this simple observation is overridden by other variables and is not consistent except that very low-resistivity germanium invariably possesses a low lifetime.

214. JUNCTION TRANSISTORS

Junction transistors are manufactured by a variety of processes which have a common characteristic—formation of a PN junction. The junction may be formed by a diffusion process,[20] during the crystal-pulling process,[21] or by the rate-grown junction method,[22] but in each case a sandwich consisting of two N or P layers separated by a P or N layer, respectively, must be achieved. The starting material for the diffusion process is in the form of a die cut from a wafer. In other methods the junction is produced during the crystal-growing operation. In all cases, the preparation of the semiconductor material is the same, and the parameters discussed, mobility, lifetime, resistivity, and impurity density, must be controlled and known before commencement of the actual transistor construction.

215. DIFFUSION PROCESS

Fundamentally, the diffusion process consists of placing a small pellet of P-forming impurity (for PNP transistors) on a die of N-type germanium followed by a suitable heating cycle.   The P-forming impurity, usually indium or gallium, diffuses into the germanium, forming a P region of germanium in intimate contact with the N-type germanium.   The process is repeated on the other side of the germanium die resulting in a second junction, and a PNP sandwich is obtained. In practice, the manufacturing techniques are somewhat involved, and if the unit is not made in a very precise and controlled manner, satisfactory junctions are not obtained.   This process has been discussed briefly in Chap. 7, but will be amplified here to indicate manufacturing techniques which are necessary for junction transistor production.

216. DETAILS OF THE PROCESS

Assuming that the germanium is of the right purity, mobility, etc., and has been properly etched and treated, the size of the die used must be correct.   If too large in area, germanium is wasted.   It may be noted in passing that it has been estimated that, after proper preparation, germanium is worth over $200 per pound.   If the thickness is too great, in addition to wastage of material, it is found that the α is poor, and hence acceptable units cannot be made.   A pellet thickness of 10 mils is considered maximum, typical values are usually less, about 0.005 in.[23]   However, this value is the final thickness desired after processing.   A thicker die is cut from the wafer since lapping and etching operations may remove as much as 0.005 in.   If the thickness is insufficient, the indium will fuse through and "short" to the diffused area on the other side.   If the dimensions are made too small, also, mechanical manufacturing difficulties are encountered, particularly in the matter of attaching leads, handling, etc.   Pellets approximately 0.1 in. on a side are preferred, the actual dimensions varying from manufacturer to manufacturer, but any one laboratory will use pellets all of the same size for convenience except where transistor-design considerations dictate otherwise.   Material with a resistivity below 10 ohm-cm is usually employed.   It has also been observed that too thick pellets produce low values of r_c although other factors also strongly affect r_c values.

The indium itself must have a high-order purity since clearly there is no point in using ultrapure germanium if the P-forming material contaminates it.   Indium with purity better than 99.9 is essential, in the manufacture of PNP transistors.   (Using a P-type material and a lead-antimony (Pb-Sb) dot, NPN transistors result.)   The size of the dot is quite important—if the emitter dot is too large, particularly with respect to the collector dot, α is low; if too small, electrical connections to it are difficult to make; in addition very low power units will result because of the very small areas involved.   If the collector dot is too large, r_c is reduced because of the large area; if too small, α is poor and the power rating low.   Usually an emitter dot is somewhat smaller than a collector dot.   A typical value of emitter dot is 0.4×10^{-7} in.[3], and for the collector approximately twice this size.   The relative size of emitter and collector dots is as important as the absolute size of each.   Alphas close to unity are achieved only if collector dots larger than emitter dots are used.

Jigs are used to align emitter and collector dots.   Very poor characteristics including low α's result from improper alignment.   Particularly vulnerable to misalignment is the base resistance, which apparently increases rapidly with the departure from alignment.   The indium dots are etched in a solution of hydrofluoric acid and nitric acid, just as are the germanium pellets, and are then washed in distilled water and dried.   Even connecting wires, usually tinned so that no copper surface is near the germanium, are etched and kept absolutely clean.   All units of the assembly are handled with tweezers which, of course, are chemically clean.   The jigs which align the pellets of indium and hold them in place against the germanium dice are similarly carefully etched and then cleansed in running water.

It may well turn out that many of these precautions are unnecessary. It may turn out also as a result of our added experience in the succeeding years that aspects to which we now give little attention, such as light intensity in the area, possible bombardment of the room by energetic particles, or the contamination of the room atmosphere by personnel, are the important things and that chemical cleanliness is a secondary matter.   Nevertheless, even today there is experimental evidence that this cleanliness is essential and failure to maintain cleanliness increases shrinkage.   In any case, quality control in transistor manufacture today is far from the state one might desire, and manufacturers are continuing to study techniques which offer promise of improving production yields.

217. FURNACE OPERATIONS

With the germanium die of the right resistivity and Hall coefficient, the indium dots pure, of right size, and properly aligned, the assembly is placed in an oven.   Accurate controls of temperature, atmosphere contamination, and time are absolutely essential.   If the temperature is too high, or the time in the oven is too great, the emitter and collector fusion areas will meet within the germanium pellet, shorting across the base region.   If the temperature is too low, or insufficient time is allowed, the diffusion is inadequate, the junction N region is too wide, and the desired characteristics, particularly frequency response and α, suffer badly. An oven temperature of approximately 530°C is an average value used, and the time necessary ranges from $1\frac{1}{2}$ to $2\frac{1}{2}$ min. In all cases, the time-temperature cycle is determined by a trial-and-error process. During the heating cycle, not only is the temperature carefully controlled, as well as the time, but in addition a dehumidified gas is constantly circulated in the oven to prevent moisture or undesired contaminants from affecting the junctions. The gas coverage and rate of circulation have a pronounced effect upon the resultant transistor since these factors control the diffusion of the P-forming material. To bring about a controlled stoppage of the extent of the diffusion, a quenching gas is circulated at the end of the desired "cooking" time, usually at a much higher flow rate than during the diffusion period.

218. FINAL STEPS

After baking, the units are again etched to clean the surfaces and to remove miscellaneous filaments of metal. Electrolytic or chemical etching may be used. The leads may be attached at any time during the process described, depending on the experiences of the individual manufacturer. Low-temperature solders such as Cerrobend (70°C) or Cerroseal (120°C) are sometimes used, but in general many manufacturers prefer to avoid use of these low-temperature solders for obvious reasons. Preference is given to attaching wires to the indium dots while still molten and to welding or brazing techniques to attach the leads to the base.

Thereafter, the unit may be vacuum sealed, hermetically sealed with some inert gas, or plastic encapsulated.

In a general way, PNP transistors appear to be characterized by a collector resistance somewhat lower than for NPN units. Because the mechanical construction renders the path from collector to emitter over the surface regions longer for the PNP units than for the NPN units, surface leakage paths, or channels,[24] are longer for the former and they appear to be somewhat less subject to humidity "aging" than the NPN units. (The foregoing considerations apply to the usual cases in which NPN units are made by crystal-growing techniques and PNP units are made by the diffusion process.)

219. GROWN CRYSTALS

Metallurgically, there are several methods by which single crystals large enough for transistor-manufacturing purposes may be grown.[1] Of these, two lend themselves specifically to the production of NPN

sandwiches—the technique of doping during the pulling process and
the rate-grown junction method.   Both have been briefly described
in Chap. 7; in this chapter, the former process will be given in more
detail.   The rate-grown junction method is not yet fully developed
and is not regarded as an established manufacturing procedure.   For
the doping-while-pulling process, very meticulous care is necessary to
obtain simultaneously a single crystal, an NPN junction of suitable
dimensions, and a resistivity variation and a P-layer thickness in the
crystal which may be tolerated.

220. PROCESS DETAILS

Reviewing once again the crystal-pulling process discussed in Sec.
196 and considering Figs. 13-3 and 13-4, it must be noted that an inert
gas, usually argon, is kept flowing in the chamber containing the
melt and the seed.   Because pulling rates differ with the type of
material being handled at any instant, provisions are necessary to vary
the rate of upward pull.   Also, the thickness of the barrier or P layer
is controllable by variation of the rate of pulling and melt temperature.
Rates of rotation while pulling vary, rates up to 150 rpm, and higher,
being in use.   Upward pulling rates similarly vary over a wide range,
from less than 0.1 in. per hr[23] to as high as 4 in. per hr and more.   It is
considered by many that rapid rates of rotation produce more uniform
mixing of the doping agents introduced and therefore more uniform
resistivity measured radially in the ingot.

Lowering the seed into the melt to initiate the crystal-growing
process requires very specific and careful manipulation.   The temperature of the melt must be correct, usually of the order of 960°C.
The seed must melt slightly at its lower end before upward pulling
commences in order to start the surface tension which is constantly
and carefully sustained during the entire process and which permits
the continuous crystal growing observed.   Further, even if the bond
between seed and melt is sufficient to maintain the surface tension and
growth, it is observed in practice that a single crystal will not result
unless an adequate bond is obtained.

As the seed is withdrawn, the molten germanium solidifies about it,
and because of the tendency of germanium to solidify as a succession of
crystals, such as shown by Fig. 5-6, the seed grows to form a large
germanium crystal, with no grain boundaries.   The diameter of the
crystal obtained is usually much larger than the maximum diameter
of the seed; a typical example is a seed with a maximum dimension on a
side of approximately 0.25 in. and the resulting crystal approximately
$1\frac{1}{2}$ in. in diameter.   The cross-sectional area of the resulting crystal

is usually not bounded by well-defined planes as one might expect by inspection of the usual pulling axes, Fig. 13-5. If the pulling axis is the 110 or 111 axis, one might expect flat, planar sides to be observed on the resulting crystal, but this is the exception rather than the rule. Most commonly observed are rounded sides, with perhaps one or two plane surfaces. With close heat control and just the correct speed of pulling and rotation, planar sides can be obtained provided the seed crystal is accurately oriented.

221. DOPING

The starting point is usually germanium of purity greater than required, as indicated by resistivity and Hall measurements, and this is doped, using antimony, arsenic, or other suitable impurities, to the desired resistivity, perhaps of the order of 1 ohm-cm. The resistivity of the three regions of the NPN sandwich is not the same, for best results, the resistivity decreasing by a factor of about 10 in each successive lower layer. Since it is not convenient to measure the resistivity of germanium when in the molten state, the quantity of impurity added is usually obtained by calculations plus experiment. The first or upper region is usually drawn at a fairly rapid rate, near the upper limit stated above, until a reasonably uniform crystal diameter is achieved. The rate is normally reduced at this point preparatory to pulling the P layer. The rate of rotation is maintained constant throughout.

When the system has stabilized at the new pulling rate, a P-forming impurity, usually indium, gallium, or an alloy of these, is added in carefully controlled amounts and of known purity, and the pulling allowed to proceed so as to establish a P layer approximately 0.001 to 0.003 in. wide. Thin layers are desirable for high α and good frequency response, but require the utmost control and pulling skill. Not only must the layers be thin, but also they must be of uniform thickness across the crystal and, in addition, of uniform resistivity measured across the sectional area. Moreover, the thickness and uniformity must be reproducible from crystal to crystal, because one crystal produces only about 200 NPN sandwiches of the dimensions required in junction transistors.

After the desired P layer has been obtained, N-forming impurities such as arsenic or antimony are again added to convert the germanium to N type again. Sometimes bismuth is added to the arsenic to obtain the desired distribution of the impurity. The crystal is then grown from another short region, $\frac{1}{2}$ in. at most. It is not feasible to grow additional junctions because the melt is now of a resistivity less than 0.1 ohm-cm and additional doping can only further decrease the resistivity. The process must be begun over again. Of course, once the steps and quantities and rates, etc., are determined by experiment, automatic programming equipments may be added to further improve uniformity.

222. FINISHING PROCESSES

The crystal is then removed, cleaned, and etched and the location of the barrier noted. Chemical etching, sandblasting, and plating techniques are used to locate the barrier region. The crystal is then sliced and diced, as explained above, into pellets each possibly 0.1 in. wide by 0.15 in. long by 0.015 in. thick, care being taken to cut parallel to the barrier. The wafers are lapped and etched, diced, and lapped and etched again. Many manufacturers perform several of the final operations in a low-humidity atmosphere. The desideratum is to obtain uniform chips or pellet sandwiches of uniform size, surface condition, and mechanical state. Polishing or grinding is known to produce amorphous polycrystalline layers, and these must be carefully etched away.

The pellet is placed in a suitable jig. Terminals are connected to the two N terminals usually by soldering directly to the germanium but sometimes by soldering to a plated surface. The entire unit is again etched, as it is after every other process, and washed. The wire is prepared for attachment to the center P region; by a rudimentary micromanipulator jig the wire is slowly moved across the surface until the P region is located. Oscilloscopic indications of correct characteristics are used to indicate when the wire is located on the P region. The center electrode is usually lightly welded. The unit is then either encapsulated in plastic or vacuum, or gas sealed, after which electrical tests are performed. Units may also be aged for a period of 24 to 96 hr, and the characteristics measured again. Shrinkage for these processes may easily reach 50 per cent, but present manufacturing experience is making great inroads into these figures. In the last few years, a vast amount of manufacturing know-how has been accumulated. Further development of many processes is still required.

223. GERMANIUM SALVAGE

During the manufacturing process, beginning with the reduction of the dioxide through the purification, etching, slicing, dicing, lapping, and associated operations, an appreciable fraction of the germanium is lost.   Because the basic material is so expensive, particularly after the purification process, it is profitable to reclaim as much of the germanium as possible.

Such pieces of germanium as may be useless for the final product because of breakage, polycrystalline structure, improper resistivity, improper size or shape, low mobility, or low lifetime are usually broken up into smaller pieces (if necessary) and remelted in the appropriate process.   The loss in the various cutting processes and the lapping and etching steps represents as large a fraction of the total germanium lost as do all the other causes combined, but the reclamation is somewhat more difficult.   It is perhaps of interest to note that, without salvage of germanium scrap, as little as 1 per cent of the germanium initially used would be included in the final product.   Also of interest is the fact that the width of the saw cuts when germanium is cut into wafers and slices is of the same order of magnitude as the resulting pellets.

224. RECOVERY FROM SLUDGE

There are two basic philosophies which may be followed in germanium recovery: (1) The waste from each step is carefully segregated and treated differently.   (2) The waste germanium or sludge is mixed from all operations; then a uniform chemical process is used to recover the metal, which is then put through the entire purification operation.

In the first method, solid germanium pieces are returned to their respective steps, depending on the known resistivity of the piece. Sludge from the slicing and dicing process is simply dried, remelted, and zone refined.   Lapping sludge is a water mixture usually; the water is decanted, the resulting mass dried and cleaned by etching. Liquid obtained from the etching process is first boiled to remove volatile compounds, then chemically treated for recovery of the germanium metal.   Many of these processes are still in quasi-experimental stages.

In method 2, chlorine gas is passed over the sludge to form germanium tetrachloride ($GeCl_4$).   The action is fortunately exothermic, and little external heat is needed.   The germanium tetrachloride is condensed and distilled, then allowed to flow into ordinary distilled water to form the dioxide.   The dioxide is dried to a powder, then put through the entire process, as explained in the first part of this chapter.

It is difficult to compare these two processes and even more difficult to select one as preferable.   But the inescapable fact that has already been observed is that the expense involved is less than the value of the germanium recovered, to say nothing of the additional control possible by use of material of known history.

225. SUMMARY

The salient points of this chapter are:

1. The essential steps in the manufacture of transistors using germanium are reduction, purification, single-crystal growing, slicing, dicing, and assembly.

2. Absolute cleanliness and the highest type of quality control are indispensable to a profitable transistor production line.

Fig. 13-13. The germanium ingot at the top is obtained from the reduction process, and the one below results from the zone-purification step. The three single crystals shown in the center are obtained from an automatic growing process. The six wafers are obtained after slicing such as may be done by the cutter shown in Fig. 13-7, and the pellets at the bottom after dicing by a machine such as shown in Fig. 13-8. (*Courtesy of the Western Electric Co.*)

3. Junction transistors are made by two principal processes: alloy or fusion, and grown junction.

4. Recovery of scrap and sludge germanium is profitable.

REFERENCES

1. Roth, L., and W. E. Taylor: Preparation of Germanium Single Crystals, *Proc. IRE*, Vol. 40, No. 11, p. 1338, November, 1952.
2. Pfann, W. G.: Principles of Zone Melting, *J. Metals*, pp. 747–754, July, 1952.
3. Pfann, W. G.: Segregation of Two Solutes, with Particular Reference to Semiconductors, *J. Metals*, pp. 861–865, August, 1952.

4. Czochralski, J.: *Z. physik. Chem.*, Vol. 92, p. 219, 1918.
5. Kittel, C.: "Introduction to Solid State Physics," John Wiley & Sons, Inc., New York, 1953.
6. Valdes, L. B.: Effect of Electrode Spacing on the Equivalent Base Resistance of Point Contact Transistors, Appendix I, *Proc. IRE*, Vol. 40, No. 11, p. 1432, November, 1952.
7. Goucher, F. S., and M. B. Prince: Alpha Values in PN Junction Transistors, *Phys. Rev.*, Vol. 89, pp. 651–653, Feb. 1, 1953.   McDonald, A., J. Soled, and C. Stearns: Four Probe Measurements for Resistivity Measurement of Germanium and Silicon, *Rev. Sci. Instr.*, September, 1953.
8. Valdes, L. B.: Resistivity Measurements on Germanium for Transistors, *Proc. IRE*, Vol. 42 pp. 420–427, February 1954.
9. Valdes, L. B.: Transistor Forming Effects in N-Type Germanium, *Proc. IRE*, Vol. 40, No. 4, April, 1952.
10. Shockley, W.: "Electrons and Holes in Semiconductors," D. Van Nostrand Company, Inc., New York, 1950.
11. Seitz, F.: "The Modern Theory of Solids," McGraw-Hill Book Company, Inc., New York, 1940.
12. Lindberg, O.: Hall Effect, *Proc. IRE*, Vol. 40, No. 11, pp. 1414–1419, November, 1952.
13. Conwell, E. M.: Properties of Silicon and Germanium, *Proc. IRE*, Vol. 40, No. 11, p. 1327, November, 1952.
14. Herkart, P. G., and J. Kurshan: Theoretical Resistivity and Hall Coefficient of Impure Germanium near Room Temperature, *RCA Rev.* Vol. 14, No. 11, pp. 427–440, September, 1953.
15. Haynes, J. R., and W. Shockley: The Mobility and Life of Injected Holes and Electrons in Germanium, *Phys. Rev.*, Vol. 81, No. 5, pp. 835–843, Mar. 1, 1951.
16. Navon, D., R. Bray, and H. Y. Fan: Lifetime of Injected Carriers in Germanium, *Proc. IRE*, Vol. 40, No. 11, pp. 1342–1347, November, 1952.
17. Valdes, L. B.: Measurement of Minority Carrier Life Time in Germanium, *Proc. IRE*, Vol. 40, No. 11, pp. 1420–1423, November, 1952.
18. Shockley, W., G. L. Pearson, and J. R. Haynes: Hole Injection in Germanium—Quantitative Studies and Filamentary Transistors, *Bell System Tech. J.*, Vol. 28, No. 3, pp. 344–366, July, 1949.
19. Bardeen, J.: Theory of Relation between Hole Concentration and Characteristics of Germanium Point Contacts, *Bell System Tech. J.*, Vol. 29, No. 4, pp. 469–495, October, 1950.
20. Saby, J. S.: Fused Impurity PNP Junction Transistors, *Proc. IRE*, Vol. 40, No. 11, pp. 1358–1360, November, 1952; and Hall, R. N., and W. C. Dunlap: PN Junctions by Impurity Diffusion, *Phys. Rev.*, Vol. 80, No. 3, p. 467, Nov. 1, 1950.
21. Teal, G. K., M. Sparks and E. Buehler: Growth of Germanium Single Crystals Containing PN Junctions, *Phys. Rev.*, Vol. 81, p. 637, Feb. 15, 1951.
22. Hall, R. N.: PN Junctions Prepared by Rate Growth Variation, *Phys. Rev.*, Vol. 88, p. 139, Oct. 1, 1952.

23. Fahnestock, J. D.: Production Techniques in Transistor Manufacture, *Electronics*, Vol. 26, No. 10, pp. 130–134, October, 1953.

24. Brown, W. L.: N-Type Surface Conductivity on P-Type Germanium, *Phys. Rev.*, Vol. 91, No. 3, pp. 518–527, Aug. 1, 1953.

25. Kikuchi, M., and T. Onishi: A Thermoelectric Study of the Electrical Forming of Germanium Rectifiers, *J. Appl. Phys.*, Vol. 24, pp. 162–166, February, 1953.

14 SILICON

The transistor effect is obtainable in silicon as well as in germanium. In their article on the physical principles involved in transistor action, Bardeen and Brattain[1] state that transistor action has been observed in silicon. In general, silicon is a semiconductor with four valence electrons, forms a cubic crystal with covalent bonds, and has an energy gap approximately 0.4 electron volt higher than that of germanium. Comparing these and other characteristics of the two elements, transistor action in silicon is understandable.

226. SILICON THE METAL

Silicon is not found on this planet in the free state although it is the second most abundant element on earth, the dioxide and its compounds comprising 87 per cent of the earth's crust.[2] Silicon forms an estimated 26 per cent of the outer regions of the earth. The most familiar silicon compound, the dioxide, is commonly found as sand and an important component of many rocks, such as quartz, flint, amethyst, etc.[3]

The first step in its preparation is generally separation from the dioxide by heating at approximately 3000°C in the presence of carbon, usually in the form of coke. Carbon dioxide is formed in the process, and by careful control of the amount of the carbon (coke), silicon in a polycrystalline form is obtainable which is about 97 per cent pure. Iron is usually one of the principal impurities. Other impurities commonly found in silicon are copper, aluminum, boron, and magnesium.

The tetrachloride may be prepared by the action of chlorine on silicon carbide (carborundum—obtained by heating sand in the presence of an excess of carbon at 3000°C); or it may be prepared by the action of chlorine directly on a heated mixture of sand and carbon. The basic reactions in the two cases are

$$2Cl_2 + SiC = SiCl_4 + C \qquad (14\text{-}1)$$
$$SiO_2 + 2C + 2Cl_2 = SiCl_4 + 2CO \qquad (14\text{-}2)$$

The tetrachloride is a colorless liquid with a low melting point (57°C). In the presence of even minute amounts of water, such as may be in moist air, a reaction takes place yielding a whitish smoke (used for smoke screens) of ammonium chloride and silicic acid (H_4SiO_4), sometimes called orthosilicic acid.

227. PURIFICATION METHODS

Purification of the 97 per cent pure metal obtained from the coke-separation process can be achieved by pulverizing and washing (or leaching) with acid, usually hydrofluorine.[4] Alternatively, melting techniques have been used[5] to separate impurities from the silicon element, simultaneously producing the crystalline structure needed for construction of silicon diodes and transistors. Some of these will be described later in this chapter.

To obtain uniformly high-purity silicon suitable for use in diodes and transistors, purification is commonly performed on silicon tetrachloride. Lyon, Olson, and Lewis[6] have described a method for the zinc reduction of silicon tetrachloride. The du Pont process for this reduction is treated by Torrey and Whitmer.[7] Other reductants, such as hydrogen,[8] may also be used to obtain a very pure form of silicon metal, with purities better than 99.90 per cent reported.

The preparation of pure silicon by the iodide method will be described briefly. This method represents one of the most recent approaches to the chemoelectrical purification of this element.

In essence, the process involves the formation of silicon tetraiodide (SiI_4) and silicon triiodide (SiI_6) by heating silicon in the presence of iodine and the subsequent decomposition of these iodides and their deposition on an electrically heated molybdenum filament.

The process is carried out in an evacuated chamber made of quartz or inconel in which pulverized silicon is held against the walls by means of a molybdenum screen. The silicon charge is heated, iodine is admitted, and the molybdenum filament in the center is heated to approximately 1000°C. The temperature of the container and silicon charge are of the order of 500°C. The purest available silicon is preferred as a starting material, such as the 99.90 per cent pure material mentioned. Figures reported for the purity after the iodide process contain as many as four nines after the decimal point. It may be remarked that even this purity is insufficient as the starting point for controlled transistor manufacture since it corresponds to less than 1 ohm-cm.

Also, the resulting material is neither single crystal nor of homogeneous constitution throughout so that further metallurgy is needed in preparation for transistor construction. The highest resistivity of silicon produced by this method is about 40 ohm-cm, whereas the maximum theoretical resistivity of silicon has been estimated variously as between 50,000 and 240,000 ohm-cm.[9,10]

228. PURIFICATION PROBLEMS

Silicon melts at approximately 1420°C (2588°F), as compared to 940°C for germanium. As noted above, silicon combines readily with carbon to form silicon carbide (SiC), a very hard substance used in carborundum abrasives and other applications where great hardness is required. Molten silicon, in general, is chemically very active and attacks the material used as a container, since it forms compounds with elements of which the containers are made (quartz, for instance, is silicon dioxide). Accordingly, the problem of contamination in the preparation of pure silicon is extremely serious and renders many techniques, hitherto used for germanium, relatively worthless. The zone-purification technique which has been used so successfully for germanium is not considered quite so suitable for silicon because the segregation constants, which determine the preference of impurities in silicon to remain in the liquid phase, are close to unity for many of the elements, particularly boron. Further, the expansion of a silicon ingot upon solidification results in cracking the crucible and producing poor-quality silicon because of brittleness caused by severe strains. The quartz boat used in the zone-purification method will also usually be broken after a single run. Also because of the segregation constants of some of the impurities, many more passes are necessary for silicon than in the case of germanium. There is no evidence that the boron, for example, usually found in silicon can be removed by any reasonable number of zone-melting passes.

As a metal to work with, silicon presents additional difficulties. Unless the cooling and solidification are suitably controlled, the resultant solid is very porous, in some cases being visibly spongy. Not only does this complicate the measurement problem, since resistivity measurements then give doubtful results, but also such spongy material is unsuitable for either diodes or transistors. Because of the high temperatures involved, degassing of associated materials occurs during the melting operation, and since silicon is so active chemically, various silicides are formed which then contaminate the melt. This necessitates special shielding and arrangements to keep contamination to a minimum. Also, silicon will react with any carbon parts in the system, forming silicon carbide films.   These films not only interfere with the normal heat-conduction processes, but in addition present a source of contamination for future runs.   In the case of crucibles of material other than quartz (or some other pure compound), the binding substance present in virtually all cases reacts with the molten silicon, producing contamination.   In melts where a considerable amount of impurity gases are occluded in the silicon, a violent boiling is observed as the gases escape.   If the volume of the charge or if the crucible dimensions are such as to greatly impede the escape of the gases, an explosion is likely to blow molten silicon completely out of the crucible and result in extensive damage to the system.   So significant is the impurity content of container materials that spectrographic analyses are made of the quartz, for instance, obtainable from different manufacturers (Thermal Syndicate, Ltd., and Hanovia Chemical and Manufacturing Co., for instance) to select the product with the minimum of contaminants.   It is interesting to note that in one such test case an improvement of almost 100 in the resistivity was effectible by selection of the highest purity quartz crucible.   As a result of difficulties such as those just mentioned, crucible materials continue to pose a first-order problem in the preparation of silicon.

229. PURIFICATION AND CRYSTAL GROWTH

To circumvent the many problems presented by the high melting point and activity of silicon, scientists and metallurgists have investigated methods of avoiding the conventional casting of a silicon ingot in a crucible.   The Czochralski method discussed in Chap. 13, the Bridgman method, and special artifices using floating liquid zones of silicon-X-metal eutectics have been successfully used to produce single crystals of high-purity silicon.

Czochralski Method.   The basic principles of this method, wherein a seed is dipped into the melt and slowly withdrawn, as applied to germanium crystal growth, have been discussed in Chap. 13.   However, additional problems are introduced when this method is applied to silicon, and these will be discussed briefly.   The problem of a seed holder is first in consideration, since the wrong supporting material either will melt, putting an end to the process, or will contaminate the resulting crystal.   Carbon and quartz have been found to be suitable materials; several others form eutectic mixtures with the silicon, severely contaminating the ingot. Freezing, and the resultant formation of "islands" in the melt, particularly near the walls, results from too low a temperature or improper temperature control, and must be carefully avoided.   Temperature control within 0.1°C is usually considered a minimum. Induction furnaces appear to be more widely used than direct heating arrangements. Purified inert gases, such as argon, are used to prevent oxidation, contamination, etc. Withdrawal rates of about 0.1 in. per min have been found satisfactory, and slow rotation rates such as 10 rpm are used. At the Signal Corps Engineering Laboratories, it has been found very desirable at the start of the operation to bring the seed to within about 3 in. of the surface of the melt and leave it there to preheat for perhaps 10 min before dipping into the melt.[11] If this is not done, uniform crystal growth is difficult to attain. The seed must be near the melting point at the lower end to easily obtain a slight "melt-back." Care must be taken in pulling as the ingot tends to break off rather easily. (In general, silicon is about half as dense as germanium, and very brittle.)

If the rate of pulling is too great, the ingot will tend to break off. The same effect is obtained if the temperature is too high, the first evidence being a tapering off in the diameter. A temperature of 1430°C has been found satisfactory. If the temperature is too low, the crystal diameter will be too large; and if the temperature control is poor, in addition to the formation of islands, an irregular ingot surface is produced. A quartz crucible greater than 2 in. in diameter has been found necessary to simplify some of the crystal-pulling problems outlined.

The general construction of a typical pulling furnace involves a pyrex glass envelope, with provision for argon inlet and exhaust; provisions for a thermocouple; and the lifting and rotating mechanisms. An outer shield of firewall material, usually alundum, is used around the heating coils, which are similarly wound on an alundum core. The quartz crucible is held in a graphite cylinder, and the entire assembly is supported on a suitable pedestal. The pyrex container volume not otherwise occupied is usually filled with alundum or similar pebbles.

The surface of the melt must be crystal-clear before the seed is dipped in, or else nucleation centers will result in polycrystalline crystal growth. The surface temperature of the melt is preferably measured by means of an optical pyrometer, since a thermocouple may or may not give the temperature of the melt, depending on its position. A preferred direction of orientation of the seed crystal appears to be the (111) direction (see Chap. 13). Single crystals up to 1 in. in diameter and 6 in. long have been successfully obtained by this method, with resistivities to 150 ohm-cm and higher. It is a characteristic of silicon crystal pulling that the reproducibility of results is not as reliable as in the case of germanium, where good reproducibility is obtainable.

There is some evidence that zirconia, beryllia, tridymite, and foster-ite are worthy of consideration as crucible and refractory materials in this process.

Bridgman Method. This method of single-crystal growth is described at length in Bridgman's original article,[12] and by Buckley.[13] Only the special adaptation to silicon will be discussed in this chapter. Since this method depends essentially on the formation of a single microscopic crystal upon cooling and the subsequent growth of additional crystals upon it in a preferred direction, provision must be made for melting, maintaining the atmosphere uncontaminated during

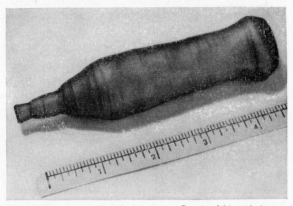

Fig. 14-1. A large silicon crystal pulled by the Czochralski technique. The crystal shown is P type, weighs approximately $\frac{1}{2}$ lb, and has a resistivity of 1 ohm-cm. (*Courtesy of the Raytheon Manufacturing Co.*)

the growth, and very slow cooling. The first two steps are of course common to the Czochralski method, but the last step introduces additional problems. It is necessary to melt the top of the charge in the crucible first, proceeding downward along the crucible. Experience has shown that, if silicon melts below granules of the material, very hard coatings form on the silicon granules, preventing successful uniform melting of the charge. When the entire crucible charge has been melted, it is raised above heating elements, and then very slowly lowered. The rate of lowering must be somewhat less than the rate of crystallization in the direction of the motion. This is very important. If this is not done the orienting influence of the advancing layer of crystals upon the subsequently formed crystals is lost—this is the essence of the Bridgman technique. If the rate of lowering exceeds the crystal growth, then the next layer may commence growth along some other preferred direction. When the originally initiated crystal front comes up to it, a grain boundary will result.

The Bridgman method is particularly useful for growing single crystals of small size, which are then useful for the Czochralski method from which somewhat larger crystals can be drawn. Because of the slow cooling rate, ingots free from strains, internal fissures, and surface cracks can be prepared.

The furnace used is very similar to that used for the Czochralski method, and somewhat simpler in that no rotational motion need be added. Further, since it is not necessary to lower a seed into the crucible, the top can be covered, thereby reducing heat losses.

Some laboratories prefer to maintain a hard vacuum in the furnace instead of an inert gas when using the Bridgman method. It appears that less contamination results. Temperature control within two- or three-tenths of a degree centigrade is essential in this method. Also, water cooling of outer parts is found necessary to protect gaskets, seals, etc.

Zone of Silicon Eutectic Method. The high melting point of silicon, its chemical activity, and the attendant difficulties in procedure have led many investigators to approach the problem from an entirely different direction, such as the interesting new approach to be described. A eutectic is a mixture of two (or more) metals or compounds which has a lower melting point than either of the two constituents. There is a gold-silicon eutectic which melts at temperatures around 400°C and a silicon-tin eutectic which melts around 900°C, certainly well below the melting point of silicon. These researchers have therefore tried, and successfully, to obtain single-crystal silicon growth upon a seed through a zone of low-melting-temperature eutectic.

H. von Wartenburg first reported silicon dissolved in aluminum, silver, and zinc,[14] and was able to precipitate pure silicon from the melts. Keck and Broder,[15] during studies of the solubility of silicon in indium and gallium, were able to grow small single crystals of silicon from saturated solutions of gallium by very slow cooling, with relatively little contamination by gallium atoms. A. J. Goss,[16] of the Bell Telephone Laboratories, reported growth of single crystals of silicon from a saturated solution of tin, at a temperature of about 900°C.

At the National Conference on Tube Techniques, Carman, Stello, and Bittman,[17] of the Hughes Aircraft Company, Culver City, Calif., reported on the regrowth of silicon through a eutectic zone of silicon and gold. In essence, a seed is dipped into a silicon-gold eutectic, which in turn rests on a layer of undissolved silicon. As the silicon is deposited on the seed, depleting the silicon-gold layer, additional silicon becomes dissolved from the bulk material underneath. The process has yielded good-grade silicon, using temperatures much below the melting point of silicon. The authors reported polycrystalline material because single-crystal silicon seeds were not available at the time of the experiment; resistivity of 4 ohm-cm and a lifetime of 2 μsec were obtained.

Speaking generally, the resultant material obtained by this method thus far has been somewhat inferior to that obtainable by the Czochralski or Bridgman methods. However, the convenience of having a lower melt temperature, the very much reduced activity of silicon at the lower temperatures, and the virtual elimination of the problems of crucible material lead one to believe that the silicon eutectic method may be further developed profitably.

230. COMPARISON OF SILICON AND GERMANIUM

The electron mobility of silicon has been reported to be about one-third that of germanium and the hole mobility about one-seventh that of germanium,[10] so that poorer frequency-response characteristics may be anticipated. In experimental investigations reported in the literature, maximum lifetime values for silicon are considerably below those for germanium, so that unless further progress is made lower current and power gains may be anticipated. In virtually every aspect the preparation of silicon is more difficult than in the case of germanium. Further, since it can be shown that to a first approximation the coefficient of temperature variation of resistivity (and therefore, roughly, of parameters) is proportional to the energy gap (1.1 electron volts for silicon and 0.72 for germanium), one would expect that the total variation in r_c, say, for a given temperature change, would be greater for silicon than for germanium. This fact can be verified experimentally. What, then, are the advantages of silicon which lead many solid state physicists to look toward silicon to effect important improvements in transistors?

It has been shown experimentally,[18] using point contact transistors, that I_{co} and r_c exhibit the largest change in values with temperature of any of the transistor parameters. In this discussion, we shall limit the analysis to these two parameters, the problem of temperature dependence of other parameters being presumably less troublesome.

Frequently, the temperature dependence of transistor parameters for a given material is considered from the standpoint of width of the forbidden gap and the resistivity. Unless this is done with great care, serious errors can be introduced by failing to consider all the factors actually involved. Considering I_{co}, the collector diode reverse current, characteristics show that this current is as much as a thousand times as large for a given temperature for germanium as it is for silicon. Such curves also show that the absolute change in I_{co}, for a given temperature change, is much less for silicon than for germanium. On a per cent basis, however, because of the lower initial (room-temperature) values of I_{co}, the change for silicon is greater than for germanium. Although data on the subject are by no means conclusive, present indications are that the degradation in collector resistance with temperature will be greater, in absolute value, for silicon compared with germanium, but on a percentage basis, less for silicon than for germanium. Both theoretical and experimental verification of these statements must await further passage of time.

It is known, however, that because of the lower value of I_{co} and higher value of r_c for silicon at room temperature, the degradation in these two parameters with temperatures as high as 150°C still leaves these parameters of acceptable value for applications in electronic circuits. At such temperatures at present, I_{co} becomes excessively large and r_c excessively small for germanium. On these bases silicon holds promise of improved temperature dependence; also, transistors made of silicon should be operable at temperatures much higher than for germanium.

231. SILICON DEVICES

Although the feasibility of silicon transistors was mentioned in 1948,[1] no silicon transistors were obtainable commercially until 1954. Grown and alloy silicon P-N junctions have been produced successfully,[19-21] as reported by the Bell Telephone Laboratories. Silicon transistors were reported by the Bell Telephone Laboratories in 1950 on an experimental basis.[22] Point contact transistors using silicon have also been reported from England,[23] but voltage and power gains were small (about 10), and current gain was approximately 1.8. In general, it appears that the technical difficulties in the preparation of the material, the marked propensity for contamination, and the difficulty of making satisfactory connections to the material have thus far blocked any rapid development of silicon-transistor devices. Some difficulties encountered in the silicon-diode construction have been ably detailed in the article by Pearson and Sawyer.[24,25]

In May, 1954, the Texas Instrument Co., Dallas, Texas, announced a limited production of silicon transistors. Since the announcement, production rates have increased, and modest amounts are available. The units are grown junction types, up to $\frac{1}{4}$ watt, and will operate satisfactorily at temperatures approximately twice the upper permissible temperature for germanium transistors.

A possible application for silicon (and germanium to a smaller extent) is in the field of lenses. At approximately 6.5 angstroms, at the higher frequency end of the infrared, silicon has a transmission coefficient of 70 per cent, and tapers off sharply toward the red end, and more slowly toward the rf end.[10] This unusual characteristic makes it suitable for the construction of solid lenses for frequencies in the infrared, from about 2 μ up to perhaps 10 μ. Germanium has a transmission coefficient somewhat less at its peak, but the peak is more sustained (2 to 10 μ), and the over-all usefulness may be considered up to about 15 μ.

REFERENCES

1. Bardeen, J., and W. H. Brattain: The Transistor: A Semiconductor Triode, *Phys. Rev.*, Vol. 74, pp. 230–231, 1948.
2. Latimer, W. M., and J. H. Hildebrand: "Reference Book of Inorganic Chemistry," The Macmillan Company, New York, 1952.
3. Ehret, W. F.: "Smith's College Chemistry," 6th ed., pp. 458ff., Appleton-Century-Crofts, New York,
4. Tucker, N. P.: *J. Iron Steel Inst.*, Vol. 15, pp. 412–416, 1927.
5. Scaff, J. H.: U.S. Patent 2,402,582, 1946.
6. Lyon, D. W., C. M. Olson, and E. D. Lewis: *Trans. Electrochem. Soc.*, Vol. 96, pp. 359–363, 1949.
7. Torrey, H. C., and C. A. Whitmer: "Crystal Rectifiers," McGraw-Hill Book Company, Inc., New York, 1948, Chapter 10.
8. Hobling, R.: *Z. angew. Chem.*, Vol. 40, pp. 655–659, 1927.
9. Lark-Horovitz, K.: Conductivity in Semiconductors, *Elec. Eng.*, Vol. 68, pp. 1047–1056, 1949.
10. Conwell, E. M.: Properties of Silicon and Germanium, *Proc. IRE*, Vol. 40, pp. 1327–1337, November, 1952.
11. Pharo, W. B.: Private communication, Signal Corps Engineering Laboratories, Fort Monmouth, N.J.
12. Bridgman, P. W.: Certain Physical Properties of Single Crystals of W, Sb, Bi, Te, Cd, Zn and Sn, *Proc. Am. Acad. Arts Sci.*, Vol. 60, pp. 303–383, 1925.
13. Buckley, H. E.: "Crystal Growth," pp. 73ff., John Wiley & Sons, Inc., New York, 1951.
14. von Wartenburg, H.: Silicon Dissolved in Aluminum, *Z. anorg. Chem.*, Vol. 265, p. 186, 1951.
15. Keck, P. H., and J. Broder: The Solubility of Silicon and Germanium in Gallium and Indium, *Phys. Rev.*, Vol. 90, pp. 521–522, May 15, 1953.
16. Goss, A. J.: Saturated Solutions of Silicon in Tin, *J. Metals*, Vol. 5, No. 9, p. 1085, September, 1953.
17. Carman, J. N., P. E. Stello, and C. A. Bittman: The Regrowth of Silicon through a Low Melting Zone of Silicon-Gold Eutectic, presented at the National Conference on Tube Techniques, October, 1953.
18. Coblenz, A., and H. L. Owens: Variation of Transistor Parameters with Temperature, *Proc. IRE*, Vol. 40, No. 11, pp. 1472, November, 1952.

19. Teal, G. K., and E. Buehler: Growth of Silicon Single Crystals and of Single Crystal PN Junctions, *Phys. Rev.*, Vol. 87, p. 190, July 1, 1952.

20. McAfee, K. B., and G. L. Pearson: The Electrical Properties of Silicon PN Junctions Grown from the Melt, *Phys. Rev.*, Vol. 87, p. 190, July 1, 1952.

21. Pearson, G. L., and P. V. Foy: Silicon PN Junction Diodes Prepared by the Alloy Process, *Phys. Rev.*, Vol. 87, p. 190, July 1, 1952.

22. Pietenpol, W. J., and R. S. Ohl: Characteristics of Silicon Transistors, presented at the Conference on Electron Devices held at the University of Michigan, June 22, 1950.

23. Granville, J. W., and W Bardsley: *Proc. Phys. Soc.*, Vol. 66, Part 3, p. 429, May 1, 1953.

24. Pearson, G. L., and B. Sawyer: Silicon PN Junction Alloy Diodes, *Proc. IRE*, Vol. 40, No. 11, pp. 1348–1351, November, 1952.

25. Johnson, W. R., and M. Hansen: Research on the Element Silicon and Silicon Alloys, AF TR No. 6383, prepared by the Armour Research Foundation, Illinois Institute of Technology, June, 1951.

15 SPECIAL TOPICS

As with the development of any new science, the major lines of advance are along a principal path, but here and there a new branch road is built leading to a new device or principle. Because it is impossible to tell whether these branch roads will run briefly and come to a dead end, or whether they may one day become major arteries of approach, it is necessary to treat each with the attention it would command if it were known that it will one day be a prominent avenue. In this chapter, several special topics will be touched upon briefly to indicate the existence of these secondary methods of approach or unproved devices. Sufficient information will be given for an understanding of the principles involved. The reader interested in more complete information is referred to the bibliography and to subsequent publications.

232. THE ANALOG TRANSISTOR

Shockley has described a theoretical type of transistor which is a semiconductor analog of the vacuum tube.[1] As far as has been reported, the unit has not been constructed physically. It is nevertheless an interesting structure to study because it suggests useful transistor-like principles. As Fig. 15-1 indicates, the device consists of a "plate," which is the peripheral N layer, a series of "grids" of P material, and a "cathode" of N material, the center, which performs the functions of an emitter (in the vacuum-tube sense of the word). The space between these elements is filled with virtually pure or intrinsic semiconductor material, corresponding to a resistivity of approximately 65 ohm-cm for germanium[2] and 240,000 ohm-cm for silicon.[3] Thus the material between the analog electrodes contributes virtually no carriers and acts as a near-insulator, being analogous to the vacuum in a tube.

As discussed in Chap. 6, if we consider that at the boundary of the N regions there are positive doNor atoms, and at the boundary of the P regions accePtor atoms, it will be seen that the polarity of applied battery voltage E_c is such as to raise the potential hill between the cathode and the grids so that only a small reverse current flows.

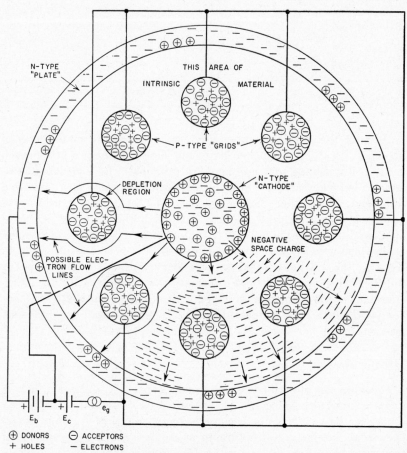

Fig. 15-1. Sketch to illustrate the theory of operation of the analog transistor. The clear area within the inner circle is intrinsic semiconductor material, the grids and cathode, as well as the plate, being of doped material of lower resistivity. The principle of operation is a close analog to the operation of a vacuum tube.

Similarly, the polarity of E_b is such that only a small reverse current flows between the grids and the N-type plate. In the P material, the majority carriers are holes, and in the N material, they are the electrons; in both cases just noted, very little majority carrier-current flow is possible because of the polarities of applied biases. Unilateral conductivity of current through the device is thus established if we assume intrinsic resistivity of the intervening material.

For the cathode-to-plate circuit, however, the conditions are somewhat different. Electrons leaving the cathode N region flow to the plate and encounter a layer of positive acceptors, positively biased with respect to the cathode, and a majority carrier flow from cathode to anode is possible. Note that the negative potential due to E_b tends to neutralize the potential hill at the cathode; and electrons can leave. On their way to the anode, the electrons must pass by the grid P regions, which are negatively charged with respect to the cathode by battery E_c. The result is the creation of a space charge and a depletion layer, as shown in the figure. When the ac generator e_g adds to the negative bias, less current is allowed to flow past the grids; and when e_g counteracts the negative bias, more current flows—as in a triode vacuum tube. Amplification can be obtained since small changes in e_g control relatively large swings in the plate circuit.

As the name implies, this structure is clearly a semiconductor analog of the vacuum tube. Shockley has pointed out a significant difference between the analog transistor and transistors discovered previously: the analog transistor current is carried by particles of one sign only—electrons in this case. Note that, while the polarity of applied biases assists the flow of holes from the plate N region to the cathode N region, not only are the holes minority carriers in N material and therefore relatively few in number, but also the positive donors at the periphery do not encourage either exit or entry of positive charges. This feature of the conduction mechanism has lead Shockley to propose the term "unipolar" to distinguish between the conduction process in the point contact and junction transistors and in this type of structure.

In point contact and junction transistors, to an equal degree, the applied biases encourage holes to move in one direction and electrons in the other—hence the name bipolar. Further, the injection of holes into N material in the case of the N-type point contact transistor and the PNP junction transistor (and of electrons into P material in the case of the NPN units) shows that minority carrier injection is a fundamental principle of operation. In the analog type of transistor, however, the intervening material (see Fig. 15-1) is intrinsic, neither P nor N type, and minority carrier injection does not take place.

Thus, the analog transistor provides a new principle for transistor action in a semiconductor—electronic control of permissible current-flow paths by means of grids of suitable semiconductor type. Obviously, an alternative arrangement to Fig. 15-1 would be plate and cathode of P material, grids of N material, with opposite polarity of batteries. Also, the device is not restricted to germanium. There is reason to believe that, because of its greater intrinsic resistivity, silicon may prove preferable.

While the model of the analog transistor in this form has not been experimentally achieved, appreciation of the new principle involved has led to a study of structures more readily realizable from a practical point of view. Shockley's first paper on the analog transistor was published in November, 1952,[4] and in August, 1953, Dacey and Ross described a unipolar transistor designed and constructed at the Bell Telephone Laboratories.[5]

233. THE UNIPOLAR FIELD-EFFECT TRANSISTOR

The unipolar field-effect transistor is based on the principle of effective widening of the PN junction or barrier upon the application of reverse bias.[6] This effect was mentioned by Shockley[7] in his analysis of PN junctions. Because this effect is not only fundamental to the transistor under discussion, but is also important in NPN and PNP junction transistors as shown by Early (see Ref. 6), it will be treated in some detail. Thereafter, the *modus operandi* of the unipolar transistor follows directly.

In Chap. 6, PN junctions, donor and acceptor arrays, and potential hills were discussed. We saw how the potential hill prevents the majority carriers from diffusing across the junction, but favors the diffusion of the minority carriers. It is easy for holes from N material to diffuse into a P region, and for electrons from a P region to diffuse into an N region. This process does not continue indefinitely for two reasons: (1) The minority carriers are limited in number, and unless they wander near the barrier, they will not, by ordinary random motion, appear in any great numbers near the junction. (2) All materials, P or N, are electrically neutral, and tend to remain so; for example, if excess diffusion of holes takes place, the N material supplying them develops a net negative charge and will tend to attract the holes, thus stopping the action. The obvious converse applies in the case of electrons. The reader is cautioned against the error of assuming that N material has a net negative charge and that P material has a net positive charge—in the absence of applied potentials, the materials are always neutral in charge.

The discussion in Chap. 6, to avoid complicating the explanation, was restricted to the action of the majority carriers, and little mention was made of the effect of the minority carriers in discussing the potential hill concept. As Fig. 15-2 shows, there are some free holes available at any time in N material as well as some acceptor atoms; similarly, there are some free electrons available in P material, as well as donor atoms. This can be understood by considering that generation of hole-electron pairs goes on all the time in germanium at room temperature. The ratio of majority to minority carriers may be anywhere from 2 to 1 to as much as 10 to 1; and it is quite accurate to consider the ratio of donors to electrons, or acceptors to holes, as 1 to 1. Sometimes, to indicate a very large ratio of electrons to holes in a given N sample, that is, to indicate a strongly N type of material, the

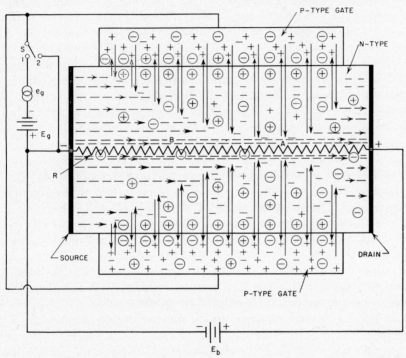

Fig. 15-2. Sketch to illustrate the theory of operation of the field effect, or unipolar, transistor. If a sector is taken from the circular figure in Fig. 15-1, the operation of the sector is analogous to that of the unipolar transistor in this sketch.

notation N^+ is used, and correspondingly P^+ is used for the case of strongly P-type material.

With these ideas in mind, let us return to Fig. 15-2 and the theory of operation of the unipolar transistor: With switch S in position 2, electrons will flow from the source, connected to the negative terminal of E_b, to the drain, through the N-type germanium body of the transistor. Resistor R is used to represent the drop through the germanium material which need not necessarily be uniform along the length of the sample. It will be seen that point A is more positive than point B in the figure, and, in general, the further one proceeds toward the drain, the more positive is the potential with respect to the source. Note that with S in position 2 both P-type gates are connected to the negative terminal of E_b. It follows, therefore, recalling the mnemonic regarding biasing in the forward and reverse directions, that the PN junctions are biased farther in the reverse direction as one proceeds along the gate toward the drain. With no applied bias, the flow of majority carriers is impeded by the potential hills, and the flow of minority carriers is impeded by the distribution of charge as discussed above. With the application of reverse bias, holes from the N material are enabled to move toward the P layer because the N material goes more positive with respect to the P-type germanium, which is at a relatively low potential with respect to it. For the same reason, electrons from the P material move toward the N germanium.

Both of these processes are, of course, intensified as one moves toward the drain, and as the arrows indicate in Fig. 15-2, the more positive the N material, the further will electrons from the P region be enabled to move. Holes in the N material will be coming from regions farther back of the barriers. In Fig. 15-2, the vertical arrows show, by the symbol at their heads, the source and movement of the carriers, as well as the extent of the effect into the N region. With the addition to the region between the gates of additional electrons from the P material, and with the removal of additional holes going to the P gates, the region outlined by the arrow heads in the N material becomes progressively more negative; the shape of the resulting negative regions is approximately as shown. We may say, therefore, that in the whale-backed regions in the N material, the germanium is N^+ compared to the remaining regions. The effect is to channel or direct the current flow from the source electrode to the drain electrode between the N^+ regions.

If E_b is increased above a value known as the pinch-off voltage, the effect of the N^+ regions in pinching off the current is counterbalanced by the smaller positive potential at point A, say, because the source-to-drain current is becoming smaller. Thereafter, further increases in applied potential will not narrow the channel further, but may cause a redistribution in its shape.

If switch S is now moved to position 1, the negative potential applied to the gates tends to further cut off the main current flow, and E_b need not be so large to obtain the same effect. When the generator e_g is plus, a potential difference counteracts E_g, and the current will increase; when the generator e_g is minus, the channel will narrow, and the source-drain current will decrease. Thus a small potential change at e_g controls the current flow, which, through a high resistance, will give a large potential change in the source-drain circuit, i.e., amplification.

234. GENERAL ASPECTS OF THE UNIPOLAR TRANSISTOR

From the appearance of the N^+ regions of Fig. 15-2 and the analysis which showed that, as the reverse bias increases, electrons penetrate deeper into the N material and holes from farther back migrate to the P gates, one can understand the meaning of the words "space-charge layer widening." The addition of electrons into and depletion of holes from a previously neutral material create an effective space charge, in this case negative. Clearly, if the gates were N type, the material between P type, and battery polarities changed accordingly, the effective space charge would be positive. But this creation of a space charge in a semiconductor, analogous to the space charge in a vacuum tube, is exceedingly important and promises to have significant applications in solid state electronics. Note the comparison with the operation of the analog transistor and the presence of the depletion layer—electrons from source to drain must move around it, so that few charge carriers of the principal current flow will be found in this region.

A significant difference between the unipolar transistor and the point contact or junction bipolar types must be considered. In the bipolar types, the controlling current or the charges bearing the controlling intelligence are flowing in the same region where charges whose density or distribution is varied by the charges bearing intelligence may flow. But in the unipolar type, the source-to-drain carriers are modulated by charges on gates involving the modulating forces, so that there is not the direct motion of both types of carriers in the same region. This is analogous to the vacuum tube, where potentials on the grid affect plate current, but the charges carrying the intelligence, in the grid circuit, do not flow in the region between cathode and plate to any significant extent. This fact leads to the important practical advantage of better frequency response in the unipolar transistor structure.

When the modulating intelligence must enter at one end and emerge amplified at the other, the transit time within the material is clearly involved. If the modulating voltage merely constricts or expands the current stream, as in the case of the unipolar transistor, the entire transit time from source to drain is not involved, thereby reducing frequency-response limitations. Dacey and Ross[5] report that an operating frequency of 140 mc should be realized with mechanically feasible designs. Point contact and junction structures operable at such frequencies would require much smaller critical dimensions.[8]

Because a potential change in an associated circuit controls current or voltage changes in another, the term transconductance can be applied in the vacuum-tube sense. The design cited as capable of

140-mc operation was computed to have a transconductance of 24,000 micromhos. The unipolar transistors appear to have excellent possibilities in the high-frequency area and for power amplification, but the noise figure is still quite high (68 db is a typical figure). An interesting aspect of the field-effect transistor is that input impedances much higher than for conventional transistors are possible.

It appears to the authors that these units should be amenable to mixer applications, in modified form. A unipolar transistor using silicon instead of germanium has been reported.[9] This unit has also been called the "transtrictor" in the literature.

235. FIELDISTORS

An entirely different approach to the control of motion of charges was taken by O. M. Stuetzer, who investigated the effect of a control electrode near, but not in contact with, point contact and junction barriers. Drawing on Bardeen's theory of surface states[10] and the experience of Shockley and Pearson with thin films of semiconductors,[11] Stuetzer developed a practical method for construction of a transistor-like device first using point contact diodes,[12] then junction diodes,[13] and obtained a device with high input impedance and some gain. As the point contact construction required special electrode-spacing techniques, Stuetzer developed microspacing methods to construct experimental models.[14]

The diode used, usually of the high-back-voltage type,[15] is biased in the reverse or high-resistance direction, and the control electrode alters the value of the reverse current by a field effect. Spacing of the control element from the device surface is of the order of 100 μ (1 micron = 1 millionth of a centimeter), and the region in between may be air or a suitable dielectric. Usually a liquid dielectric is used as the medium between the control or "grid" element, and the dielectric and its properties materially affect the characteristics of the device. In the case of the point-contact fieldistors, Stuetzer has used a hexagonally spaced set of fine wires; in the junction unit, a small rectangular piece of metal set near the junction. The characteristics of the junction fieldistor vary with placement of the electrode with respect to the junction.

Except for the capacity involved, the input circuit including the battery, control element, and ac source is virtually open, and input impedances of many megohms are possible. The author quotes 100 megohms "on dry days." Output impedances of several to tens of thousands of ohms are possible; frequency response is below 1 mc, and gains are rather small, although for the point contact units

Stuetzer reports power gains of about 40 db. Mutual conductances of 200 are possible with the point contact units and below 1,000 with junction fieldistors. Noise figures are high, of the order of noise in point contact diodes—60 db.

Although these units are not yet considered sufficiently understood or developed for practical circuit applications, the fieldistor is interesting because it represents a type of device which nevertheless serves as an additional research tool. During investigations of the fieldistors, important data on surface states and high-back-voltage diode characteristics were added to the store of our knowledge of the solid state.

236. COAXIAL TRANSISTOR

When Bardeen and Brattain announced the discovery of the point contact transistor in 1948,[16] they referred to a construction wherein both contacts were on the same surface of the germanium pellet. A few months later, Shive reported the presence of transistor action when the point contacts were on opposite sides of a thin wafer,[17] thus showing that transistor action was possible as a bulk semiconductor process. He reported current and resistance gains similar to point contact units and indicated that, with this double-surface approach, physical spacings between emitter and collector somewhat greater than those possible with single-surface transistors were feasible.

The double-surface transistor suggested to Kock and Wallace the possibility of a coaxial type of transistor,[18] made along the lines of a tubular resistor. The device is made in a simple cartridge with a disk of germanium having a thin cross section at its center and to which two oppositely directed cat whiskers making up the emitter and collector are brought into pressure contact. The cartridge serves as the third electrode or base. Best operating results are obtainable by high polishing of the germanium surfaces and aligning the cat whiskers exactly opposite each other on the thinnest part of the germanium disk. Advantages claimed are stability, shielding of input from output, and simplicity of construction.

As in the case of the fieldistor, this device demonstrated conclusively another point of importance in solid state theory: transistor action is not solely a surface phenomenon. Transistor action may also take place within the semiconductor itself.

237. ADDITIONAL SPECIAL TRANSISTORS

Several special transistors will be described briefly in this section with the purpose of indicating their existence and possible fields of application. For additional details, which incidentally are quite limited in the available literature, the reader may refer to the references cited.

In his book, "Transistor Circuits,"[19] R. F. Shea describes the double-base diode which performs transistor-like functions using only a single PN junction. The device consists of a long rod of germanium with a PN junction formed at its center by the diffusion process. An interesting phenomenon results when the indium dot which forms the junction is biased at half the difference of potential between the ends of the rod. The P region performs the function of an emitter over the negative portion of the rod, with respect to which it is biased positively, and the function of a collector over the positive portion of the rod, with respect to which it is biased negatively. Negative resistance characteristics are shown to be feasible.

Variations of the double-base diode are also discussed, as well as variations of the double-base transistor (tetrode, see Chap. 7). Applications to push-pull amplifiers and high-frequency operation are also given. By addition of further base contacts and PN junctions, pentodes and multielement devices having a variety of applications suggest themselves. No extensive applications of these devices have been announced.

In Chap. 7 the phototransistor was described as a diode whose third element was the light source, creating hole-electron pairs and thereby altering the conductivity. A modification of the phototransistor uses an actual NPN or PNP unit as the base device; with the presence of incident radiation the conductivity is altered so that the transistor properties change in a predictable manner.[20] The change in transistor characteristics is then used to indicate the presence, and in some cases the intensity, of the incident radiation. For the latter purpose, the light must be "chopped," *i.e.*, transformed into a series of light pulses to make use of the ac response. Values of light-chopping frequency may be as high as 25 kc.

Lehovec has proposed devices based on transistor-like mechanisms.[21] In phototransistors, absorption of the light energy by the semiconductor atoms alters the carrier concentration and distribution, and in this way influences the carrier injection process. It is known that the opposite effect is also possible, *viz.*, injection of suitable carriers produces hole-electron recombinations, and radiation, which may or may not be in the visible range, is produced.[22] Lehovec has used these concepts to produce a modulation of incident light by means of injected carriers. A PN junction is used across which an ac potential causes, for example, a sinusoidal variation of carrier injection. A beam of light focused on the junction will be modulated in passing through the semiconductor. In order that the light may not be absorbed by the semiconductor, the wavelength of the light modulated must be outside the range of light absorption of the PN junction.

Lehovec has also described a device which minimizes the loss of light energy when radiation is directed on a semiconductor material but must pass through a layer of material before impinging on the barrier or junction itself.

As intimated above, many of these devices may find only limited practical application and in time may be relegated to the museums where are stored the galena crystal, phlogiston, and similar historic devices. But the multifarious possibilities of these new solid state concepts, some of which are only a few years old, are repeatedly exemplified by these new devices and, by inference, point to vast hitherto unexplored and undiscovered fields for investigation and application. Therein lie untold possibilities in the solid state field.

238. GERMANIUM-SILICON ALLOYS

Among the avenues of investigation for the development of materials from which improved transistors can be made, several research teams have considered the silicon-germanium alloys. In mixing, atomic per cent concentrations are used because electrical properties are more directly related to the number of atoms involved than volume or weight ratios. When we speak of 50 atomic per cent, we mean 50 per cent of, say, germanium atoms and, in this case, 50 per cent silicon atoms. It is of interest to observe in passing that, while the method of mixtures by atomic per cent is not new, it has received increased stimulus with the advent of crystal diodes and transistors, where very pure materials are essential and one literally "counts the atoms." (A weight in grams of an element equal to its atomic weight contains Avogadro's number of atoms, 6×10^{23}.)

Despite serious metallurgical problems, it appears to be feasible to obtain germanium-silicon alloys. In general, difficulties with internal cracks and fissures are encountered because of the different coefficients of contraction, and very slow and controlled cooling is essential. Materials hitherto reported have been of the N and P type, with a resistivity up to 200 ohm-cm and mobility below 400 cm per sec per volt per cm. Apparent variations from the Stohr and Klemm[23] phase diagrams have been investigated. Solidus temperatures ranging from 1420°C, for pure silicon, to 940°C, for pure germanium, are observed with the solidus temperatures varying monotonically. To date, information regarding the electrical properties of germanium-silicon alloys is quite incomplete. In addition, no conclusive results have been reported in so far as transistor action in these materials is concerned. However, the investigations continue to add to our store of knowledge regarding the ramifications of the behavior of semiconductors and will undoubtedly contribute to the effort for improved transistors.

An interesting side light on the germanium-silicon alloys is the fact that because the lattice structure of silicon and germanium is so similar, and their interatomic distances so nearly equal, germanium is the only element which forms a continuous series of solid solutions with silicon.[24] All other elements will not mix with silicon in *all* possible proportions.

239. THE INTERMETALLIC COMPOUNDS

The principal difficulty with germanium appears to be its relatively high per cent change of resistivity with temperature; silicon is difficult to work with, and marked over-all advantages over germanium have yet to be demonstrated. These considerations have led investigators to consider the possibility of the intermetallic compounds, since it is known that compounds of elements from groups III and V of the periodic table often have characteristics similar to those of group IV. Germanium and silicon both are in group IV.

To be suitable as semiconducting materials, the compounds must possess several of the characteristics which characterize the known semiconductors: isotropy, or structure which has identical properties in all directions; interatomic distances approximately equal to those of the crystals in group IV, *i.e.*, about 2.5 angstrom units ($1 A = 10^{-8}$ cm); the sum of the valence electrons of the elements in the compound must be 8; finally, the energy gap should fall in the range of the semiconductors, below approximately 4 electron volts. Semiconductors suitable for transistor action must be capable of acting as good diode-forming substances. While these are not all of the criteria, they nevertheless serve as an initial basis for elimination. On such bases, the possible semiconducting compounds which seem to show promise are: indium antimonide (InSb), gallium antimonide (GaSb), aluminum antimonide (AlSb), aluminum phosphide (AlP), indium phosphide (InP), gallium phosphide (GaP), aluminum arsenide (AlAs), gallium arsenide (GaAs), and indium arsenide (InAs). In addition to these, semiconductors which must be seriously considered are lead sulfide (PbS), lead selenide (PbSe), and lead telluride (PbTe), which are group IV-IV compounds. These latter have been investigated quite carefully by British physicists.[25-27] It is interesting to observe that the British investigated transistor action in lead sulfide in 1950.[28]

In considering these compounds as possible transistor materials, it is natural to ask what parameters shall be used as criteria for selection of the best compounds for optimum transistor action. A comprehensive and complete study of this question has not been made, but it appears that certain limits can be set and certain criterial parameters identified which can be used as a basis for evaluation. Based on the current research work in semiconducting materials, the parameters usually investigated when considering a possible transistor material are the width of the energy gap, intrinsic resistivity, mobility, and lifetime. An additional parameter might be β, the temperature coefficient of energy gap, but the parameters of interest in electronics vary so differently with β in practical cases, that it is better considered in conjunction with the resistivity. The Hall coefficient and thermoelectric power are also often investigated, but these are contained in the four characteristics already mentioned.

240. RANGES OF THE MATERIAL PARAMETERS

If the energy gap is too high, the material approaches the insulators and too few carriers are available at room temperature for transistor use. If the gap is too small, the properties of the material approach those of the conductors, ionization or valence-bond disruption is excessive at room temperature, and satisfactory control of majority carriers is difficult. For a suitable transistor material, a range of energy gap from approximately 0.05 electron volt to a maximum of 4 electron volts appears to be desirable.

The present indications are that the resistivity cannot be too high since transistors made of such materials would have prohibitively high impedance levels. Similarly, if too low, the impedance levels and gains would be low. The resistivity is, of course, connected with the width of the gap, and remarks similar to those above also apply. In general, the resistivity range is preferably greater than 0.1 ohm-cm and less than approximately 1 megohm-cm.

Too high a mobility will not usually be encountered in a semiconducting material, and in general, high mobility contributes to high-frequency response and is no disadvantage. Too low mobility, however, will limit the frequency response and hence restrict the range of usefulness of transistors made from such material. Mobility greater than 50 cm per sec per volt per cm is desirable.

Too high a lifetime is similarly unlikely in semiconductors, and it appears from data already available that increase of lifetime beyond values now possible will be a continuing problem. Too low a lifetime, on the other hand, will seriously interfere with current gain, and may well render a material entirely unfit for transistor usage. From information presently available, lifetimes of less than 0.1 μsec are undesirable.

In addition to these physicoelectrical parameters, availability of the material should be satisfactory and its preparation should not create health hazards for working personnel. It should be amenable to purification and single-crystal growth and should be reasonably facile with regard to handling. As noted in Chap. 14, silicon may well be considered cautiously because of this last desideratum.

241. PROMISING INTERMETALLIC COMPOUNDS

In Table 15-1 are shown some of the parameters discussed above for several compounds and for tellurium. Germanium and silicon are

TABLE 15-1. INTERMETALLIC COMPOUNDS

Substance	ρ_i, ohm-cm	μ_e, cm^2/ volt sec	μ_h, cm^2/ volt sec	β, electron volts/°K	τ, μsec	ΔE_g, electron volts
Germanium.	65	3,600	1,700	4×10^{-4}	1,000 and higher	0.72
Silicon.....	2.4×10^5	1,200	300	3×10^{-4}	200 and higher	1.12
Tellurium..	1.0*	900	550	2.35×10^{-4}	....	0.33
InSb.......	1.0*	40,000	500	4×10^{-4}	....	1.8–0.40
PbS........	1.17*	1,400	350	4×10^{-4}	....	1.17
PbTe......	2.0*	3,200	800	4×10^{-4}	....	0.62
GaSb......	0.1*	1,600	400	4×10^{-4}	....	0.5–1.23
AlSb.......	0.1*	300	100	$4* \times 10^{-4}$	....	1.65

* Approximately.

shown for comparison. Data for the table have been obtained from Refs. 29 to 40. It cannot be impressed too strongly upon the reader that the values for the compounds must be considered as tentative, since the amount of work in the field has been insufficient to provide conclusive data. As an illustration, data for the mobilities given by Welker, Breckenridge, Pearson, and Tannenbaum, et al., do not agree; neither do the data on energy gap. However, the general range of values given, by comparison with silicon and germanium, does give a good guide to results that may be anticipated. Except for the lead sulfide transistors mentioned in Ref. 28, no data regarding successful transistors made with compounds are available at present. Units have been constructed on a laboratory scale only. The marked incidence of data on indium antimonide as a material in the literature in 1953 seems to indicate that this material has some promising features. Certainly the mobilities are encouraging.

Looking over the table, and considering the desiderata of the preceding section, one observes that, while lifetime data are lacking, in other respects these compounds appear to meet the requirements. But upon close circumspection, certain difficulties become evident. Hogarth[34] has reported transistor action in lead telluride—at 90°K, or −183°C. This is hardly a transistor in the practical sense of the word. The Hall coefficient of some of the compounds exhibits very anomalous behavior, particularly with temperature, with changes of sign sometimes at several points, indicating transition from P to N material, or vice versa. The resistivity given is not always attainable at room temperatures, and similar remarks refer to the mobilities. Many of the energy gaps given are admittedly not far removed from guesses. In short, the technology of even these few compounds is incomplete, and the amount of information still needed is enormous. But the significance of the trend of investigations cannot be unheeded, and one is intuitively led to the conclusion that somewhere there lurks a compound, perhaps not yet even under consideration, which will prove to be more nearly ideal than germanium. It is well to remember that transistors were not invented because germanium happens to be the best material, but rather because at the time of the discovery the inventors were investigating germanium (see Chap. 1). In view of the capabilities and limitations which have been found in all materials explored to date, there is good reason to assume that a single ideal material will not be found. Rather a variety of materials may become of practical importance because of optimum performance for particular sets of design and application requirements.

242. P AND N SEMICONDUCTORS BY RADIATION

On the basis of the valence-bond picture introduced in Chap. 5, it is understandable that any influence which will disrupt the valence bonds will alter the conductivity of the material. Further, consideration of the donor and acceptor picture indicates that if an external influence were to create donors or acceptors, as opposed to the creation of these ionized atoms by impurity additions, the P or N character might be changed thereby.

That marked changes in conductivity of semiconductors can be produced by subjecting them to bombardment by suitable particles had been known, but it was not until 1947 that Prof. K. Lark-Horovitz was able to produce permanent effects by use of sufficiently high-energy particles. These particles are collectively called nucleons since they are obtained from the nucleus of specified elements, and include deuterons, neutrons, protons, and α particles; but successful semiconductor effects are obtainable using high-energy electrons also. Table 15-2 shows the origins of these particles, some information about their mass relative to that of an electron, and the energy levels required for successful semiconductor bombardment. Also given are possible sources of high-energy particles and references where further information about these particles may be found.

TABLE 15-2. NUCLEONICS

Particle	Mass compared to that of electron (approx.)	Min. energy for bombardment (approx.), mev*	Possible source of particle	Ref.
Deuteron....	3,600 times (nucleus of deuterium, heavy isotope of hydrogen)	10	Cyclotron	40
Neutron.....	1,850 times (slightly heavier than nucleus of hydrogen but with no charge)	2	Cyclotron; reactors in atomic-energy plants	41
Proton......	1,800 times (hydrogen nucleus)	2	Radium-beryllium; cyclotron; action of α particles on hydrogen	41
α particles...	7,500 times (doubly charged helium atom)	2	Cyclotron; any radioactive source such as polonium, radium	42
Electrons....	1 $\times$	0.5	Cyclotron; Van de Graaff generator	43

* mev = million electron volts

When bombarded by such high-energy particles, P- and N-type germanium or silicon material may be obtained,[44] and the effects are permanent. This technique is superior to diffusion methods or grown-junction methods in that no near-melting or molten materials are involved. It is also clearly amenable to the formation of junctions whose shape or extent can be controlled by the use of shielding patterns.[45] One need merely cut a pattern from a nucleon-opaque material such as lead, silver, cadmium, etc. This is placed on the sample between the radiation source and the germanium (or silicon), and the shielded areas will be unaffected, since the motion of the nucleons is virtually a straight-line path. In this way, junctions may be formed of any size or shape; PNPN arrangements, unipolar arrangements, etc., are feasible; these possibilities have been explored only to a very limited extent.

243. THEORETICAL ASPECTS OF THE NUCLEON BOMBARDMENT

Some very interesting theoretical aspects of the formation of P and N regions by nucleon bombardment must be considered, since they throw further light on our knowledge of the solid state. The high-energy particles may dislodge electrons from pentavalent impurities; but by collision with the atoms of the lattice, they may also either move the atom bodily out of place, producing interstitials, or they may disrupt covalent bonds producing hole-electron pairs. Or, of course, they may do all of these simultaneously.

When an atom has been displaced from its normal position in the lattice, there is created a vacancy, of course, and simultaneously an interstitial (atom). One must consider that in this process relatively large forces are involved, both elastic and electrical, of the coulomb attraction type. Such lattice defects or dislocations give rise to "disorder" in the crystal structure, and the interstitial atoms, as well as the vacant sites previously occupied, introduce new characteristics of the crystal and, hence, of the substance itself. Fast neutrons produce just such dislocations, but slow neutrons may actually produce a more permanent effect resulting in transmutations, where the germanium character of the material is lost, and the characteristics of arsenic, gallium, or selenium are observed. Usually, the transmutations are observed to a lesser extent than the interstitials and vacancies.[46]

Experimentally, it is observed that if N-type germanium is bombarded with neutrons the resistivity increases, reaches a maximum, then becomes P type, with resistivity steadily decreasing if radiation is continued. For silicon, the resistivity increases as radiation is continued, but the rate of increase is greater for P material than for N-type silicon. Resistivities, not necessarily permanent, as high as 10,000 ohm-cm for silicon have been achieved in this manner by the Purdue group.[46] The effects observed may be removed by suitable heat-treatment. This can be understood by reasoning that, when the lattice atoms are dislocated, there is no force to restore them to their normal positions once the radiating particle is past. With the addition of thermal energy and the lapse of time, the displaced atoms may be expected to return to their preferred positions in the lattice structure, restoring the properties of the material. Accompanying the radiation is a certain amount of local or spot heating which introduces relatively macroscopic internal strains and dislocations; in practice, this is inhibited by controlled cooling of the sample during the radiation process. Of particular interest is the theoretical explanation for the behavior of the resistivity of germanium under prolonged radiation.

It has been suggested by Professor Lark-Horovitz[47] that, when the atoms are displaced from their lattice sites, the vacancies are tantamount to holes and act essentially as might an acceptor atom. This implies that the region where the vacancy has been created acts as a trap for electrons. The interstitial atom itself, in the process of dislocation due to the bombardment, may act as a donor atom, in that it may contribute electrons into the conduction band. These assumptions must be viewed seriously since Hall effect measurements as well as resistivity measurements verify predicted behavior quite well. The question of whether the donor or acceptor effect will outweigh hinges on the energy of the incident particles, the available energy levels of the material, new energy levels created, and the nature of the collision (for instance, whether direct or glancing). But it is possible to show that the energy-level distribution of N-type germanium is such that the acceptor effect predominates. Then, as radiation commences, acceptor levels are formed, electrons become trapped, lesser numbers appear in the conduction band, and the observed resistivity increases. After a time of continued irradiation, an equilibrium between acceptor levels and available electrons is reached, and the conduction reaches a minimum, i.e., the resistivity is at a maximum. Thereafter, continued action by the acceptors created by the bombardment creates an excess of holes, and conduction by holes is observed, i.e., the material is P type. Continued radiation merely increases the number of holes, and P-type resistivity continues to decrease. As stated, this agrees with experiment.

The corresponding behavior of silicon is explainable because of differences in the distribution of energy levels created during the bombardment. The behavior with respect to N-type silicon is very nearly the same as for germanium. For P type, there are certain unfilled energy levels for silicon which trap electrons produced by the bombardment in hole-electron recombinations, thus decreasing the available hole supply, and resistivity increases monotonically. It must be emphasized that this technique of bombardment is new and the entire theoretical foundation not yet fully set.

244. NO-CRUCIBLE SILICON ZONE PURIFICATION

In Chap. 14 mention was made of the difficulties in silicon preparation due to container problems. To circumvent this source of contamination, Keck and Golay[48] proposed a method of zone melting where the high surface tension of liquid silicon is used to retain a short cylindrical section of a vertical silicon bar in position after it has been melted by a circumlocated heater ring. As the heater ring, either resistively heated or representing the tank coil of an rf bombarder, is moved up or down slowly, the molten section is moved along and impurities which prefer the liquid zone will be segregated, as explained under zone purification in Chap. 13. It is clear that, by enclosing the apparatus in an inert gas or vacuum, the source of contaminants may be reduced to a minimum. The disadvantages of the method are: (1) It is not yet ascertained that zone purification of silicon is commercially feasible. (2) Rods of very limited diameter can be so treated, since the surface tension is the only force available to hold the molten zone in place. Notwithstanding, the fundamental idea is extensible to other applications, such as single-crystal growth, and appears to be of more than casual interest, particularly for laboratory techniques.

245. METAL TO SEMICONDUCTOR AREA CONTACTS

The Philco Corporation has introduced an innovation into transistor techniques by establishing the feasibility of minority carrier injection between metal and semiconductor in area contact.[49] The point contact transistor is, of course, representative of the metal-to-semiconductor point contact and the junction transistor of the semiconductor-to-semiconductor area contact. The semiconductor is abraded by a fine stream of carbon disulfide, to a thickness of fractions of a mil. Thereafter, zinc or other suitable metals are electroplated to either surface, to make a junction type of transistor with values of frequency for α cutoff of 50 mc or better. The concept should be applicable to power units, silicon devices, unipolar transistors, and the like.

246. PNIP AND NPIN JUNCTION TRANSISTORS

In May, 1954, the Bell Telephone Laboratories published an account of theoretical and experimental work being done on PNIP and NPIN transistors.[50] A relatively wide intrinsic region of germanium, that is, a region almost free of donors and acceptors, separates N and P regions, markedly reducing the collector capacitance, providing smaller values of base resistance, and increasing the upper frequency limit without resorting to fragile-thin webs. Upper frequency limits attained on a laboratory basis are 25 mc as amplifiers, and 95 mc as oscillators. Theoretically possible frequency limits are in the neighborhood of 1,000 mc, without resorting to prohibitively thin N or P separating regions. The structure is also considered amenable to power transistor applications.

REFERENCES

1. Shockley, W.: Transistor Electronics: Imperfections, Unipolar and Analog Transistors, *Proc. IRE*, Vol. 40, No. 11, pp. 1289–1313, November, 1952.
2. Herkert, P. G., and J. Kurshan: Theoretical Resistivity and Hall Coefficient of Impure Germanium near Room Temperature, *RCA Rev.*, Vol. 14, No. 11, pp. 427–440, 1953.
3. Lark-Horovitz, K.: Conductivity in Semiconductors, *Elec. Eng.*, Vol. 68, pp. 1047–1056, 1949.
4. Shockley, W.: A Unipolar Field Effect Transistor, *Proc. IRE*, Vol. 4, No. 11, pp. 1365–1376, November, 1952.
5. Dacey, G. C., and I. M. Ross: Unipolar Field Effect Transistor, *Proc. IRE*, Vol. 41, No. 8, pp. 970–979, August, 1953.
6. Early, J. M.: Effects of Space Charge Widening in Junction Transistors, *Proc. IRE*, Vol. 40, No. 11, pp. 1401–1406, November, 1952; and Early, J. M.: Design Theory of Junction Transistors, *Bell System Tech. J.*, Vol. 32, pp. 1271–1312, November, 1953.
7. Shockley, W.: The Theory of PN Junctions in Semiconductors and PN Junction Transistors, *Bell System Tech. J.*, Vol. 28, pp. 435–489, 1949.
8. Slade, B. N.: The Control of Frequency Response and Stability of Point Contact Transistors, *Proc. IRE*, Vol. 40, No. 11, pp. 1382–1384, November, 1952.
9. Pearson, G. L.: A High Impedance Field-Effect Silicon Transistor, *Phys. Rev.*, Vol. 90, No. 2, p. 336, Apr. 15, 1953.
10. Bardeen, J.: Surface States and Rectification at a Metal-Semiconductor Contact, *Phys. Rev.*, Vol. 71, pp. 717–727, 1947.
11. Shockley, W., and G. L. Pearson: Modulation of Conductance of Thin Films of Semiconductors by Surface Charges, *Phys. Rev.*, Vol. 74, No. 2, pp. 232–233, July 15, 1948.
12. Electrostatic Field Controlled Semiconductors, MCREE-49-9 (GS-USAF-Wright-Patterson AFB-173), Feb. 21, 1949; and Stuetzer, O. M.: A Crystal Amplifier with High Input Impedance, *Proc. IRE*, Vol. 38, No. 8, pp. 868–871, August, 1950.
13. Stuetzer, O. M.: Junction Fieldistors, *Proc. IRE*, Vol. 40, No. 11, pp. 1377–1381, November, 1952.
14. Stuetzer, O. M.: Microspacer Electrode Technique, *Proc. IRE*, Vol. 38, No. 8, pp. 871–876, August, 1950.
15. Benzer, S.: The High Voltage Germanium Rectifier, *National Defense Research Council 14-342*, Purdue University, Nov. 1, 1944.
16. Bardeen, J., and W. H. Brattain: The Transistor, a Semiconductor Triode, *Phys. Rev.*, Vol. 74, pp. 230–231, July 15, 1948.

17. Shive, J. N.: The Double Surface Transistor, *Phys. Rev.*, Vol. 75, No. 4, p. 69, Feb. 15, 1949.

18. Kock, W. E., and R. L. Wallace, Jr.: The Coaxial Transistor, *Elec. Eng.*, Vol. 68, pp. 222–223, March, 1949.

19. Shea, R. F.: "Transistor Circuits," John Wiley & Sons, Inc., New York, 1953.

20. Shive, J. N.: The Properties of Germanium Photocells, *J. Opt. Soc. Am.*, Vol. 43, pp. 239–244, April, 1953.

21. Lehovec, K.: New Photoelectric Devices Utilizing Carrier Injection, *Proc. IRE*, Vol. 40, No. 11, pp. 1407–1409, November, 1952.

22. Haynes, J. R., and H. B. Briggs.: Radiation Produced in Germanium and Silicon by Electron-hole Recombinations, *Bull. Am. Phys. Soc.*, Vol. 27, p. 14, 1952.

23. Stohr, H., and W. Klemm: Uber Zweistoffsysteme mit Germanium (Part I), Ge-Al, Ge-Sn, Ge-Si, *Z. anorg. Chem.*, Vol. 4, p. 305, 1939.

24. Johnson, W. R., and M. Hansen: Research on the Element Silicon and Silicon Alloys, AF TR No. 6383, prepared by the Armour Research Foundation, Illinois Institute of Technology, June, 1951.

25. Gibson, A. F.: Single Contact Lead Telluride Photocells, *Proc. Phys. Soc. (London)*, Vol. 65, p. 196, 1952.

26. Putley, E. H.: *Proc. Phys. Soc. (London)*, Vol. 65, Sec. B, pp. 388–389, 993, 736–737, 1952.

27. Hogarth, C. A.: Transistor Action and Related Phenomena in PbS, Using Specimens from Various Sources, *Proc. Phys. Soc. (London)*, Vol. 66, Part 3, pp. 216–220, Mar. 1, 1953.

28. Banbury, P. C., H. A. Gebbie, and C. A. Hogarth: "Semiconducting Materials," ed. H. K. Henish, Butterworth's Scientific Publications, pp. 78ff, 1951.

29. Pearson, G. L., and M. Tanenbaum: The Magnetoresistance Effect in InSb, *Phys. Rev.*, Vol. 90, No. 1, p. 153, Apr. 1, 1953.

30. Breckenridge, R. G.: Semiconducting Intermetallic Compounds, *Phys. Rev.*, Vol. 90, No. 3, p. 488, May 1, 1953.

31. Tanenbaum, M., and J. P. Maita: Hall Effect and Conductivity of InSb Single Crystals, *Phys. Rev.*, Vol. 91, No. 4, pp. 1009–1010, Aug. 15, 1953.

32. Tanenbaum, M., and H. B. Briggs: Optical Properties of Indium Antimonide, *Phys. Rev.*, Vol. 91, No. 6, p. 1561, Sept. 15, 1953.

33. Scanlon, W. W., R. L. Petritz, and F. L. Lummis: *Phys. Rev.*, Vol. 86, No. 4, pp. 659–660, 1952.

34. Hogarth, C. A.: Transistor Action in Crystals of Lead Telluride, *Proc. Phys. Soc. (London)*, Vol. 65, Sec. B, pp. 958–963, 1952.

35. Justi, E., and G. Lautz: *Abhandl. braunschweig. wiss. Ges.*, Vol. 4, pp. 107–116, 1952.

36. Hintenberger, H.: *Z. Physik*, Vol. 119, pp 1ff., 1942.

37. Bauer, K.: *Ann. Physik*, Vol. 38, pp. 84ff., 1940.

38. Welker, H.: *Z. Naturforsch.*, Vol. 7A, p. 744, 1952; also Vol. 8A, p. 248, 1953.

39. Semiconductor Research, Seventh Quarterly Report, Contr. DA36-039 sc-15339, pp. 31 and 51, Purdue Research Foundation, Purdue University, Department of Physics, Jan. 1, 1953, to Mar. 31, 1953; and Madelung, O., and H. Welker: *Z. angew. Physik*, Vol. 5, pp. 12–14, January, 1953.
40. Freeman, I. M.: "Modern Introductory Physics," pp. 427–451, McGraw-Hill Book Company, Inc., New York, 1949.
41. "Outline of Atomic Physics" by members of the staff, Physics Department, University of Pittsburgh, John Wiley & Sons, Inc., New York, 1936.
42. Prutton, C. F., and S. H. Maron: "Fundamental Principles of Physical Chemistry," The Macmillan Company, New York, 1951.
43. Ruark, A. E., and H. C. Urey: "Atoms, Molecules and Quanta," McGraw-Hill Book Company, Inc., New York, 1930.
44. Lark-Horovitz, K.: Nucleon Bombarded Semiconductors, in "Semiconducting Materials," ed. H. K. Henish, Butterworth's Scientific Publications, 1951.
45. Johnson, V. A., and K. Lark-Horovitz: Final Report, Semiconductor Research, Contr. W-36-039 sc-32020, Purdue University, Department of Physics, January, 1946–December, 1948.
46. Final Report, PRF-489, Semiconductor Research, Contr. W36-039 sc-38151, pp. 80–92, Purdue University Department of Physics, September, 1948, to Nov. 30, 1951.
47. James, H. M., and K. Lark-Horovitz: *Z. physik. Chem.*, Vol. 198, p. 4, 1951. (Excellent list of references on this subject.)
48. Keck, P. H., and M. J. E. Golay: Crystallization of Silicon from a Floating Liquid Zone, *Phys. Rev.*, Vol. 89, No. 6, p. 1297, Mar. 15, 1953.
49. Technical Staff of Philco Research Division: The Surface Barrier Transistor, *Proc. IRE*, Vol. 41, pp. 1702–1720, December, 1953.
50. Early, J. M.: PNIP and NPIN Junction Transistor Triodes, *Bell. System Tech. J.*, Vol. 33, No. 3, pp. 517–533, May, 1954.

APPENDIX I.   FOUR-POLE PARAMETER

TRANSFORMATION EQUATIONS

$$h_{11} = r_{11} - \frac{r_{12}r_{21}}{r_{22}} \tag{1}$$

$$h_{12} = \frac{r_{12}}{r_{22}} \tag{2}$$

$$h_{21} = -\frac{r_{21}}{r_{22}} = -\alpha \tag{3}$$

$$h_{22} = \frac{1}{r_{22}} \tag{4}$$

$$g_{11} = \frac{r_{22}}{r_{11}r_{22} - r_{12}r_{21}} \tag{5}$$

$$g_{12} = \frac{-r_{12}}{r_{11}r_{22} - r_{12}r_{21}} \tag{6}$$

$$g_{21} = \frac{-r_{21}}{r_{11}r_{22} - r_{12}r_{21}} \tag{7}$$

$$g_{22} = \frac{r_{11}}{r_{11}r_{22} - r_{12}r_{21}} \tag{8}$$

$$r_{11} = h_{11} - \frac{h_{12}h_{21}}{h_{22}} \tag{9}$$

$$r_{12} = \frac{h_{12}}{h_{22}} \tag{10}$$

$$r_{21} = -\frac{h_{21}}{h_{22}} \tag{11}$$

$$r_{22} = \frac{1}{h_{22}} \tag{12}$$

$$h_{11} = \frac{1}{g_{11}} \tag{13}$$

$$h_{12} = -\frac{g_{12}}{g_{11}} \tag{14}$$

$$h_{21} = \frac{g_{21}}{g_{11}} = -\alpha \tag{15}$$

$$h_{22} = g_{22} - \frac{g_{12}g_{21}}{g_{11}} \tag{16}$$

$$g_{11} = \frac{1}{h_{11}} \tag{17}$$

$$g_{12} = -\frac{h_{12}}{h_{11}} \tag{18}$$

$$g_{21} = \frac{h_{21}}{h_{11}} \tag{19}$$

$$g_{22} = h_{22} - \frac{h_{12}h_{21}}{h_{11}} \tag{20}$$

$$r_{11} = \frac{g_{22}}{g_{11}g_{22} - g_{12}g_{21}} \tag{21}$$

$$r_{12} = \frac{-g_{12}}{g_{11}g_{22} - g_{12}g_{21}} \tag{22}$$

$$r_{21} = \frac{-g_{21}}{g_{11}g_{22} - g_{12}g_{21}} \tag{23}$$

$$r_{22} = \frac{g_{11}}{g_{11}g_{22} - g_{12}g_{21}} \tag{24}$$

NOTES: Z's may be substituted for r's, Y's for g's in the above formulas. All parameters are based on small-signal grounded-base operation.

REFERENCES: G. Knight, Jr., R. A. Johnson, and R. B. Holt, Measurement of Small Signal Parameters of Transistors, *Proc. IRE*, Vol. 41, pp. 983–989, 1953.

L. J. Giacoletto, Terminology and Equations for Linear Active Four-Terminal Networks Including Transistors, *RCA Rev.*, Vol. 14, No. 1, pp. 28–46, 1953.

See also Ref. 4, Chap. 9.

APPENDIX II. GENERALIZED EQUATIONS FOR

TRANSISTORS IN CASCADE

Consider the system of Eqs. (12-1) to (12-4), and write these in the general form:

$$A_1i_1 + B_1i_2 + C_1i_3 + D_1i_4 = e_g \qquad (12\text{-}1')$$
$$A_2i_1 + B_2i_2 + C_2i_3 + D_2i_4 = 0 \qquad (12\text{-}2')$$
$$A_3i_1 + B_3i_2 + C_3i_3 + D_3i_4 = 0 \qquad (12\text{-}3')$$
$$A_4i_1 + B_4i_2 + C_4i_3 + D_4i_4 = 0 \qquad (12\text{-}4')$$

The system determinant, to be denoted by SD, is then:

$$SD = \begin{vmatrix} A_1 & B_1 & C_1 & D_1 \\ A_2 & B_2 & C_2 & D_2 \\ A_3 & B_3 & C_3 & D_3 \\ A_4 & B_4 & C_4 & D_4 \end{vmatrix}$$

The system determinant is then conveniently expanded by the minors of the first column:

$$SD = A_1\begin{vmatrix} B_2 & C_2 & D_2 \\ B_3 & C_3 & D_3 \\ B_4 & C_4 & D_4 \end{vmatrix} - A_2\begin{vmatrix} B_1 & C_1 & D_1 \\ B_3 & C_3 & D_3 \\ B_4 & C_4 & D_4 \end{vmatrix} + A_3\begin{vmatrix} B_1 & C_1 & D_1 \\ B_2 & C_2 & D_2 \\ B_4 & C_4 & D_4 \end{vmatrix}$$
$$- A_4\begin{vmatrix} B_1 & C_1 & D_1 \\ B_2 & C_2 & D_2 \\ B_3 & C_3 & D_3 \end{vmatrix}$$

By examination of Eqs. (12-1) to (12-4), it is seen that $A_3 = 0 = A_4$, and we need merely expand the first two minors. This yields:

$$SD = A_1B_2C_3D_4 + A_1B_4C_2D_3 + A_1B_3C_4D_2 + A_2B_4C_3D_1$$
$$+ A_2B_3C_1D_4 + A_2B_1C_4D_3 - A_1B_4C_3D_2 - A_1B_3C_2D_4 - A_1B_2C_4D_3$$
$$- A_2B_1C_3D_4 - A_2B_4C_1D_3 - A_2B_3C_4D_1$$

Terms in D_2 also vanish, but the general form is given for further reference. We shall also need the generalized form of Eqs. (12-13) to (12-15), given below:

$$A_1 i_1 + B_1 i_2 + C_1 i_3 = e_g \qquad (12\text{-}13')$$
$$A_2 i_1 + B_2 i_2 + C_2 i_3 = 0 \qquad (12\text{-}14')$$
$$A_3 i_1 + B_3 i_2 + C_3 i_3 = 0 \qquad (12\text{-}15')$$

Examination of the Kirchhoff equations for all the cascading arrangements reveals that in all cases $C_1 = 0$ and $A_3 = 0$. Therefore, upon expanding the system determinant, we will in all cases have only three terms:

$$D = A_1 B_2 C_3 - A_1 B_3 C_2 - A_2 B_1 C_3$$

Solving, it is found that, for Eqs. (12-13') to (12-15'):

$$i_1 = \frac{e_g(B_2 C_3 - C_2 B_3)}{D}$$

$$i_2 = - \frac{e_g A_2 C_3}{D}$$

$$i_3 = \frac{e_g A_2 B_3}{D}$$

$i_3'' =$ loop III current when e_g is placed in loop III

$$= \frac{e_g(A_1 B_2 - A_2 B_1)}{D}$$

Using these relations, with the coefficients A, B, and C replaced by the corresponding functions of the parameters obtained from the Kirchhoff equations, it is not difficult to show that:

$$R_i = A_1 - R_g - \frac{A_2 B_1 C_3}{B_2 C_3 - B_3 C_2}$$

$$R_o = C_3 - R_L - \frac{A_1 B_3 C_2}{A_1 B_2 - A_2 B_1}$$

$$VG_\mathrm{I} = \frac{A_2 C_3(A_1 - R_g) - A_2 B_3 C_2}{D}$$

$$VG_\mathrm{II} = \frac{-B_3 R_L}{(A_1 - R_g)C_3 - B_3 C_2}$$

$$VG_o = \frac{-A_2 B_3 R_L}{D}$$

$$CG_\mathrm{I} = \frac{-A_2 C_3}{B_2 C_3 - B_3 C_2}$$

$$CG_\mathrm{II} = \frac{-B_3}{C_3}$$

$$CG_o = \frac{A_2 B_3}{B_2 C_3 - B_3 C_2}$$

$$PG_{\mathrm{I}} = \frac{4R_g(A_2C_3)^2R_{i\mathrm{II}}}{D^2}$$

$$PG_{\mathrm{II}} = \frac{B_3{}^2R_L}{C_3{}^2R_{i\mathrm{II}}}$$

$$PG_o = \frac{4R_gR_L(A_2B_3)^2}{D^2}$$

APPENDIX III.   EXCERPTS FROM MIL-T-12679A

(SIG C)

Early in 1953 the Signal Corps Engineering Laboratories initiated a series of conferences leading to the establishment of a specification of tests to be used in the evaluation of transistors—in military parlance this is called a Basic Section.   Approximately 25 separate conferences were held, involving the expenditure of over 10,000 engineering man-hours, with the following organizations acting in a consultant or advisory capacity:

Western Electric Co.

Bell Telephone Laboratories

General Electric Co.

Raytheon Manufacturing Co.

Sylvania Electric Products Inc.

Bureau of Ships, US Navy

Wright Air Development Center, Dayton, Ohio.

On Sept. 23, 1953, the Basic Section, identified as MIL-T-12679A (Sig C) became an official procurement document for transistors and crystal diodes.   Pertinent excerpts from this specification are reproduced in this book as a guide to testing procedures for transistors and crystal diodes.

3.2.1 *Transistor.* A transistor is an active transducer which depends for its essential behavior on the transport and control of charges in semiconductors.

3.2.2 *Crystal diode.* A crystal diode is a passive, asymmetrical, nonlinear circuit element which depends for its essential behavior on the transport and control of charges in semiconductors.

3.2.3 *Phototransistor.* A phototransistor is a semiconductor photo-electric transducer which depends for its essential behavior on the transport of charges and their control by light.

276

3.2.4 *Reference point for transistors.* The reference point for transistors is the transistor electrode that is common to both input and output circuits.

3.2.5 *Reference point for crystal diodes and phototransistors.* The reference point for electrode potentials on crystal diodes and phototransistors is the N (cathode) terminal.

3.2.6 *Vb: Base voltage.* The base voltage is the potential between the base terminal and the reference point.

3.2.7 *Vc: Collector voltage.* The collector voltage is the potential between the collector terminal and the reference point.

3.2.8 *Ve: Emitter voltage.* The emitter voltage is the potential between the emitter terminal and the reference point.

3.2.9 *Applied potential.* The applied potential on an electrode is the potential between the electrode and the reference point.

3.2.10 *Supply potential.* The supply potential is the potential furnished to a circuit containing a semiconductor device.

3.2.11 *Polarity.* All potentials are designated by polarity with respect to the reference point.

3.2.12 *Permanent shorts and opens.* A permanent short or open is a short-circuit or open-circuit, respectively, which exists for an appreciable time when there is no accelerating force applied to the semiconductor device. This class includes sustained short-circuits and open-circuits which may be corrected by subsequent acceleration.

3.2.13 *Temporary shorts or opens.* A temporary short or open is a short-circuit or open-circuit, respectively, resulting from and lasting during the application of the accelerating force. Temporary shorts are classified as follows:

(a) A tap short or open is a temporary short or open as determined with a relatively low accelerating force, as specified in paragraph 4.8.

(b) A transient short or open is a temporary short or open occurring during a high-level shock impact, as specified in 4.20.

3.2.16 *Co: Output capacitance.* The output capacitance is the capacitance between the output terminals.

3.2.17 *Ci: Input capacitance.* The input capacitance is the capacitance between the input terminals.

3.2.18 *Z11: Small-signal, open-circuit, input-impedance.* Small-signal, open-circuit, input impedance is the ratio of the ac input potential to ac input current, with zero ac output current. The real and reactive parts of Z11 are defined by: Z11 = R11 + j11 (4.2.11).

3.2.19 *Z12: Small-signal, open-circuit, reverse-transfer impedance.*

Small-signal, open-circuit, reverse-transfer impedance is the ratio of the ac input potential to ac output current, with zero ac input current. The real and reactive parts of Z12 are defined by: Z12 = R12 + j12 (4.2.11).

3.2.20 *Z21: Small-signal, open-circuit, forward-transfer impedance.* Small-signal, open-circuit, forward-transfer impedance is the ratio of the ac output potential to ac input current, with zero ac output current. The real and reactive parts of Z21 are defined by: Z21 = R21 + j21 (4.2.11).

3.2.21 *Z22: Small-signal, open-circuit, output-impedance.* Small-signal, open-circuit, output impedance is the ratio of the ac output potential to ac output current, with zero ac input current. The real and reactive parts of Z22 are defined by: Z22 = R22 + j22 (4.2.11).

3.2.22 *αce: Small-signal, short-circuit, current-multiplication ratio.* Small-signal, short-circuit, current-multiplication ratio is the ratio of the ac output current to ac input current, with zero ac output potential (4.2.12).

3.2.23 *face: Small-signal, short-circuit, current-multiplication ratio cut-off frequency.* Small-signal, short-circuit, current-multiplication ratio cut-off frequency is the frequency in cycles per second at which the absolute value of the small-signal, short-circuit, current-multiplication ratio is 0.707 times its value at the specified reference frequency (see 4.2.12 and 4.55).

3.2.24 *h11: Small-signal, short-circuit, input-impedance.* Small-signal, short-circuit, input impedance is the ratio of the ac input potential to ac input current, with zero ac output potential. (4.2.12)

3.2.25 *h12: Small-signal, open-circuit, feedback-potential ratio.* Small-signal, open-circuit, feedback-potential ratio is the ratio of the ac input potential to ac output potential, with zero ac input current. (4.2.11)

3.2.26 *h21: Small-signal, short-circuit, current-transfer ratio.* Small-signal, short-circuit, current-transfer ratio is the ratio of the ac output current to ac input current, with zero ac output potential. (4.2.12)

3.2.27 *h22: Small-signal, open-circuit, output-admittance.* Small-signal, open-circuit, output admittance is the ratio of the ac output current to ac output potential, with zero ac input current. (4.2.11)

3.2.28 *Y11: Small-signal, short-circuit, input-admittance.* Small-signal, short-circuit, input admittance is the ratio of the ac input current to ac input potential, with zero ac output potential. (4.2.12)

3.2.29 *Y12: Small-signal, short-circuit, feedback-admittance.* Small-signal, short-circuit, feedback admittance is the ratio of the ac input current to ac output potential, with zero ac input potential. (4.2.12)

3.2.30 *Y21: Small-signal, short-circuit, transfer-admittance.* Small-signal, short-circuit, transfer admittance is the ratio of the ac output current to ac input potential, with zero ac output potential. (4.2.12)

3.2.31 *Y22: Small-signal, short-circuit, output-admittance.* Small-signal, short-circuit, output admittance is the ratio of the ac output current to ac output potential, with zero ac input potential. (4.2.12)

3.2.32 *NF: Noise figure.* In decibels NF = $10 \log_{10}$ (Noise Factor).

3.2.33 *Noise factor.* For a linear system at a selected input frequency, the noise factor is the ratio of the total noise power per unit bandwidth (at a corresponding output frequency) available at the output terminals, to the portion thereof engendered at the input frequency by the input termination, whose noise temperature is standard (290°K) at all frequencies.

3.2.34 *Pulse.* A pulse is a recurrent flow of energy of short time duration.

3.2.35 *Spike.* A spike is a transient of very short time duration, during which the amplitude appreciably exceeds the average amplitude of the pulse.

3.2.36 *tr: Rise time.* The rise time of the pulse or spike is that time duration of the pulse or spike during which the amplitude of its leading edge is increasing from 10% to 90% of the maximum amplitude of the pulse or spike.

3.2.37 *tf: Fall time.* The fall time of the pulse or spike is that time duration of the pulse or spike during which the amplitude of its trailing edge is decreasing from 90% to 10% of the maximum amplitude of the pulse or spike.

3.2.38 *tp: Pulse time.* The pulse time of a pulse or spike is the time duration from a point on the leading edge which is 90% of the maximum amplitude of the pulse or spike, to a point on the trailing edge which is 90% of the maximum amplitude of the pulse or spike.

3.2.39 *tw: Average pulse time.* The average pulse time of a pulse or spike is the time duration from a point on the leading edge which is 50% of the maximum amplitude of the pulse or spike, to a point on the trailing edge which is 50% of the maximum amplitude of the pulse or spike.

3.2.40 *Vif: Floating potential.* Floating potential is the dc potential which appears at an open-circuit ith-electrode when dc potentials are applied to other electrodes.

3.2.41 *Probe frequency.* Probe frequency is the frequency of the small signal applied to the emitter, in the oscilloscopic display of α ce vs Ie. (The output amplitude of the probe frequency signal varies with α ce.)

3.2.42 *Sweep frequency.* Sweep frequency is the repetition frequency of the time base used to provide the recurrent deflection on an oscilloscope.

3.2.43 *Display bandwidth.* Display bandwidth is the bandwidth, in cycles per second, of the oscilloscope and associated equipment in the oscilloscopic display of αce vs Ie.

3.2.44 *Photoconductance effect.* Photoconductance effect is the change in a parameter of a semiconductor device when the device is exposed to light.

3.2.45 *Light.* Light is any radiation of wavelengths within the range of detectability of the semiconductor device.

3.2.46 *ID: Dark current.* Dark current is the current flowing to the reference electrode when further reduction of light incident on the semiconductor device produces no measurable change in current.

3.2.47 *IL: Light current.* Light current is the current which flows to the reference electrode when light from the standard radiation light source (see 4.2.5) falls on the semiconductor device.

3.2.48 *Ac light response.* Ac light response is the ac current which flows to the reference electrode when the sensitive area of the photo-transistor is exposed to intensity-modulated light.

3.2.49 *Spectral response.* Spectral response is the distribution of the photoelectric sensitivity with the frequency of the incident light, at constant applied potential.

3.2.50 *Photoelectric sensitivity.* Photoelectric sensitivity is the change in current in the semiconductor device per unit change in incident light flux at the specified frequency or band of frequencies.

3.2.51 *Forward current.* Forward current is the conventional current that passes through the semiconductor device in the direction of easy flow.

3.2.52 *Reverse current.* Reverse current is the conventional current that passes through the semiconductor device in the opposite direction to the direction of easy flow.

3.2.53 *EZ: Zener voltage.* Zener voltage is the voltage associated with that portion of the reverse E vs I characteristic of a semiconductor device wherein the voltage remains substantially constant over a considerable range of current values.

3.2.54 *Limits.* The term "within the limits specified" includes the minimum or maximum values, or both, shown on the specification sheet.

3.2.55 *Maximum ratings.* The maximum ratings are limiting values above which the serviceability of any individual semiconductor device may be temporarily impaired. The values specified on the specification sheet under "maximum" are based on the "absolute arithmetic system" and shall not be exceeded during manufacture or inspection. (It does not follow that combinations of maximum ratings can be obtained simultaneously.)

3.2.55.1 *Absolute maximum ratings.* Absolute maximum ratings are the limiting values beyond which the performance of any individual semiconductor device may be permanently impaired. (It does not follow that combinations of absolute maximum ratings can be obtained simultaneously.)

3.2.56 *Rectification efficiency.* Rectification efficiency is the ratio, expressed as a percentage, of the dc load voltage to the peak ac input voltage in a half-wave rectifier circuit.

3.2.57 *epx: Peak reverse voltage, crystal diodes.* The crystal diode peak reverse voltage is the voltage at which further increase in the current through the crystal diode does not result in an increase in the voltage across the crystal diode.

4.2.1 *Holding period.* The semiconductor device shall be held non-operating for a period of at least 24 hours. This holding period shall be initiated after the completion of all manufacturing processes.

4.2.2 *Test frequency.* Measurements shall be made at 270 ± 30 cps. A frequency of measurement other than 270 ± 30 cps may be used provided the manufacturer or contractor demonstrates that the results obtained correlate with those obtained at 270 ± 30 cps.

4.2.3 *Reference temperature.* The reference temperature shall be $25°$ C. The ambient air temperature shall be $25°$ C $\pm 1.5°$ C with no direct draft on the device under test.

4.2.4 *Common base.* The following transistor parameters shall refer to the common base, emitter input connection: $Z11$, $Z12$, $Z21$, $Z22$, $Y11$, $Y12$, $Y21$, $Y22$, $h11$, $h12$, $h21$, $h22$, αce, $f\alpha ce$, NF, Co, and Ci.

4.2.5 *Standard radiation light source.* The standard radiation light source shall be a lamp consisting of a coiled tungsten filament inclosed in a lead-glass or lime-glass envelope. The lamp shall operate at a color temperature of $2870 \pm 5°$ K. Periodically, the following calibrating tests shall be made on the test lamp:

(a) The electric current necessary to produce the specified color temperature shall be determined by comparison with a secondary standard lamp. The latter lamp shall be calibrated by a recognized certification laboratory approved by the contracting officer.

(b) A photometer method shall be used to determine the intensity of the test lamp.

4.2.6 *Orientation.* Orientations shall be defined as follows and as shown in figure 1:

(a) *X1.* The orientation of a semiconductor device with the main axis of the device and the major cross section of the device normal to the direction of accelerating force.

(b) *X2.*   The orientation of a semiconductor device with the main axis of the device normal and the major cross section parallel to the accelerating force.

(c) *Y1.*   The orientation of a semiconductor device with the main axis of the device parallel to the direction of the accelerating force and the principal base away from the point of application of the accelerating force.

(d) *Y2.*   The orientation of a semiconductor device with the main axis parallel to the direction of accelerating force and the principal base toward the point of application of the accelerating force.

4.2.7 *Handling precautions.* The following handling precautions shall be observed in the testing of semiconductor devices:

4.2.7.1 *Transients.* The semiconductor device shall not be subjected to conditions in which transients cause the ratings to be

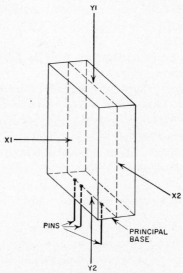

Figure 1. Orientation of X1, X2, Y1 and Y2 directions of accelerating forces for transistors.

exceeded, such as may result from inserting the semiconductor device into or removing it from the circuit with power on.

4.2.7.2 *Order of connection of leads.* When the semiconductor device is connected to the power source, the base lead shall be connected first or second.

4.2.7.3 *Radiation precautions.* Due precautions shall be used in storing or operating semiconductor devices in substantial fields of X-rays, cosmic rays, neutrons or other energetic particles.

4.2.8 *Test value*. Tests shall be conducted only at the specified test value or within the specified test range.

4.2.9 *Pulse voltages and currents*. The values of pulse time, rise time, fall time, repetition rate and pulse amplitude shall be as specified. No part of the pulse which occurs after the rise time and prior to the fall time shall have an amplitude less than 85 percent of the maximum amplitude of the pulse. At least 85 percent of the time duration of that portion of the pulse which occurs after the rise time and prior to the fall time, shall have an amplitude which is at least 90 percent of the maximum amplitude of the pulse. This 85 percent time duration may be composed of separate portions of the pulse.

4.2.10 *Small-signal*. To attain a small signal, the amplitude of the test signal shall be progressively decreased until any further decrease in amplitude produces no change, within specified accuracy, in the value of the parameter.

4.2.11 *Open-circuit*. In the measurement of small-signal, open-circuit parameters, the words "open circuit" shall mean the following:

(a) In the measurement of Z11 and Z21 the output circuit shall be considered "open" or output ac current zero if, at the test frequency, halving the magnitude of the output circuit impedance produces no change, within the specified accuracy, in the small-signal values of Z11 and Z21.

(b) In the measurement of Z12, Z22, h12 and h22, the input circuit shall be considered "open" or the input ac current zero if, at the test frequency, halving the magnitude of the input circuit impedance produces no change within the specified accuracy in the small signal value of Z12, Z22, h12, and h22.

4.2.12 *Short-circuit*. In the measurement of small-signal, short-circuit parameters, the words "short circuit" shall mean the following:

(a) In the measurement of h11, h21, Y11, Y21 and αce, the output circuit shall be considered "short-circuited" or the ac output potential zero, if at the test frequency, increasing the magnitude of the output circuit impedance by 50 percent produces no change within the specified accuracy in the small signal value of h11, h21, Y11, Y21 and αce.

(b) In the measurement of Y12 and Y22, the input circuit shall be considered "short-circuited" or the ac input potential zero, if, at the test frequency, increasing the magnitude of the input impedance by 50 percent produces no change within the specified accuracy in the small signal value of Y12 and Y22.

4.8 *Tap shorts and opens test.*   The semiconductor devices shall be tested for tap shorts and opens as follows: The semiconductor device shall be mounted in an approved manner and tapped three times on each of two sides, 90° apart.   Sharp blows shall be delivered with an approved mallet or equivalent mechanical device.   When any tap short or open indication is obtained, the test shall be repeated.   When any short or open indication is again obtained, the semiconductor device fails this test.   For purposes of this test, an approved mallet is described as follows: an 1/8 inch diameter fibre rod shall be fully inserted concentrically into the small end of a #8 cork; the mallet shall have an overall length of 6 inches.

4.9 *Base, cap, and insert torque test.*   First the semiconductor device shall be immersed in water at a temperature of 50° C for 42 hours, and then removed and cooled for 1 hour at room temperature.   Then a torque of the applicable value specified in Table VIII shall be gradu-

Table VIII—Torque

Base or cap size	Torque lb-inches
Base, 0.65 inch diameter (major) or less	12
Base having a maximum overall diameter of 0.65 to 1.5 inches	20
Medium, small, or miniature caps	1.5

ally applied between the elements specified in Table IX.   There shall be no loosening of cemented joints.

Table IX—Torque elements

Design	Torque between
Base, cemented	Base and bulb, or pins and bulb
Cap, cemented	Cap and bulb

4.11 *Lead fatigue test.*   The lead fatigue test shall be conducted on two leads of each specimen of the sample.   The leads shall be selected in a cyclical manner (regular recurring): for example, leads No. 1 and 2 of the first specimen; leads No. 2 and 3 on the second specimen, etc. The lead fatigue test shall be made by subjecting each lead under test to a pull of 16 ± 1 ounces.   Each lead so weighted shall withstand the minimum number, as specified on the specification sheet, of 90-degree arcs at the header.   An arc is defined as the movement of the lead away from the semiconductor device through 90° from normal and back to normal.   All arcs on a single lead shall be made in the same direction from its normal position and in the same plane.   A lead shall be considered to have failed when it breaks off from the device.

4.12 *Axial strain test.* With one axial lead of the semiconductor device clamped, a force of 1 pound shall be applied, without shock, at right angles to the axis of the semiconductor device at the farther end of the other lead. Leads showing any loosening shall be considered to have failed.

4.13 *Glass envelope strain test.* The glass envelope, but not the base, of the semiconductor device shall be completely immersed in boiling water for 15 seconds and immediately thereafter immersed in ice water for 5 seconds. The volume of water shall be large enough not to be affected appreciably in temperature by this test. The glass envelope shall not crack or break. For all-glass types, the entire device shall be immersed. In case of doubt, compliance with this test shall be determined by ability to meet the requirements of the hermetic seal test of 4.14 or 4.15.

4.14 *Gas filled hermetic seal test.* The semiconductor device shall be completely immersed in water that partially fills a vessel from which the air can be evacuated. Evacuation shall proceed to an approximate absolute pressure of one (1) inch (25 mm of mercury) during which time the semiconductor device shall not leak as evidenced by gas bubbles rising to the surface of the water from any portion of the semiconductor device.

4.15 *Evacuated hermetic seal test.* The semiconductor device shall be placed in a suitable vessel and shall be subjected to a water vapor pressure of not less than 433.6 mm of mercury for a period of 8 hours. The device shall then be removed and dried for a period not to exceed 20 hours at room temperature.

4.16 *Drop test.* The semiconductor device shall be dropped three times. The height from which the semiconductor device is dropped shall be as specified. The barrier receiving the impact shall be a 1-inch thick maple wood block. Both the length and width of the block shall be at least 6 inches each.

4.17 *Vibration test, low acceleration.* The semiconductor device shall be fastened rigidly on the vibration platform. The device shall be vibrated successively in orientations X1, X2, and Y1, over a frequency range of 10 to 100 cycles per second, covering the frequency range in not less than 1 minute with uniform variation of frequency and constant peak acceleration of 2G. The voltages and currents specified on the specification sheet shall be applied to the semiconductor device during this test. With the specified emitter load resistance, the value of the alternating voltage produced across the specified collector load resistance shall be measured with an average responding, rms calibrated ac vacuum tube voltmeter. This meter shall have appropriate voltage ranges and shall have the ability to measure, with an error of less than 3 percent, the rms value of a sine wave voltage at 1000 cps. The calibration of the meter shall be ± 1 db of the 1,000 cps reading, between 20 and 20,000 cps, with an attenuation rate below 20 cps and above 20,000 cps of 6 db ± 2 db per octave. Maximum inherent noise in the meter shall be 20 db below the voltages specified on the specification sheet.

4.18 *Vibration test, high acceleration.* The semiconductor device shall be fastened rigidly on the vibration platform. The device shall be vibrated successively in orientations X1, X2, and Y1, over a frequency range of 100 to 1000 cycles per second, covering the vibration frequency range four times in no less than 16 minutes, with uniform variation of frequency and constant peak acceleration of 10G. The voltages and currents specified on the specification sheet shall be applied to the semiconductor device during this test. With the specified emitter load resistance, the value of the alternating voltages produced across the specified collector load resistance shall be measured with an average responding, rms calibrated ac vacuum tube voltmeter. This meter shall have appropriate voltage ranges and shall have the ability to measure, with an error of less than 3 percent, the rms value of a sine wave voltage at 1000 cps. The calibration of the meter shall be ± 1 db of the 1,000 cps reading, between 20 and 20,000 cps, with an attenuation rate below 20 cps and above 20,000 cps of 6 db ± 2 db per octave. Maximum inherent noise in the meter shall be 20 db below the voltages specified on the specification sheet.

4.19 *Vibration fatigue test.* The semiconductor device shall be fastened rigidly on the vibration platform and shall be vibrated with simple harmonic motion at any single frequency between 45 and 100 cps, with a constant peak acceleration of 10G. The semiconductor device shall be vibrated for a total of 96 hours, 32 hours in each of the three orientations X1, X2, and Y1.

4.20 *Shock test.* The semiconductor device shall be tested in accordance with Method 202 of Military Standard MIL-STD-202 or on the Navy type high impact (fly-weight) shock machine shown on Drawing 180-JAN. The semiconductor device shall be subjected to three 500G shocks of approximately 1 millisecond duration in each of the three orientations X1, X2, and Y2, (a total of nine shocks). The voltages and currents specified in the specification sheet shall be applied to the semiconductor device during test. With emitter and collector load resistances as specified on the specification sheet, the value of the peak voltage produced across the collector load resistor shall be measured by means of a peak reading device with a sensitivity as specified on the specification sheet, whose characteristics are as follows: flat, within ± 1 db of the 1000 cps readings, between 20 and 20,000 cps, with an attenuation rate below 20 cps and above 20,000 cps of 6 db ± 2 db per octave. Maximum inherent noise in the meter shall be 20 db below the voltages specified on the specification sheet. The maximum error at 1000 cps shall be 3 percent. The peak output voltage shall not exceed the value specified on the specification sheet. Thyratron devices calibrated to indicate acceptable levels may be used.

4.21 *Centrifuge test.* The semiconductor devices shall be subjected to a centrifugal acceleration of 20,000 G's in each of the three orientations, X1, X2, and Y2. The centrifuge shall be held at the maximum speed until a stable reading of the tachometer is obtained.

4.25 *Temperature test, non-operating.* The semiconductor device shall be subjected to the number of temperature cycles specified on the specification sheet. Low temperature shall be $-55°$ C or lower; high temperature shall be $85°$ C or higher. The device shall be maintained at each end temperature for sufficient time to reach thermal equilibrium, but not for less than 15 minutes. The time for changing the temperature from end point to end point shall not exceed 30 minutes. The test may be started at any point in the cycle. A cycle is a series including both end point temperatures and return. Example: Room temperature to $-55°$ C to $85°$ C to room temperature.

4.26 *High temperature operation test.* With the specified voltages applied, the semiconductor device shall be operated at the specified high temperature. After thermal equilibrium has been reached at the specified high temperature, performance measurements shall be made.

4.28 *Moisture resistance test.* The semiconductor device shall be tested in accordance with Method 106 per Military Standard MIL-STD-202.

4.29 *Immersion test.* The semiconductor devices shall be immersed in a water bath at $40°$ C for a period of 15 minutes. At the conclusion of this period they shall be transferred to a water bath at $25°$ C for 15 minutes. The surface of the semiconductor devices shall then be wiped dry, and the electrical tests as required on the specification sheet shall be conducted within 1 hour after the drying operation.

4.30 *Salt-spray corrosion test.* The device shall be subjected for 96 hours to the salt spray test in accordance with Method 101 per Military Standard MIL-STD-202. At the end of this test, the device shall be washed, shaken, and air-blasted, and then permitted to dry for 24 hours at $40°$ C. There shall be no visible damage which might cause nonconformance with specified requirements.

4.32 *Transistor life test.* The transistor shall be subjected to intermittent (see 4.32.2) or continuous operation life test in accordance with the following procedures:

(a) The emitter current and the collector voltage shall be held constant to within ±5%.

(b) The emitter current and collector voltage shall be chosen in the following manner: As illustrated in figure 2, make a diagram of the collector characteristics of the transistor, drawing curves for the maximum rated collector voltage, current, and power. Connect the origin with the abscissa and ordinate corresponding to the maximum rated current and voltage. The intersection

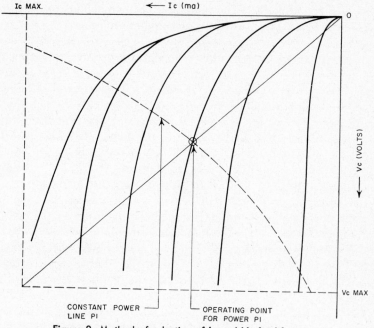

Figure 2. Method of selection of Ic and Vc for life test.

of this diagonal line with the maximum rated power curve is the operating point. The ambient temperature shall be between 20° C and 35° C.

(c) Specified measurements to determine compliance with specified life test end points shall be made at the end of the first twenty-four hours and at intervals thereafter as specified until completion of the life test. The duration of the life test shall be as specified on the specification sheet.

4.32.1 *Criteria for life test end point.* The criteria for life test end point shall be as specified on the specification sheet. A semiconductor device shall have reached the end of its life when it fails the specified life test end point limit(s) when measured under the specified test conditions. When two or more tests are specified for the life test end points, failure of any one of these tests shall constitute failure of the semiconductor device. When optional tests are specified on the specification sheet, the one selected by the contractor at the start of the test shall govern.

4.32.2 *Intermittent life test operation.* When intermittent life test operation is specified on the specification sheet, the semiconductor device shall be subjected to the life test under the following conditions: The semiconductor device shall be intermittently operated under specified test conditions, and the "ON" periods shall consist of from 12 to 25 interruptions (at uniform intervals) per 24 hours of life test with approximately 20 hours of operation in a 24-hour period. The on and off periods shall be initiated by immediate application or removal, respectively, of the full specified voltage values: that is, the voltages shall not be gradually increased or decreased. Other electrode potentials may be applied continuously. The accumulation of the "ON" time shall be the only time considered in determining compliance with minimum specified time.

4.33 *Crystal diode life test.* The crystal diode shall be subjected to intermittent (see 4.32.2) or continuous operation life test in accordance with the following procedure:

(a) Insert the crystal diode in a half-wave rectifier circuit as shown in figure 3.

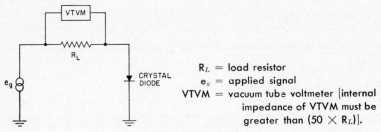

R_L = load resistor
e_g = applied signal
VTVM = vacuum tube voltmeter [internal impedance of VTVM must be greater than $(50 \times R_L)$].

Figure 3. Crystal diode life test.

(b) The applied signal amplitude, frequency and wave-shape, the value of the load resistor, and the duration of the test shall be as specified on the specification sheet.

(c) Specified measurements to determine compliance with the specified life test end points shall be made at the end of the first twenty-four hours and at intervals thereafter as specified until the completion of the life test. The duration of the life test shall be as specified on the specification sheet.

4.34 *Phototransistor life test.* The phototransistor shall be subjected to intermittent (see 4.32.2) or continuous operation life test in accordance with the following procedure:

(a) Insert the phototransistor in the circuit shown in figure 4.

(b) The phototransistor shall be exposed to an intermittent light which is incident normally upon the sensitive area. The ratio of "off" time to "on" time per cycle of the intermittent light shall be as specified in the specification sheet. The light source shall be the standard radiation light source (4.2.5) and the intensity shall be as specified.

(c) The value of the voltage across the phototransistor and the value of the limiting resistor shall be as specified.

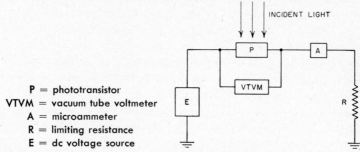

P = phototransistor
VTVM = vacuum tube voltmeter
A = microammeter
R = limiting resistance
E = dc voltage source

Figure 4. Phototransistor life test.

(d) Specified measurement to determine compliance with the specified life test end points shall be made at the end of the first twenty-four hours and at intervals thereafter as specified, until the completion of the life test. The duration of the life test shall be as specified on the specification sheet.

4.34.1 *Criteria for life test end point.* See 4.32.1.

4.34.2 *Intermittent life test operation.* See 4.32.2.

4.35 *Ic: Collector current test.* With specified voltages and currents applied to the electrodes, the collector current shall be measured. See 4.2.13.

4.36 *Ie: Emitter current test.* With specified voltages and currents applied to the electrodes, the emitter current shall be measured. See 4.2.13.

4.37 *Ib: Base current test.* With specified voltages and currents applied to the electrodes, the base current shall be measured. See 4.2.13.

4.38 *Vc: Collector voltage test.* With specified voltages and currents applied to the electrodes, the collector voltage shall be measured. See 4.2.13.

4.39 *Ve: Emitter voltage test.*   With specified voltages and currents applied to the electrodes, the emitter voltage shall be measured. See 4.2.13.

4.40 *Vb: Base voltage test.*   With specified voltages and currents applied to the electrodes, the base voltage shall be measured.   See 4.2.13.

4.41 *Z11: Small-signal, open-circuit, input-impedance test.*   With the specified dc voltages and currents applied to the electrodes, an ac small-signal applied to the input terminals, and an open-circuited output, the magnitude (without regard to phase angle) of Z11 shall be determined.

4.42 *Z12: Small-signal, open-circuit, reverse-transfer, impedance test.*   With the specified dc voltages and currents applied to the electrodes, an ac small-signal applied to the output terminals, and an open-circuited input, the magnitude (without regard to phase angle) of Z12 shall be determined.

4.43 *Z21: Small-signal, open-circuit, forward-transfer, impedance test.*   With the specified dc voltages and currents applied to the electrodes, an ac small-signal applied to the input terminals, and an open-circuited output, the magnitude (without regard to phase angle) of Z21 shall be determined.

4.44 *Z22: Small-signal, open-circuit, output-impedance test.*   With the specified dc voltages and currents applied to the electrodes, an ac small signal applied to the output terminals, and an open-circuited input, the magnitude (without regard to phase angle) of Z22 shall be determined.

4.45 *h11: Small-signal, short-circuit, input-impedance.*   With the specified dc voltages and currents applied to the electrodes, an ac small-signal applied to the input terminals, and the output short-circuited, the magnitude (without regard to phase angle) of h11 shall be determined.

4.46 *h12: Small-signal, open-circuit, feedback-potential ratio test.*   With the specified dc voltages and currents applied to the electrodes, the specified connections, an ac small-signal applied to the output terminals, and the input open-circuited, the magnitude (without regard to phase angle) of h12 shall be determined.

4.47 *h21: Small-signal, short-circuit, current-transfer ratio test.*   With the specified dc voltages and currents applied to the electrodes, an ac small-signal applied to the input terminals, and the output short-circuited, the magnitude (without regard to phase angle) of h21 shall be determined.

4.48 *h22: Small-signal, open-circuit, output-admittance test.*   With the specified dc voltages and currents applied to the electrodes, an ac small-signal applied to the output terminals, and the input open-circuited, the magnitude (without regard to phase angle) of h22 shall be determined.

4.49 *Y11: Small-signal, short-circuit, input-admittance test.* With the specified dc voltages and currents applied to the electrodes, an ac small-signal applied to the input terminals, and the output short-circuited, the magnitude (without regard to phase angle) of Y11 shall be determined.

4.50 *Y12: Small-signal, short-circuit, feedback-admittance test.* With the specified dc voltages and currents applied to the electrodes, an ac small-signal applied to the output terminals, and the input short-circuited, the magnitude (without regard to phase angle) of Y12 shall be determined.

4.51 *Y21: Small-signal, short circuit, transfer-admittance test.* With the specified dc voltages and currents applied to the electrodes, an ac small-signal applied to the input terminals, and the output short-circuited, the magnitude (without regard to phase angle) of Y21 shall be determined.

4.52 *Y22: Small-signal, short-circuit, output-admittance test.* With the specified dc voltages and currents applied to the electrodes, an ac small-signal applied to the output terminals, and the input short-circuited, the magnitude (without regard to phase angle) of Y22 shall be determined.

4.53 *Small-signal, short-circuit, grounded-base, driving-point imped-ance test.* With the specified dc voltages and currents applied to the electrodes, an ac small-signal applied to the input terminals, and the output short-circuited, the polarity of the small-signal, short-circuit, grounded-base, driving-point impedance shall be determined.

4.54 *αce: Small-signal, short-circuit, current-multiplication ratio test.* With the specified dc voltages and currents applied to the elec-trodes, an ac small-signal applied to the input terminals, and a short-circuit output, αce shall be determined.

4.55 *$f\alpha ce$: Small-signal, short-circuit, current-multiplication ratio cut-off frequency test.* The conditions for measurement of αce to determine $f\alpha ce$, shall be as indicated in 4.54. Measurements shall be taken at the specified reference frequency and at different frequencies thereafter until $f\alpha ce$ is determined. ($f\alpha ce$ is greater than the refer-ence frequency.)

4.56 *NF: Noise figure test.* With the specified dc voltages and cur-rents applied to the semiconductor device, the noise figure, measured at 1000 cps $\pm 10\%$ with an input resistance of 1000 ohms $\pm 10\%$ and as referred to a 1-cycle bandwidth, shall be determined. In making the measurements, the detector shall be an average responding rms cali-brated indicator.

4.57 *Characteristic curve irregularities test.* The grounded base, static output characteristic (Vc vs Ic with Ie as the parameter) shall be displayed on an oscilloscope having voltage and current sensitivities as specified. The characteristic curve shall, within the range of voltages and currents specified, exhibit no irregularities greater than those specified on the specification sheet. The emitter and collector load impedances and the collector sweep frequency shall be as specified. Irregularities, for the purpose of this test, are illustrated by figures 5A, 5B, 5C, and 5D.

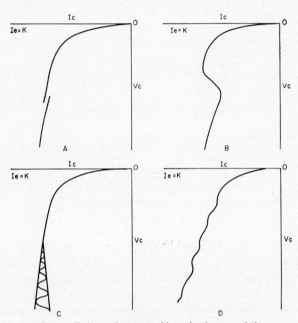

Figure 5. Irregularities in Vc vs Ic characteristic.

4.58 *Characteristic curve instability test.* The grounded base, static output characteristic (Vc vs Ic with Ie as the parameter) shall be displayed on an oscilloscope having voltages and currents sensitivities as specified. The characteristic curve shall, within the range of voltage and current specified, exhibit no instabilities greater than the limits indicated on the specification sheet. For the purpose of this test, the emitter and collector load impedances and the collector sweep frequency shall be as specified. Instability, for the purpose of this test, is defined as a sudden change in trace position as shown in figure 6.

4.59 *Small-signal, grounded-base, short-circuit, current-multiplication ratio vs emitter-current test.* The αce vs Ie curve shall be displayed on an oscilloscope. The horizontal and vertical sensitivities of the oscilloscope, the scope face display region, and the emitter current sweep range shall be as specified. The following frequency ratios shall be approximated by the test equipment: (See 3.2.41, 3.2.42, and 3.2.43

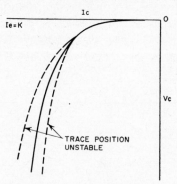

Figure 6. Trace position instability.

for definitions of probe frequency, sweep frequency and display bandwidth.)

$$\frac{\text{Display Bandwidth}}{\text{Emitter Sweep Current Frequency}} = 300$$

$$\frac{\text{Emitter Probing Current Frequency}}{\text{Display Bandwidth}} = 10$$

The amplitude of the emitter probing current shall be as specified. The collector load impedance shall be equal to or less than 100 ohms at the emitter probing current frequency. When operating at the voltages and current specified, the αce vs Ie curve shall remain within the unshaded area of the scope face display region specified on the specification sheet. A sample scope face display is shown in figure 7.

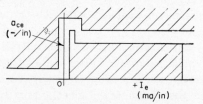

Figure 7. Oscilloscope overlay for αce vs Ie curve.

4.60 *tt: Turn-off time test.* The transistor shall be operated in the test circuit shown in figure 8. The pulse or square wave generator shall be adjusted to present a 5000 cps signal having a positive peak amplitude of +15 volts at the transistor base terminal when the

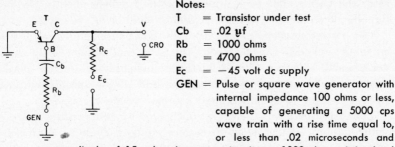

Notes:

T   = Transistor under test
Cb = .02 µf
Rb = 1000 ohms
Rc = 4700 ohms
Ec = −45 volt dc supply
GEN = Pulse or square wave generator with
      internal impedance 100 ohms or less,
      capable of generating a 5000 cps
      wave train with a rise time equal to,
      or less than .02 microseconds and
an amplitude of 15 volts when operating into a 1000 ohm resistive load
CRO = Oscilloscope capable of presenting an input wave form of 0.1 microsecond
      per centimeter
V   = Vertical terminal of oscilloscope

Figure 8. Circuit for measuring turn-off time.

collector is open circuited. The time duration, t1, as defined by figure 9, shall be adjusted to be greater than the turn off time, tt, also defined by figure 9. The oscilloscope shall be adjusted so that its sweep is synchronized with the pulse generator. The turn-off time, tt, shall be within the limits specified.

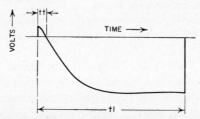

Figure 9. Measurement of turn-off time off.

4.61 *Co: Output capacitance test.* With the specified dc voltages and currents applied to the electrodes and an ac signal applied, the output capacitance of the semiconductor device shall be measured by measuring the capacitance between the output terminals. The amplitude of the signal used and a choice of either 10 kc or 1 Mc as the signal frequency shall be as specified.

4.62 *Ci: Input capacitance test.* With the specified dc voltages and currents applied to the electrodes and an ac signal applied, the input capacitance of the semiconductor device shall be measured by measuring the capacitance between the input terminals. The amplitude of the signal used and a choice of either 10 kc or 1 Mc as the signal frequency shall be as specified.

4.63 *Vif: Floating potential test.* With the specified dc voltage applied to the collector, the floating potential at the emitter shall be measured. The floating potential at the emitter shall be measured after the voltage has been applied for the time specified. The input impedance of the measuring instrument shall be as specified.

4.64 *Photoconductance effect test.* With the specified dc voltages and currents applied to the electrodes, the photoconductance effect shall be determined. During this test the semiconductor device shall be exposed (in the manner specified) to light of the specified intensity from the standard radiation light source. (See 4.2.5.)

4.65 *Semiconductor device characteristic vs temperature test.* The semiconductor device shall be subjected to a cycle of temperature beginning at the reference temperature (see 4.2.3), thence to the extreme of the operating temperature range, as specified on the specification sheet, in 10-degree intervals, and back to the reference temperature in 10 degree intervals. When raising and lowering the temperature, the semiconductor device shall be maintained at each temperature step for the minimum time as specified. At each temperature step, the specified parameters shall be determined.

M1 = dc vacuum tube voltmeter (VTVM)
M2 = dc milliameter
E_{bb} = variable voltage source
R1 = 25,000Ω protective resistor

Figure 10. Circuit for measuring peak reverse voltages.

4.66 *Ib: Forward current.* With the specified dc voltage applied to the electrodes the forward current of the semiconductor device shall be measured. This test may be made utilizing volt-ammeter methods or by oscilloscope presentation with a sweep frequency of 10,000 cps or less.

4.67 *LIb: Reverse current.* With the specified dc voltage applied to the electrodes the reverse current of the semiconductor device shall be measured. This test may be made utilizing volt-ammeter methods or by oscilloscope presentation with a sweep frequency of 10,000 cps or less.

4.68 *+Eb or −Eb: Voltage drop test.* With the specified current flowing through the crystal diode, the voltage drop across its terminals shall be measured. This test may be made utilizing volt-ammeter methods or by oscilloscope presentation with a sweep frequency of 10,000 cps or less.

4.69 *epx: Peak reverse voltage test.* The peak reverse voltage shall be measured using the circuit in figure 10, or its equivalent.

4.70 *EZ: Zener voltage test.* If Zener voltage is specified, the specified value of current from a controlled current source shall be passed through the semiconductor device and the value of voltage across its terminals shall be measured.   If Zener voltage regulation is specified, the voltages shall be measured at the two values of current specified on the specification sheet and the difference between these voltages determined.

4.71 *trt: Reverse transient response time test.*

4.71.1 *trt: Reverse transient response time test, Method A.*   Reverse transient response time shall be measured in the circuit shown in figure 11.

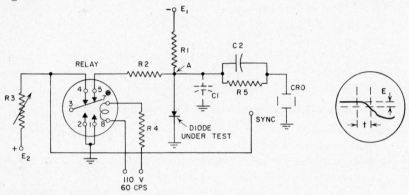

Notes:

    CRO Tektronix 513D or equivalent

    Relay Western Electric 276B Mercury SW, or equivalent

    R1 as specified on specification sheet

    R2 470 ohms

    R3 as specified on specification sheet

    R4 39K, 2W

    R5 9.1 megohms

    C1 20 μμf (Total capacity, point A to GND. including relay)

    C2 Approximately 5 μμf (Adjust for good square wave response on CRO)

    E1 (Well filtered or batteries) as specified on specification sheet

    E2 As specified on specification sheet

    E   As specified on specification sheet

    t   As specified on specification sheet

Figure 11.   Circuit for reverse transient response time, Method A.

(a) CRO response shall be dc to 18 Mc and rise time (10% to 90%) shall not exceed 0.025 μs.

(b) Attenuator R5, C2 has as its purpose the reduction of capacitance from point A to ground.   Using Tektronix Type 513D CRO, or equal, (nominal input impedance 1 megohm and 40 uuf) R5 results in a 10:1 attenuation.   C2 shall be adjusted for best square wave transmission.

(c) Relay shall operate at 60 cps with positive chatterless contact; the mercury type is recommended.

(d) With relay operating at 60 cps, observe pattern on CRO (see sketch on schematic); the time "t", to right of the negative step in the curve, required for voltage across the diode to increase to "E" shall be within the limits specified on the specification sheet.

(e) Lead length is important.

4.71.2 *trt: Reverse transient response time test. Method B.* The reverse transient response time shall be measured in the circuit shown in figure 12.

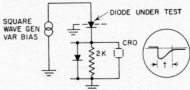

Figure 12. Circuit for reverse transient response, Method B.

(a) CRO response shall be dc to 18 Mc and rise time (10% to 90%), shall not exceed 0.025 μs.

(b) Square wave generator: rise time 0.1 μs max., internal impedance approximately 300 ohms, variable bias.

(c) Adjust bias in square wave generator to produce specified value for forward current in the crystal diode. During measurement the voltage across the crystal diode shall be reversed to the value specified in 0.1 μ sec or less. The time that the crystal diode operates in the forward direction shall be equal to the time of operation in the reverse direction. The time, as observed on the oscilloscope, after the voltage reversal until the reverse current is reduced to less than the value specified for LIb on the specification sheet, shall be within the limits specified.

4.72 *tft: Forward transient response test.* Forward transient response shall be measured in a circuit as shown in figure 13.

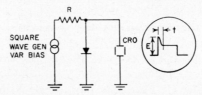

Figure 13. Circuit for forward transient response.

(a) CRO response shall be dc to 18 Mc and rise time (10% to 90%) shall not exceed 0.025 μs.

(b) The square wave generator and resistor R represent a source of constant current. The generator shall have a maximum rise time of 0.1 microsecond.

(c) With the value of R and the voltage output of the generator set at the values specified, the initial voltage peak (E) observed on the oscilloscope shall be within the limits specified. This circuit shall also be used to measure time "t" for the forward voltage drop to reach its specified value when this parameter is specified.

4.73 *RE: Rectification efficiency test.* The rectification efficiency shall be measured with 2 volts rms at the specified frequency input. The load resistance shall be 5000 ohms and the load capacitance shall be 20 $\mu\mu$f.

4.74 *Io: Rectified current test.* The crystal diode shall be placed in a simple half wave rectifier circuit. With the specified value of 60 cps alternating current applied to the circuit and with the specified load resistance, the rectified current shall be measured.

4.75 *ID: Dark current test.* With the specified potential applied across the phototransistor, the dark current shall be measured.

4.76 *IL: Light current test.* With the specified potential applied across the phototransistor, the light current shall be determined. The active surface of the phototransistor shall be illuminated by radiation of specified intensity from the standard light source. All tests shall be made in an inclosure such that no radiation to which the phototransistor is sensitive, other than direct radiation from the standard light source, shall impinge on the active surface of the phototransistor. Apertures and focusing devices may be used to limit the light upon the phototransistor to a uniform distribution over the area specified, if the spectral distribution of the incident radiation on the phototransistor is the same as from the standard radiation light source. The geometry and intensity of this radiation shall be as specified.

4.77 *Frequency response test.* Light having the same spectral distribution as the standard light source and having its intensity modulated sinusoidally, shall be directed on the sensitive area of the phototransistor. With the specified voltages and currents applied to the phototransistor, the ac light response (3.2.48) for each of the specified modulation frequencies shall be measured. The ac light response at the higher of the two light modulation frequencies specified, shall not be less than 0.707 times the ac light response at the lower modulation frequency. The general test conditions of 4.76 shall also apply. (If other than sinusoidal modulation is employed, an appropriate compensation shall be made in the measurement to yield the same result as that obtained with sinusoidal modulation.)

4.78 *Spectral response.* With the specified potentials and currents applied to the phototransistor, the spectral response shall be determined by using the standard light source and a series of light filters as specified. The filters shall be placed into and normal to the light path, between the light source and the phototransistor. The response to each filter or combination of filters shall be determined as a percentage of the response of the phototransistor to the unfiltered radiation.

4.79 *Soldering test.* Each lead of the semiconductor device shall be immersed in molten solder at a temperature of 230 $\pm 5°$ C, to a point $\frac{1}{16}$ inch $\pm \frac{1}{32}$ inch from the body of the device for 15 seconds, after which the device shall be removed and wiped dry.

INDEX